Prentice Hall Advanced Reference Series

ULTRA LARGE SCALE INTEGRATED MICROELECTRONICS

David K. Ferry
Arizona State University, Tempe

Lex A. Akers
Arizona State University, Tempe

Edwin W. Greeneich
Arizona State University, Tempe

PRENTICE HALL
Englewood Cliffs, New Jersey 07632

Library of Congress Cataloging-in-Publication Data

Ferry, David K.
    Ultra large scale integrated microelectronics / David K. Ferry,
Lex A. Akers, Edwin W. Greeneich.
        p.   cm. -- (Prentice Hall advanced reference series)
    Bibliography: p.
    Includes index.
    ISBN 0-13-935735-1
    1. Integrated circuits--Very large scale integration.   I. Akers,
Lex A.,   . II. Greeneich, Edwin W.,   III. Title.
TK7874.F46 1988
621.381'73--dc19   87-25078
                                                        CIP

The publisher offers discounts on this book when ordered in bulk quantities. For more information, write:

Special Sales/College Marketing
Prentice Hall
College Technical and Reference Division
Englewood Cliffs, NJ 07632

Editorial/production supervision and
    interior design: Linda Zuk, Wordcrafters Editorial Services, Inc.
Cover design: Wanda Lubelska

Printed in the United States of America

10 9 8 7 6 5 4 3 2 1

ISBN 0-13-935735-1

Prentice-Hall International (UK) Limited, *London*
Prentice-Hall of Australia Pty. Limited, *Sydney*
Prentice-Hall Canada Inc., *Toronto*
Prentice-Hall Hispanoamericana, S.A., *Mexico*
Prentice-Hall of India Private Limited, *New Delhi*
Prentice-Hall of Japan, Inc., *Tokyo*
Simon & Schuster Southeast Asia Pte. Ltd., *Singapore*
Editora Prentice-Hall do Brasil, Ltda., *Rio de Janeiro*

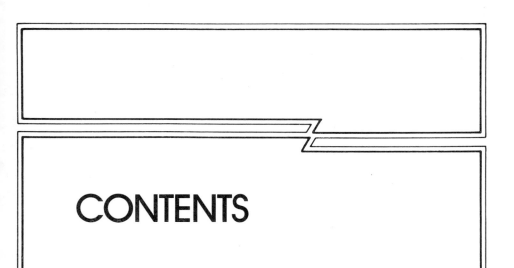

CONTENTS

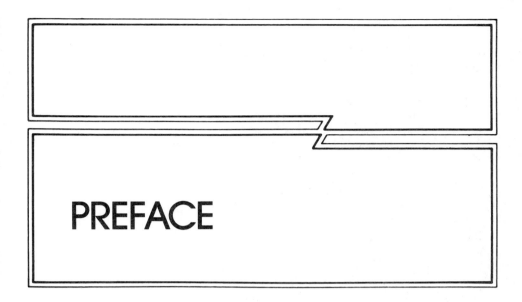

PREFACE

Since the text on VLSI design by Carver Mead and Lynn Conway was written, the growth of interest in VLSI has been dramatic. The application of these design principles has propelled interest into many new and important areas, such as digital signal processing and application-specific integrated circuits. This growth of interest in the layout and design of circuits has been coupled with an equally impressive growth in the density of individual devices on a semiconductor chip. As a consequence, we are arriving at chips with densities of more than 30 million individual devices. What is the next phase? Several answers, and several questions, are included in this elementary question— perhaps the least of which is, "What should this next level of integration be called?" We have chosen Ultra-Large Scale Integration (ULSI) to stand for chips with more than $1-5 \times 10^6$ individual devices. Indeed, such terminology is already beginning to be used quite commonly in the industry.

The more serious questions that must be raised for ULSI certainly address the limits of packing density. These questions have been around for more than a decade, and new limits seem to be promulgated yearly (and always smaller than the most recent chip has demonstrated to be possible). In this book we are trying to address these questions on a more systematic basis by dealing with the modeling of the devices and the circuit topology. In the first four chapters, we discuss the rationale for ULSI and the physics of the three major technologies that are being discussed for ULSI—Si MOS, Si bipolar, and GaAs field-effect transistors. In these chapters, we also discuss the "so-called second order effects," which cause major deviations from the simplified one-dimensional analysis presented in many texts. While nearly all of these effects have been discussed quite extensively in the literature, they have not really been brought together in a single text.

In Chapter 5 we begin to discuss the circuit aspects that will limit ULSI. Here we go beyond a mere treatment of device physics and try to begin to understand how packing density can be limited by pin-outs and the architecture chosen for the circuits. In this latter concept, we point out the difference between gate arrays, which are principally highly partitioned circuits, and the VLSI design concept of Mead and Conway, which leads to functionally partitioned circuits. The differences are more than simply terms, as the architectural differences lead to different functional forms for Rent's Rule and different numbers of required pins on the chip.

Finally, in the last two chapters, we go to the more esoteric limitations that can arise in ULSI circuits. First are the direct interactions between individual devices in a dense circuit—interactions that go far beyond those programmed by interconnection levels included in the layout. We treat the cooperative and parasitic interactions that can arise. The last chapter deals more with the fundamental limits on the speed-power product that can be expected in ULSI. Here we examine the basic concepts of doing digital computations and processing in ULSI in order to arrive at the thermodynamic and quantum mechanical limits.

The text material is drawn from material that the authors use in several different courses at ASU. Primarily these courses are at the first and second year of graduate study. However, some of the material has never appeared in print before and represents novel approaches to the physics of these devices.

David K. Ferry
Lex A. Akers
Edwin W. Greeneich

1

INTRODUCTION

The microelectronics age, the micro-millenium, the computer age, the information revolution, the second industrial revolution; whatever one chooses to call it, we have all been inundated with popular press accounts of the changes very-large-scale integration (VLSI) has made within our society. Whatever the name, it is clear that we are riding the crest of a wave of technological growth. In the microelectronics industry, we see progress as a steady increase in the packing density of individual devices upon a single integrated circuit "chip." Gordon Moore [1] summarized this growth with his now famous conclusion that the density doubles each two years. He saw this growth in circuit complexity arising from three main sources: (1) increases in die size, (2) increases in circuit cleverness, and (3) decreases in the size of an individual transistor. The first of these factors arises from normal improvements in manufacturing technology. The second factor led to desires to develop regularity in design, as represented in the text by Carver Mead and Lynn Conway [2]. This and the third factor are the subject of this book, which we further discuss and define below.

It is not unusual to put more than a half-million transistors onto a single integrated circuit chip. By nearly all measures, this may be called VLSI density. The engineering profession likes to scale technology by factors of ten —by orders of magnitude. Initial circuits of a few hundred transistors on a single chip were simply called "integrated circuits." When a density of a thousand transistors on a single chip was achieved, we began to use the phrase large-scale integration, or LSI. Somewhere beyond 10,000 to 30,000 transistors, we may safely begin to use the descriptor VLSI. Where do we go in the

1

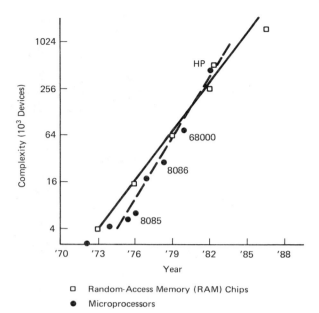

Figure 1.1   Growth of integrated circuit complexity over the last decade.

future? In 1986, there were circuits with more than a million transistors. In light of this, we felt that we should remain in the traditional mold which follows a logical progression, and have chosen to delimit ultra-large-scale integration (ULSI) at a level of one million transistors on a single chip.

In Figure 1.1, the growth of circuit complexity is illustrated for a series of familiar microprocessors and memory chips. Two factors are immediately obvious. First, the growth has been fairly constant since the early 1970s. Second, there does not appear to be a significant difference today between the two types of circuits. This is primarily because there is little true random logic utilized today. The use of read-only memory (ROM) and programmable-logic arrays (PLA), indeed the general drift toward array-oriented architecture for both logic and microcode implementation, has led to a highly paralleled architecture whose structure differs little from a memory chip.

Concurrent with the complexity growth has been the shrinking of design rules (item 3 above), which lead to smaller and smaller devices. In Figure 1.2, we show the manner in which the "minimum dimension," for which lithography is used, has been reduced over the past decade. Again, the rate has been relatively constant over this period. Now we are at the key question: Just how long can this decrease, and the attendant growth in complexity, continue? Various estimates, all based upon sound reasoning, have been given for this lower limit. These estimates have ranged from 2.0 micrometer [3] to 0.2 micrometer [4]. Yet, at least one suggestion for a device an order of magnitude smaller has been made [5], and devices with gate lengths in this range have

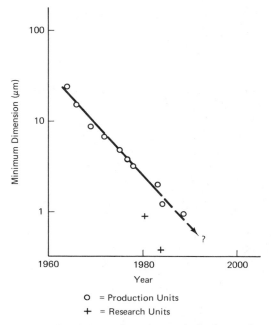

Figure 1.2 Decrease of the minimum dimension, typically the gate length in MOS, over the last decades.

been fabricated in our laboratories [6]. However, it is not particularly likely that the true limits will be set by the properties of individual devices, but rather by the combined considerations of devices and circuits. It is not our aim here to set a new value for the limit. Technology has always shown a penchant for violating limits, and hopefully this will continue in microelectronics. What we do want to achieve here is a thorough discussion of what is currently known about the various factors that are likely to contribute to these limits. In doing this, we will need to touch upon many effects: second-order effects, circuit effects, architecture effects, and so on through what is hopefully (at least defined by us to be) a finite list.

In the remainder of this first chapter, we want to examine the past, present, and future of microelectronics *per se*. In this, we want to discuss how we got where we are, what the current driving forces are, and what the future is likely to hold.

1.1 OF CALCULATORS AND COMPUTERS

The microprocessor is generally agreed to have arrived in 1969 with Intel's 4004 and 8008 machines, although contemporary efforts by Texas Instruments were also producing these types of machines. These were the first devices to put the basic central processing unit on one chip and allowed for the advance in calculators. In doing this, they were in fact merely one more step in a long evolution of "mechanical" calculating machines. More than a third of a millenium earlier, Wilhelm Schickard had begun the long march to microcomputers. In 1623, Schickard apparently built a working, mechanical calculator capable of addition and subtraction along with some partial capability for multiplication and division. Unfortunately, most of his work was destroyed during the Thirty Years War (1618–1648).

In 1642, Blaise Pascal designed a small counting machine which was limited to addition and subtraction. Some thirty years later, Leibniz enlarged this machine, adding the functions of multiplication and division. Many of the concepts developed by these two, including the use of rotating wheels, remained in use in small calculators until the advent of the all-electronic microprocessor itself. Finally, over a period of years in the early nineteenth century, Charles Babbage gave us first the "difference engine" and then the "analytical engine."

The analytical engine was a remarkable concept, in that it essentially contained most of the concepts of the modern computer. First, there was the "mill" to carry out the calculations themselves. This corresponds to today's arithmetic logic unit (ALU) and control unit combined. The mill operated from external program cards for variables and operands. Internal to the machine, however, was a memory, which was appropriately enough called the "store." Although Babbage apparently failed to complete a working model, one was built by Pehr Scheutz, a Swede who exhibited the machine in London in 1854. The natural evolution was the punched card tabulating machine introduced by Herman Hollerith in the 1880s for the census (his company evolved into IBM).

The modern electronic computer has its later roots in the work of John Atanasoff at Iowa State University and Konrad Zuse in Berlin. The latter, in particular, worked in isolation so that he had little impact in the West. Yet, in 1931, he proposed the use of a binary number system and worked on a vacuum tube model of his computer in the mid-1930s. The former scientist was the American pioneer, who apparently affected both Bell Labs and the later effort at the University of Pennsylvania. The 1930s were pivotal as many events occurred at this time. Whether or not the stimulus came from Atanasoff, Bell Labs' Stibbutz had constructed a relay calculator prior to the end of that decade. Also by this time, Norbert Wiener had done considerable theoretical work on computation and Vaniver Bush had done experiments on the topic. In England, Alan Turing had carried out his fundamental theoretical work on computation of numbers (work that led to the wartime work on the Colossus machine for code breaking).

As is still true today, the need for massive numerical calculators was even then a strong driving force for evolution in computers. In 1940, the driving force was largely the calculation of ballistics tables for the military. To speed this project, the ENIAC (Electronic Numerical Integrator And Computer) was begun at the University of Pennsylvania in 1942, with funding from the Ballistic Research Laboratory. This machine was huge, containing 17,000 vacuum tubes. The ENIAC worked with a 100 kHz clock, and was a primitive "data flow" structure in that operations were performed by any of the 20 accumulators, each with 10 decimal digits of accuracy. John Mauchly headed the effort, which included a great many people before its demonstration in 1945. Yet, one of these stands out from the rest—John von Neumann. Von Neumann's impact was enormous, for it was his influence which dictated that future generations of computers would be:

1. Binary,
2. Stored program, and
3. Sequential.

In particular, the stored program concept, in which the program was placed in the main memory with the data, was crucial. These three attributes describe the Von Neumann architecture as we know it today.

From these beginnings, progress was rapid. In 1955, only seven years after the invention of the transistor, an all transistor computer was introduced. The 2000 transistor 4004 chip was introduced in 1969, only thirteen years after the first primitive integrated circuit. And today, less than two decades later, we have single chips with 10^6 transistors.

As with much of science, we seem to be on an exponential growth of knowledge. The microelectronics revolution, as we are prone to call it, is making extensive changes in society today. The first industrial revolution introduced mechanical leverage to the work-place, thereby multiplying man's muscle power. The current revolution is multiplying man's thinking and reasoning power [7], once again making dramatic changes in the work place. The possibilities for this growth are strong driving functions for continued growth beyond VLSI, and we shall examine these next.

1.2 THE MARKET PRESSURE FOR ULSI

The early pushes to higher levels of complexity in integrated circuits have been from the computer groups, who desired more processing power in each chip. Today, we see the push coming as well from the signal processing community. Indeed, a great deal of effort is being expended in seeking purely architectural solutions to large signal and/or data processing problems that are implementable in VLSI. To achieve this, it is necessary to solve the problem of economic constraints (particular to a specific task) on design costs, fabrication costs, and completion time limitations.

The extremely low level of surface defects in the best silicon wafers means that the limiting defects are mostly process induced. Still, very good processing yields can be achieved even for highly complex circuitry. Even so, the size of the individual die remains below roughly 1.0 square centimeter, so that increases in complexity (and gate count) must be accompanied by reductions in device power dissipation if the power level on the chip is to remain within bounds. Decreases in the gate lengths of silicon FETs in turn result in speed improvements of the individual transistors, yet the complex circuits often have the speed of the circuit limited by the complex interconnections. Because of this, the ability to fabricate very small transistors will more than likely be exploited to allow compacting greater numbers of devices on a single chip rather than for achieving greater speed. This result tends to follow from the enthusiasm in the computer architecture community for higher gate counts arising from the introduction of parallelism. As a consequence, the principle driving force toward ULSI is to produce ever more dense circuits, such as memory, microprocessors, and general purpose signal processing modules, that can be produced in large numbers. In this way, the traditional learning curve of technology will continue to allow reasonable cost levels per chip to be achieved.

To understand how this driving force occurs, we can refer to Figure 1.3, where we plot the cost per function versus the number of functions on an integrated circuit chip. The assembly and test costs of a chip tend to be related to the size of the chip more than any other single factor, so that as the number of functions increases, the cost per function decreases. On the other hand, the manufacturing cost of a chip increases as the complexity goes up, so that the silicon chip cost is a rising function. When these two factors are combined, a minimum appears in the total cost per function. This minimum gives the optimum functionality for a chip. However, the latter cost, that of manufactur-

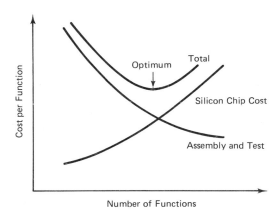

Figure 1.3 Optimum numbers of functions per chip.

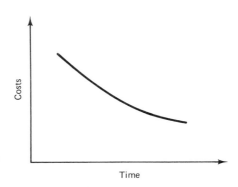

Figure 1.4 Learning curve reduction of optimum number of components per chip.

ing the silicon chip, is subject to the famous "learning curve," shown in Figure 1.4. Thus, this curve decreases with time, so that the optimum functionality moves toward larger numbers of functions per chip as time progresses. For chips that will be produced in very large volumes, it becomes economically advantageous to incorporate larger numbers of functions on each chip. It is to capitalize on these economics that many custom designs are implemented in master slices, or gate arrays, in order to utilize as much commonality as possible.

1.3 THE MICROPROCESSOR

In 1879, the British government appointed a committee to examine the progress made by Charles Babbage, and indeed to ascertain whether there was any real possibility of useful results to be obtained from his inventions. The committee concluded that [8]:

> If intelligently directed and saved from wasteful use, such a machine might mark an era in the history of computation,... Care might be required to guard against misuse....

While we might laugh at this last comment, it certainly must rank as one of the earliest registered concerns about the impending computer revolution. Nevertheless, perhaps the committee's foresight is now being attended to with the increasing concern over the security of computer data files. It is clear that once the computer decades were opened, the size and capability of the computer was steadily increased, and this continues to be the case. However, this increase meant that the cost also rose so that the availability of computers to all groups was reduced. The spin-off was first the minicomputer, and ultimately the microcomputer or microprocessor, which have reversed this trend.

Mainframe computers have evolved to the fourth generation, by popular accounts. The current push to develop large supercomputers and the development of artificial intelligence for design are the onset of what has become called the fifth generation. This current fourth generation includes a number of major steps away from the classic Von Neumann architecture, including parallel or vector processors, pipelining techniques, and data flow architectures. On the other hand, the first rash of 8 bit microprocessors shared most in common with the early first generation machines. Today, the complex microprocessors have reached perhaps the second or third equivalent generation of the mainframe machines, and people are now discussing the fourth generation concepts for the new proposed microprocessors.

Indeed, current microprocessors include such features as microcoded control units, PLA sequencers and arithmetic units, modest pipelining and parallelism, and multi-MHz operations with large, fast memory banks off-chip. However, these machines still consist primarily of the Babbage/Von Neumann architecture in that a single microprocessor chip is structured around an arithmetic logic unit, control unit, and some parts of the input/output systems and memory. The latter is at least implemented as the operations registers, which can function as temporary storage. To make a complete computer system, we still need to complete the input/output structure, provide the hopefully vast memory banks, and provide the buses for signals and communications.

As the size of the microprocessor has increased, in terms of density and number of gates, the word size has increased accordingly. The first microprocessors were 4 bit machines. These were followed by a great number of different 8 bit machines, then hybrid 8/16 bit machines as well as true 16 bit machines. Currently, we have available 32 bit architectures from a number of manufacturers. Ultimately, it is not unreasonable to expect to see 64 bit machines available before the end of the century, and probably a good deal sooner.

The power that is now available in the microprocessor is the driving force for the microelectronics revolution. It is now sufficiently easy to get massive computing power in a small size. As a consequence, it is feasible to build significant levels of automation into machines, whether mechanical or electrical. The former is rapidly changing the factory floor while the latter is rapidly changing the nature of electrical instrumentation. Progress in both of these areas now depends upon the continued evolution of the basic electronic marvel, the microprocessor, which generated the movement itself. To what extent can we expect this basic evolution to continue? Are there absolute limits to the packing density that can be achieved? What are the physical laws which determine how small individual devices can be made or fabricated? These are the questions to which we want to address ourselves in this text.

We can get an insight into some of the problems by an example. It is generally conceded that computers 1000 times faster than today's supercomputers will be required in the future to process image and other array signals in the coming decades. This has led computer scientists to direct their efforts toward the area of large-scale multiprocessor networks in which speed is gained through massive parallel arrays of relatively slow processors. Indeed, the clock speeds envisioned in individual processing elements in nearly all proposed supercomputers, including the Japanese fifth generation project, are slower than either the Iliac IV or current supercomputers such as the Cray I or the CDC 205. This is also true in microcomputers. In fact, the Department of Defense program in very-high-speed integrated circuits (VHSIC) has goals of 100 MHz (with 0.5 micrometer technology), which exceeds the speeds of all of the above machines. On the other hand, clock speeds and data rates are often set not by the switching speed of individual devices, but by the requirements of off-chip communications [9]. Still, it becomes feasible to conceive of a supercomputer based upon a microprocessor chip set.

As mentioned, speeds in multi-chip systems or multiprocessors have been held down due to inter-chip communications that requires driving long transmission lines between chips. Even though we discuss microprocessors, this is still the case even in supercomputers where word lengths are 64 bits or more. For example, the Motorola 68020 is a 32 bit I/O machine and would still compose only one bit-slice portion of a multi-chip processor element were it to be used in a supercomputer. When full VHSIC capabilities are achieved, one can readily conceive of changing this with a 64 bit machine on a single chip with nominal linewidths of 0.5 micrometer or less. This chip would have to have some on-board memory, which is crucial if speeds are to be increased. This memory must compose not only the quick access local register stack, but also the intermediate cache memory. Thus, only large block data moves are made at slower off-chip time limitations, and this process is sped up by transmitting several words in parallel. In future sub-micron technology, such a chip will probably remain at today's 1 cm^2 area limitation, yet will be powerful enough to serve as the processing element in the supercomputer.

The requirements of electromagnetic propagation across the chip suggest that delay times as large as 100 psec can be encountered, so that the clock speed is limited to less than, say, 3 GHz, if clock skew and signal propagation across the chip is not to be a limiting factor. At this point, we have to ask whether we can hope to achieve this speed with any expected extrapolation from today's devices. In doing this, we can draw upon ring-oscillator results, although these devices operate with little inter-stage load capacitance, while logic circuits with multi-device fan-outs may be limited by inter-device capacitances. Consequently, ring-oscillator results must be 4–5 times faster than speeds expected in logic circuits; e.g., delay times of 20–25 psec are required for logic families that can be used in this processor. This speed is marginal in silicon technology, although one must confess that only silicon has demonstrated the integration of levels conceived here. On the other hand, this delay time is well within the capabilities of expected performance in GaAs and InP circuitry.

This leads us to some interesting conclusions. First, the demands of ultimate functional throughput require large parallelism in the overall system. However, the limitations of the much discussed Amdahl's Law (that speed enhancement is a sublinear function of parallelism) requires that the highest possible speed be achieved within a single processing element. Thus, we are faced with another driving force toward continued miniaturization.

1.4 FUTURE GROWTH

The driving force for continued growth in the number of devices on a chip is usually felt first in the implementation of memories. The reason for this lies in the inherent regularity of the layout of semiconductor memories. The natural tendency of these devices to be constructed with regular arrays means that it is here that the impact of scaling down size is felt first. Memories, in turn, highlight a number of physical problems which must be addressed in future (and present) system designs. First, the memory is a system for storing information. In a read-only memory (ROM), this information is usually hard-wired into the structure, and therefore is not particularly susceptible to decay. On the other hand, we must have voltage levels in read-out that are sufficiently large compared to those arising from noise in the system. An important point can be illustrated here, to which we shall ultimately return later. This is, the requirement of uniformity in signal levels throughout the system requires that the output levels of the memory must be such that degradation does not drop the signal below the standard level. This implies that the variability of component parameters, in particular threshold, is equivalent to adding noise to the system and must be taken into consideration.

The addition of read/write memory, known commonly as random-access memory (RAM), introduces the additional requirement that the storage time must be long enough to satisfy the standard level requirement above. Thus, we must design "refresh" circuitry to re-establish the operating level of charge in the storage system and maintain the standard operating levels. In both cases, we require that logic amplifiers downstream from the memory must be nonlinear in order to sustain operation between these standard signal levels, with little operating time in the transition between levels. This ensures against noise in the logic system as well as the introduction of errors. However, we note that time is required in this transition, and this time is associated with the fundamental levels of charge that must be moved in the circuitry. Thus, there are delay times that must be accommodated. The thermal noise at 300 K (room temperature) is about 26 mV, so that signal levels must be much greater than this. This means that practical voltages must be a significant fraction of a volt. This sets the basic device type and parameters, as well as the amount of charge that is required to store a single bit of information in the memory. Thus, we find that the implementation of memories leads technology because of the regularity of the circuits and the ease of scaledown. However, this also pushes memories to be the first circuits which challenge new levels of circuit limitations as well.

We still see quite some controversy in the discussions of alternative materials to silicon, particularly GaAs. The latter material is the most well developed material for integrated circuits that are non-silicon based. While these arguments touch a great many issues, it is important to note that in general the system implementation functions that are carried out with GaAs will be fundamentally different from, and probably complementary to, those of silicon VLSI. As we have pointed out above, silicon circuitry is fundamentally drifting toward circuitry that is array oriented. As a consequence, the circuits tend to be heavily influenced by large interconnection capacitances and may not be able to fully implement any fundamental device speeds. In fact, many well-known supercomputer architects have stated that, without major architectural improvements, the availability of devices with zero gate delay would not improve the operation of their machine by more than 20%, since interconnect delays would by then be the dominant limiting factor.

As a consequence of the above factors, it is only in special architectures for very-high-speed signal processing that high-speed devices can really be utilized. These different architectures would retain all operands on each portion of each chip for a maximum time, thus minimizing any off-chip excursions. Specific examples of such layouts are iterative and recursive algorithms which are executed at high clock rates, systolic or cellular arrays whose devices communicate only with near neighbor devices, and some types of elemental pixel operation arrays. In short, architectures which require high system clock rates or real time processing, and which are not limited by long interconnection capacitances, would appear to be those systems that can utilize very high speed silicon and alternative GaAs devices.

Let us return to the limitation of the interconnection capacitance. Keyes [9] recently pointed out an example of a gate array chip with 1500 gates. This chip had 4 m of wire even though it was only 0.57×0.57 cm^2. Each wire track was 6.7 micron wide. A more modern chip is the Hewlett-Packard 32 bit microprocessor. This chip contains 470,000 transistors and is thought to have some 7 m of wire. The wiring has a nominal width of 1.25 micron, and the chip is about 1 cm^2. It is interesting to note that the length-to-width ratio of the wiring, if it were strung out, would be 5.6×10^6, which is equivalent to a 100 ft wide highway running for 100,000 miles (nearly four times around the earth at the equator). This is a lot of wire. However, Keyes' example is also illustrative in another way. In his example, we note that the wirelength is some 800 times longer than the chip edge. If the average length of an interconnection is equal to the chip edge (which is an upper limit), then there are an average of 400 wires in each of the two directions on the chip. This leads to 160,000 wire crossings. If the 1500 gates are in a 40×40 array, then there are on the average 20 wires passing through each cell. This is a blueprint for disaster, and it is no wonder that gate arrays are called wire-dominated chips. Clearly, the shear number of wires in this type of circuit limits its usefulness for VLSI.

The above discussions illustrate how the presence of excess interconnection capacitance can limit the speed of integrated circuits. We can illustrate this further with some numbers. First, we note that

$$P < QA \tag{1.1}$$

where P is the power dissipation of the chip in W, Q is the heat removal flux, and A is the area of the chip. Now, our requirement of propagation across a cell gives

$$A^{1/2} < c_1 t_d \tag{1.2}$$

where c_1 is the propagation speed and t_d is the delay time. We can combine these two equations to eliminate A and obtain

$$t_d^2 > P/Qc_1^2 \tag{1.3}$$

But, we can introduce the minimum energy to switch $E_m = Pt_d$, so that

$$t_d^3 > E_m/Qc_1^2 \tag{1.4}$$

We can clearly take one electrical charge as the minimum energy (at 1.0 V), and c_1 as the speed of light. A good (although large) number for Q is 10 W/cm^2, so that we find that $t_d > 0.026$ psec. This is some 2.5 orders of magnitude smaller than the fastest reported semiconductor switch, so it is a relatively safe lower limit.

On the other hand, the wire dominated chip has considerable energy stored in the interconnections rather than the devices. Keyes [9] has suggested that in this case, the energy required to switch is given by

$$Pt_d = (CwV_BV_S)(K^2/M)f \tag{1.5}$$

where C is the line capacitance, w is the width of the line, V_B is the bias voltage, V_S is the signal voltage, K is the number of wire tracks per cell, M is the number of wire layers, and f is the fraction of wire tracks occupied. In Equation (1.5), the first term in parentheses is the energy stored in a single wire per cell and the second term is the number of wires per cell when combined with f. Now, the area of a cell is given by

$$a = (Kw/M)^2 \tag{1.6}$$

and

$$Pt_d^2 > (CfKV_BV_S)^2/Q \tag{1.7}$$

Using (1.2) with $A = Na$, we finally arrive at

$$t_d^2 > N^{1/2}(CfKV_BV_S)/Q_c \tag{1.8}$$

Using $K = 20$, $N = 1000$, $f = 1$, $V_B = 5$, $V_s = 1$, $C = 0.1$ fF/micron, and the previous values for the other parameters, we find that $t_d > 0.1$ nsec. Clearly, this limit is considerably less advantageous for future integrated circuits, and shows that we must be very careful in the architectural design of ULSI to eliminate large numbers of long interconnection circuits.

1.5 CONCURRENT ARCHITECTURES FOR THE FUTURE

The transition to ultra-large-scale integration, in which more than one million active devices will be incorporated on a single chip, and the prospects for another 10–100-fold multiplication in this number, confronts the micro-electronics industry with two major tasks: how to manage the enormous complexity of such systems, not to mention the design problems, and how to manage to overcome the reliability of individual elements within the integrated circuit. The latter problem can be addressed via redundancy and better quality of processing, while the former problem is perhaps of more significance. While the complexity is a problem, it is also an opportunity, in that the sheer number of devices opens the possibility of constructing massively concurrent processing structures. As we pointed out above, the trend in Si VLSI is toward more regularity and parallelism in the architecture. Still, the presence of long interconnection lengths is a problem. This latter is alleviated in architectures which are concurrent, i.e., the architecture is composed of structured layers that are derived from several hundred or more distributed processing elements, rather than a single processor. Such concurrent structures offer considerable opportunity for advanced computer design, innovation in complex control tasks, perceptual systems, signal processing, and artificial intelligence machines.

The design "bottleneck" is already perceived to exist in VLSI, and is expected to be worse in ULSI. It is because of this bottleneck that random logic designs such as microprocessors lagged behind simpler memory chips. If the true potential of ULSI is to be fully realized, then there must be a continuation, indeed an acceleration, in the inclusion of structured regularity of design. However, this cannot be unfettered repetition of regular standard cells, as the long interconnections will begin to dominate the time response of the circuit, forcing the overall chip to be rather slower than the devices themselves would support. In short, if downscaling is to be meaningful in ULSI, then structured architectures must be devised which minimize the interconnect area, rather than the number of gates. This implies that highly concurrent architectures, such as pipeline or parallel arrays or even tree structure arrays, are much more favorable. Some authors have even argued that the full capabilities of ULSI can only be achieved, and the problems of temporal management of the complex concurrent architectures solved, if self-timed non-synchronous clocking of individual subunits is introduced [2].

The prototype of structured concurrent architecture is cellular logic. Here, cellular logic is a descriptor for the more general concept of cellular automata, in which operations are carried out locally at a site within an array of processors. Thus, this array could be operating on an array of data, and each local processing site operates on a single element of the data array. Thus the array $A(i, j)$ is transformed into a new array $A'(i, j)$, where in each element in the new array A' has a value that is determined from the corresponding element of A and those values of a small neighborhood of elements around the specific site. Cellular logic machines are already commonplace in image processing and certain types of signal processors, such as systolic arrays, are examples of this technique. Moreover, the earliest parallel computers, the Iliac IV and the CLIP series at the University of London, were synchronous implementations of cellular logic machines. We introduce this point here merely to illustrate that a wealth of concurrent architectures has already been investigated and implemented, utilizing discrete logic. While current microprocessor design still holds to the basic Von Neumann architecture, it is only a matter of time until the design complexity leads us to adopt more concurrent structures. We will return to a discussion of cellular logic in a later chapter, where we discuss the possibility of synergetic processing.

The introduction of concurrent architectures, however, is already beginning to be seen in another aspect of ULSI—whole wafer integration. By whole wafer integration, we are referring to the possibility of a single silicon system that encompasses the entire 5–6″ wafer. Although current yields are such that processing induced defects would pretty much prevent achieving full operation across the entire wafer, other schemes in which standard super-cells are implemented are going forward. In these latter approaches, arrays of microprocessors are fabricated on a single wafer, and these elements are placed around a central memory area. Such arrays are little different from current designs where one wafer may contain hundreds of identical microprocessors. However, rather than dicing them apart, they are interconnected with the memory and with each other. Redundancy in design allows selection of functional units, just as is currently done in some 256K and larger memory chips today. An alternative approach uses the wafer just as a chip carrier, with the individual processing elements bonded onto the wafer. In either case, the selection of operational units from smaller standard sized chips allows the overall functional yield to be greatly increased. This approach to whole wafer integration may in fact be the first step toward the massive supercomputer on a wafer. However, caution is still to be exercised as these designs encompass long interconnection runs across the wafer, and it has not yet been ascertained that these off-chip excursions (even though they remain on Si or GaAs) offer substantially better performance than off-chip excursions on a normal chip carrier using unpackaged chips. In either case, total performance of the overall system will be achieved only if the inter-chip communications are designed with full electromagnetic propagation considerations, just as is done in today's microwave integrated circuits.

The above paragraphs have touched upon a number of the driving forces and questions for future ULSI. In the following chapters, we shall address these points in more detail.

REFERENCES

1. G. Moore, *Proceedings IEDM 1975*, p. 11 (IEEE Press, New York, 1975).
2. C. A. Mead and L. Conway, *Introduction to VLSI Systems* (Addison-Wesley, Reading MA, 1980).
3. J. T. Wallmark, in *Solid State Devices 1975*, vol. 25 conf. ser., p. 133 (Inst. Phys., London, 1975).
4. B. Hoeseisen and C. A. Mead, *Solid State Electronics*, vol. 15, p. 819 (1972).
5. J. R. Barker and D. K. Ferry, *Solid State Electronics*, vol. 23, p. 531 (1980).
6. G. Bernstein and D. K. Ferry, *Superlattices and Microstructures*, vol. 2, p. 147 (1986); vol. 2, p. 373 (1986).
7. P. E. Haggarty, B. R. Mayo, and C. H. Phipps, in *VLSI Electronics: Microstructure Science*, ed. N. Einspruch, vol. 1 (Academic Press, New York, 1981).
8. "Report of the Committee, consisting of Professor Cayley, Dr. Farr, Mr. J. W. L. Glaisher, Dr. Pole, Professor Fuller, Professor A. B. W. Kennedy, Professor Clifford, and Mr. C. W. Merrifield, appointed to consider the advisability and to estimate the expense of constructing Mr. Babbage's Analytical Machine, and of printing Tables by its means. Drawn up by Mr. Merrifield (1879)," reprinted in *The Origins of Digital Computers: Selected Papers*, ed. B. Randell, pp. 53–64 (Springer-Verlag, Berlin, 1973).
9. R. Keyes, *Proc. IEEE*, vol. 63, p. 740 (1975).

2

SMALL-GEOMETRY
MOSFETs

The metal-oxide-semiconductor field effect transistor, commonly called the MOSFET, is currently expected to satisfy the majority of requirements for ULSI. The MOSFET structure was proposed as early as 1930 by Lilienfeld [1], but the first working device was not fabricated until 1960 by Kahng and Atalla [2]. While the term MOSFET generally refers to any gate-insulator-semiconductor structure, for ULSI a MOSFET using a heavily doped polysilicon or a polysilicon and refractory metal combination for the gate, silicon dioxide or silicon nitride as the insulator, and silicon for the semiconductor will be the most commonly used structure.

In this chapter we will review the MOSFET and examine its use in ULSI. First the basic MOS structure will be described, then the classical MOSFET characteristics will be derived. Once a basic foundation in the operation of the MOSFET has been established, the so called second-order effects which actually dominate the behavior of small-geometry MOSFETs will be examined.

2.1 MOS

For this discussion, the MOS structure shown in Figure 2.1 is composed of a conductor of heavily n doped polysilicon, an insulator of silicon dioxide (SiO_2), and a semiconductor which is p-type silicon. The thickness of insulators in current production is in the 150–400 Å range, with thickness as small as 100 Å in developmental stages. The silicon bulk region is contacted with an ohmic Al contact on the back of the wafer.

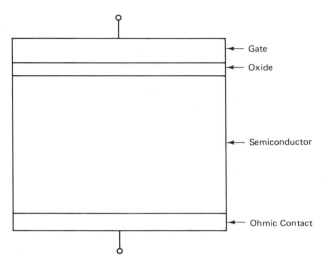

Figure 2.1 Cross section of a MOS capacitor.

To analyze this structure, we initially make the following approxima-tions:

1. The insulator is ideal with zero current flowing through it for all dc bias conditions,
2. The gate conductor is considered to be an equipotential region,
3. No trapped charge or interface states exist,
4. The semiconductor is uniformly doped,
5. The substrate is sufficiently thick that a quasi-neutral region exists, and
6. The length and width of the structure is sufficiently large that edge effects may be neglected allowing a one-dimensional analysis to be used.

The gate is characterized by a gate Fermi energy, E_{FM}, and a gate work function, $q\phi_M$. $q\phi_M$ is the difference between the vacuum energy level, E_0, and the Fermi energy level of the gate. $q\phi_M$ thus represents the energy required to remove an electron from the gate material. The oxide is char-acterized by a thickness, t_{ox}, and an insulator electron affinity, $q\chi_i$. This insulator electron affinity is measured from the conduction band edge in the oxide to the vacuum level. The semiconductor is characterized by a conduction band edge, the Fermi energy, the intrinsic Fermi energy, a valence band edge, the electron affinity, and a semiconductor work function. These are denoted by E_C, E_F, E_i, E_V, $q\chi_S$, and $q\phi_{sc}$, respectively. The semiconductor electron affinity, $q\chi_S$, is measured from the conduction band edge in the semiconduc-tor to the vacuum energy level. The semiconductor work function, $q\phi_{sc}$, is

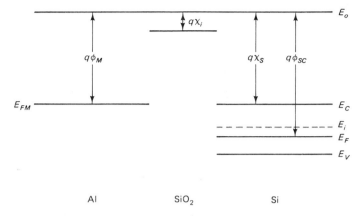

Figure 2.2   Energy levels in the three separate components of the MOS system.

defined as the difference between the vacuum energy level and the Fermi energy level in the semiconductor. These definitions are shown in Figure 2.2.

The MOS system's band diagram is formed when the three regions are brought in contact. When $\phi_m + V_G = \phi_{sc}$, where V_G is the gate voltage relative to the substrate, as shown in Figure 2.3, the flatband condition is formed. From Figure 2.3, ϕ_{sc} is found to be

$$\phi_{sc} = \left(\chi_s + \frac{E_G}{2q} + \phi_B \right) \tag{2.1}$$

where E_G is the semiconductor gap energy, and ϕ_B is the bulk potential

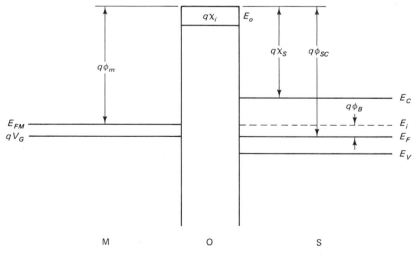

Figure 2.3   Flatband condition.

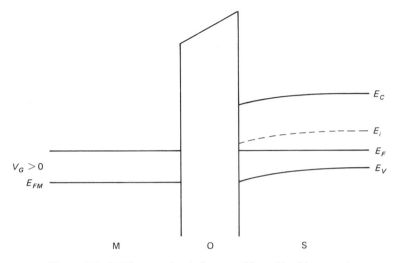

Figure 2.4   MOS energy band diagram with positive bias on gate.

defined as

$$\phi_B = (E_F - E_i)/q \qquad (2.2)$$

If the substrate (p-type in this example) is grounded and a positive voltage is applied to the gate, the bands will bend downward as illustrated in Figure 2.4. Since we have assumed no current can flow through the oxide, the Fermi energy must remain constant as a function of position. This implies that for the static case the MOS structure always remains in thermal equilibrium regardless of gate voltage. Even though the Fermi energy is constant within each material, the values in the gate and the semiconductor will split in magnitude by an amount determined by the gate voltage

$$E_{FM} = -qV_G + E_F \qquad (2.3)$$

Defining $y = 0$ to be the interface between the SiO$_2$–Si boundary, the following statements can be made about various V_G bias conditions. If V_G is sufficiently large to cause

$$E_F = E_i(0) \qquad (2.4)$$

as shown in Figure 2.5, the semiconductor surface is depleted of mobile carriers. The depletion region, W_D, extends into the substrate a distance of

$$W_D = \sqrt{\frac{2\varepsilon_s \phi_B}{qN_A}} \qquad (2.5)$$

where ε_s is the permittivity of the semiconductor and N_A is the substrate doping concentration. Since the majority and minority carrier concentrations,

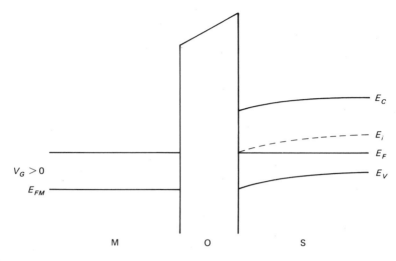

Figure 2.5   MOS energy band diagram in depletion.

p_p and n_p, in the depletion region are significantly smaller in magnitude than the substrate doping concentration, they can be neglected in most calculations involving this region.

If the gate voltage is further increased to cause

$$E_F - E_i(0) = q\phi_B \qquad (2.6)$$

the system is defined as being in strong inversion, as shown in Figure 2.6. The Fermi level has crossed over the intrinsic Fermi level and the concentration of

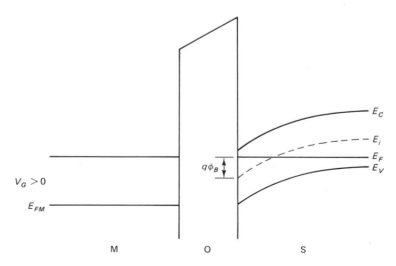

Figure 2.6   MOS energy band diagram in strong inversion.

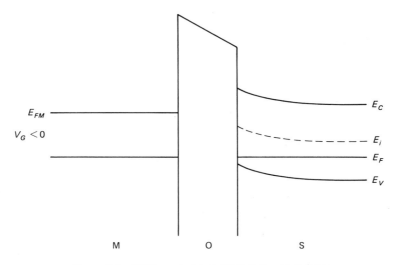

Figure 2.7   MOS energy band diagram in accumulation.

minority carriers at the surface, electrons in this case, is equal in magnitude to the substrate doping concentration. This inversion layer is approximately 100 Å thick and produces a highly conductive electron skin along the surface.

If a negative voltage is applied to the gate, holes are attracted to the surface and the device is said to be in accumulation, as shown in Figure 2.7.

A solution of the electrostatic potential, ψ, as a function of y into the semiconductor allows a complete description of the carrier concentration. The electrostatic potential is defined as

$$\psi \triangleq \left[E_i(y) - E_i(\text{bulk}) \right]/q \qquad (2.7)$$

The electrostatic potential evaluated at the surface, $y = 0$, will be called the surface potential, ψ_s. For a grounded bulk, the potential and the electric field, related by

$$E = -\nabla\psi \qquad (2.8)$$

both go to zero as $y \rightarrow \infty$ in the bulk.

To obtain a solution for ψ, we must solve Poisson's equation. In one dimension, Poisson's equation is

$$\frac{d^2\psi}{dy^2} = -\frac{\rho}{\varepsilon_s} \qquad (2.9)$$

where ρ, the charge density is

$$\rho = q\left(p_p - n_p + N_D - N_A \right) \qquad (2.10)$$

The majority carrier concentration, p_p, and the minority carrier concentration, n_p, can be expressed as

$$p_p = n_i e^{\beta(\phi_B - \psi)} \tag{2.11}$$

and

$$n_p = n_i e^{\beta(\psi - \phi_B)} \tag{2.12}$$

where n_i is the intrinsic carrier concentration and $\beta = q/kT$ is the inverse of thermal voltage. In the bulk, $\psi = 0$ and $\rho = 0$, hence

$$N_D - N_A = n_{po} - p_{po}, \tag{2.13}$$

where

$$p_{po} = n_i e^{\beta \phi_B} \tag{2.14}$$

and

$$n_{po} = n_i e^{-\beta \phi_B} \tag{2.15}$$

Therefore, Poisson's equation may be expressed as

$$\frac{d^2\psi}{dy^2} = \frac{-q}{\varepsilon_s} \left[p_{po}(e^{-\beta\psi} - 1) - n_{po}(e^{\beta\psi} - 1) \right] \tag{2.16}$$

Integrating from the bulk toward the surface gives

$$\int_0^\psi \frac{d^2\psi}{dy^2} d\psi = \frac{-q}{\varepsilon_s} \int_0^\psi \left[p_{po}(e^{-\beta\psi} - 1) - n_{po}(e^{\beta\psi} - 1) \right] d\psi \tag{2.17}$$

The left-hand-side of (2.17) can be transformed into

$$\int_0^\psi \frac{d^2\psi}{dy^2} d\psi = \int_0^{\partial\psi/\partial x} \left(\frac{d\psi}{dx} \right) d\left(\frac{d\psi}{dx} \right) \tag{2.18}$$

With this transformation, (2.17) may be integrated to give

$$E^2 = \left(\frac{2}{\beta} \right)^2 \left(\frac{qp_{po}\beta}{2\varepsilon_s} \right) \left[(e^{-\beta\psi} + \beta\psi - 1) + \frac{n_{po}}{p_{po}}(e^{\beta\psi} - \beta\psi - 1) \right] \tag{2.19}$$

Unfortunately, (2.19) does not give an expression relating ψ to y, but rather ψ to the electric field.

For convenience [3], we define

$$F(\psi) \triangleq \left[(e^{-\beta\psi} + \beta\psi - 1) + \frac{n_{po}}{p_{po}}(e^{\beta\psi} - \beta\psi - 1) \right]^{1/2} \tag{2.20}$$

Therefore the electric field is

$$E = \pm \frac{\sqrt{2}}{\beta L_D} F(\psi) \tag{2.21}$$

where L_D is the extrinsic Debye length for holes defined as

$$L_D = \sqrt{\frac{\varepsilon_s}{q p_{po} \beta}} \tag{2.22}$$

Using Gauss's law, the space charge per unit area in the semiconductor is

$$Q_s = -\varepsilon_s E_s = -\frac{\sqrt{2}\,\varepsilon_s}{\beta L_D} F(\psi_s) \tag{2.23}$$

Figure 2.8 shows the variation in the space charge as a function of the surface potential. Notice the sharp increase in change as ψ_s increases past $2\phi_B$. Hence, the onset of strong inversion is defined as occurring when

$$\psi_s = 2\phi_B = \frac{2kT}{q} \ln\left(\frac{N_A}{n_i}\right) \tag{2.24}$$

We have so far neglected a very important characteristic of the MOS system, traps at the SiO_2–Si interface and oxide fixed charge. The influence of

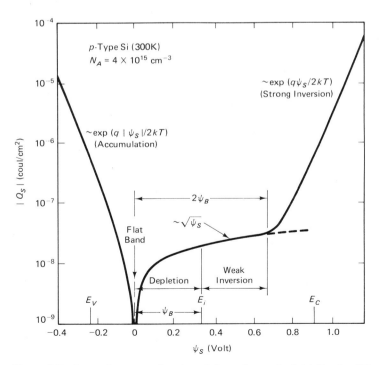

Figure 2.8 Space charge as a function of the surface potential (after Sze [3]).

a nonideal interface and oxide can cause significant changes in the electrical behavior of the MOS system and devices made from this structure. Surface properties can be the dominant influence on the electrical stability and reproductivity of the MOS system. To illustrate the importance of charge at the surface of the substrate on the electrical behavior of the MOS system, consider the surface density of the mobile charge in the inversion layer. For strong inversion, the number of electrons per unit area, Q_n/q, where Q_n is the electron charge per unit area, is equal to the substrate doping per unit area. For a uniformly doped substrate of $1 \times 10^{16}/cm^3$, Qn/q is $4.6 \times 10^{10}/cm^2$. Compared to the area density of Si atoms of $1.36 \times 10^{15}/cm^2$, a surface density of electrons of 3×10^{-5} times the atomic surface density can cause major electrical changes in the MOS system.

There are two types of charge centers at the SiO_2–Si interface, interface trap charge, Q_{it}, and oxide fixed charge, Q_f. Interface traps are defects located at the interface. Part of the interface traps arise from uncompleted silicon-silicon bonds at the surface. Interface trap charges are localized at centers that can exchange their charge with mobile carriers in the silicon. The charge in the interface traps can change states with gate voltage if the trap level is below the Fermi level. This voltage dependent Q_{it} will cause a distortion of the C–V curve as shown in Figure 2.9.

The second type of charge is oxide fixed charge. There are two main types of oxide fixed charge. The first type are localized charge centers that cannot change their charge state with mobile inversion layer carriers. These centers are predominantly positive, although a small number of negative centers may exist.

The second type of fixed oxide charge is mobile ionic charge. This type of charge is commonly caused by ionized alkali metal atoms such as sodium or

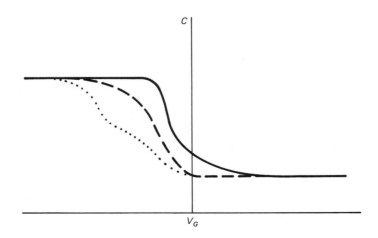

Figure 2.9 C–V curve. Ideal curve (solid line), addition of oxide fixed charge (dashed line), and charge that is influenced by the gate voltage (dotted line).

potassium. Sodium is especially troublesome since it is present in many metals and easily transmitted by human contact. These ions can drift in SiO_2 at relatively low gate voltages and can cause unstable device characteristics.

Two methods which introduce fixed oxide charge and interface traps are radiation and hot carrier injection. Hot carrier injection is enhanced in small-geometry structures by the large electric fields present and can cause serious time dependent device instabilities. Hot carriers are discussed in Section 2.6.

Interface traps and oxide fixed charge affect the electrical behavior of the capacitors and devices made from this structure. Interface traps can affect device gain at inversion since fields leaving from the gate are not compensated by additional mobile carriers, but by charged interface traps. Hence, interface traps reduce conductivity modulation of the inversion layer. High interface trap level densities (greater than $10^{11}/cm^2$ eV) can also cause increased noise as the traps fill and discharge [4].

The localization of interface traps and oxide fixed charge can be important in small surface area devices. Interface traps are very sensitive to mobile carrier densities near the traps. Just before the surface is inverted, the surface carriers are especially sensitive to the localized nature of interface traps. Oxide fixed charge near the drain in a small MOSFET can influence the voltage required for strong inversion and the symmetry of the device under interchange of the source and drain.

Interface traps and oxide fixed charge are sensitive to the fabrication process. Oxidation conditions, annealing, and contaminants are especially important. After fabrication, densities of $10^{11}/cm^2$ are common. This density level is unacceptable and may be reduced to an acceptable level of $10^{10}/cm^2$ by annealing in forming gas (a hydrogen-nitrogen mixture at 450°C for 30 minutes).

To illustrate the effect of fixed oxide charge on the MOS system's behavior, we will approximate Q_f as residing in a plane at $y = y_1$, inside the oxide. As this plane of charge moves from $y = -t_{ox}$, the gate electrode, to the Si–SiO$_2$ interface, $y = 0$, a greater fraction of charge will be induced in the substrate. From Gauss's law,

$$E_{ox} = -Q_f/\varepsilon_{ox} \quad \text{for} \quad -t_{ox} < y < y_1 \qquad (2.25)$$

The gate voltage resulting from this charge sheet is $(y_1 + t_{ox})E_{ox}$ also expressed as $Q_f(y_1 + t_{ox})/C_{ox}t_{ox}$. For a reference, the voltage required to force the energy bands to be flat is termed the flatband voltage, V_{FB}. For the ideal case, the flatband voltage is equal to the difference in the work function of the gate and the semiconductor. For the non-ideal case the voltage resulting from a charge sheet will add to the ideal flatband voltage giving

$$V_{FB} = \phi_{ms} - \frac{Q_f(y_1 + t_{ox})}{C_{ox}t_{ox}} \qquad (2.26)$$

Maximum shift in V_{FB} will occur when the sheet of charge is located at the SiO_2–Si interface.

The approximation of all oxide fixed charge contained in a uniform charge sheet is, of course, not accurate. The charge will be distributed throughout the oxide with a distribution of charge $\rho_{ox}(y)$. Integrating the product of the charge distribution and its location gives the contribution to the V_{FB} from the fixed oxide charge as

$$-\frac{1}{C_{ox}} \int_{-t_{ox}}^{0} \frac{y\rho_{ox}(y)\,dy}{t_{ox}} \tag{2.27}$$

The last component of the flatband voltage is the interface trap charge, Q_{it}. Its contribution is

$$-Q_{it}/C_{ox} \tag{2.28}$$

Hence, the V_{FB} is the sum of three terms: the gate-semiconductor work function difference, the oxide fixed charge distributed throughout the oxide, and the interface charge. Combining the terms gives

$$V_{FB} = \phi_{ms} - \frac{Q_{it}}{C_{ox}} - \frac{1}{C_{ox}} \int_{-t_{ox}}^{0} \frac{y\rho_{ox}(y)}{t_{ox}}\,dy \tag{2.29}$$

A typical value of V_{FB} for n^+ doped polysilicon gate is $-.9$ V for a $1 \times 10^{16}/cm^3$ substrate doping.

The purpose in discussing the MOS structure has been to introduce the effects of an insulated gate on a semiconductor without adding the complexities of current flow in the semiconductor. We will now extend this description to include a source and drain and hence the possibility of current flow to develop an understanding of the MOSFET.

2.2 MOSFET: QUALITATIVE THEORY OF OPERATION

Figure 2.10 is a three-dimensional view of a simplified MOSFET structure, with cross sections shown in Figures 2.11 and 2.12. Physically, the MOSFET is simply a MOS device with two implanted regions at each end. The substrate is either n-type or p-type for PMOS or NMOS, respectively, and the sources and drains are heavily doped with an opposite species. Also shown in Figure 2.10 is the standard voltage notation. In the normal operation of an NMOS structure, the source is taken as the reference point and is typically grounded. The substrate is either grounded or biased negative for NMOS, and the drain and gate are biased positive. The substrate contact, while shown at the back of the wafer, is often connected with an ohmic contact at the surface of the substrate outside the channel area, but electrically the surface or substrate back are the same. For proper field effect operation, the polarities of the

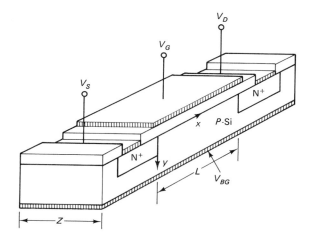

Figure 2.10   Three-dimensional view of a MOSFET.

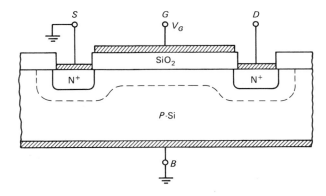

Figure 2.11   MOSFET length cross section.

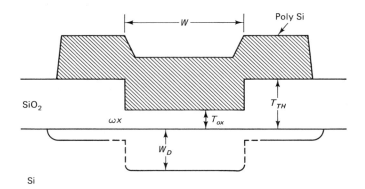

Figure 2.12   MOS width cross section.

source and drain junction are such as to always produce zero or reverse biased diodes with the substrate.

First, consider the case with the drain-to-source voltage, V_{DS}, grounded, and vary the gate-to-source voltage, V_{GS}, in the positive direction. For $V_{GS} <$ V_T, where V_T, the threshold voltage, is the voltage required to form an inversion layer, the device is in the subthreshold mode. A depletion region exists from the surface to a depth W_D into the substrate, where W_D is

$$W_D = \sqrt{\frac{2\varepsilon_s(\psi_s)}{qN_A}} \qquad (2.30)$$

This depletion region is assumed to be uniform over both the length and width directions—an approximation that is not valid in small MOSFET devices.

When V_{GS} is biased greater than V_T, the depth of the depletion region saturates at

$$W_{D\,max} = \sqrt{\frac{2\varepsilon_s(2\phi_B)}{qN_A}} \qquad (2.31)$$

and electrons are attracted to the surface to form an inversion layer. This inversion layer is typically considered to be a rectangular region uniformly filled with carriers to a depth of approximately 100 Å. Actually, the carrier density in the inversion layer decays approximately exponentially toward the bulk. The carriers in the inversion region are mobile and form a conductive skin, near the surface, connecting the source and drain. As V_{GS} is further increased, the surface potential increases only slowly beyond $2\phi_B$, and the increased gate voltage is dropped across the oxide. Hence, the gate voltage is used to create a conductive channel between the source and drain.

The drain bias provides for the flow of electrons from the source to the drain. For $V_{GS} < V_T$ and $V_{DS} > 0$, the subthreshold mode, a small but potentially important current flows. Since the region between the source and drain is depleted, the current flows by diffusion. This current, as will be shown, is constant for all drain voltages > 100 mV. This subthreshold current affects the speed at which the device can turn on or off, as well as the standby power dissipation. If V_{GS} is increased beyond V_T, and V_{DS} is kept less than $V_{GS} - V_T$, the inversion layer thus formed allows current to flow and the structure behaves like a voltage controlled resistor. This corresponds to region 1 of the static $I_D - V_{DS}$ output curve of Figure 2.13. As V_{DS} is increased further, the drain depletion region expands since it is reversed biased (as shown in Figure 2.14), and the inversion region starts to decrease near the drain. Further increases in the drain voltage cause additional reductions in the inversion layer depth, resulting in sublinear channel current behavior, as

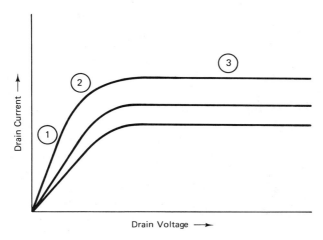

Figure 2.13   Static output curves: (1) linear region, (2) near saturation region, and (3) saturation region.

shown in region 2 of Figure 2.13. Continued increases in V_{DS} cause complete depletion of the inversion region at the drain edge and result in a condition called pinch-off. In pinch-off, a depletion region exists between the end of the inversion region and the drain junction. The drain voltage that causes pinch-off is defined as the saturation voltage, $V_{DS\,sat}$. As V_{DS} is increased above $V_{DS\,sat}$, the pinch-off region expands toward the source. Below pinch-off, the voltage drop along the channel is approximately linear. However, once the device is biased past pinch-off, the additional increase in voltage past pinch-off is dropped across the region from the pinch-off point to the drain. Therefore, the current, which is determined by the voltage drop from the pinch-off point to the source, will remain approximately constant, as shown in region 3 of Figure 2.13.

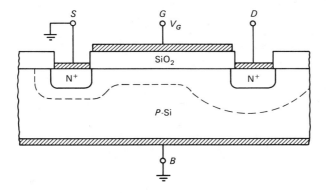

Figure 2.14   Depletion profile.

This section qualitatively explains the MOSFET behavior when the channel length and width are large, e.g., 4 μm or greater. As we shall see, reduction in these dimensions causes significant changes in device behavior which must be understood.

2.3 CLASSICAL MOSFET BEHAVIOR

To obtain the total charge within the inversion layer and the electrostatic potential, as a function of position, Poisson's equation must be solved for the MOSFET structure in nonequilibrium. The solution procedure is similar to that described in Section 2.1, except that source and drain junctions are introduced and a voltage is applied between these junctions. In nonequilibrium, the potential in the inversion region at a point x may be approximated as

$$\psi(x) = 2\phi_B + V_c(x) \tag{2.32}$$

where $V_c(x)$ is the voltage drop from the source to the point x.

Assuming ψ varies approximately linear with x, Poisson's equation at point x is

$$\frac{d^2\psi(y)}{dy^2} = \frac{-q}{\varepsilon_s}\left(N_D^+ - N_A^- + p_p - n_p\right) \tag{2.33}$$

where

$$p_p = n_i e^{-\beta(\psi - \phi_B)} \tag{2.34}$$

and

$$n_p = n_i e^{\beta(\psi - \phi_B - V_c(x))} \tag{2.35}$$

Equation (2.35) results from the electron and hole Fermi energies, E_{FN} and E_{FP}, respectively, splitting by $V_c(x)$, as shown in Figure 2.15. With no applied substrate bias, the voltage and the electric field in the bulk are zero. Charge neutrality requires in the bulk

$$N_D^+ - N_A^- = n_i e^{-\beta\phi_B} + n_i e^{\beta\phi_B} \tag{2.36}$$

Therefore, Equation (2.33) can be expressed as

$$\frac{d^2\psi(y)}{dy^2} = \frac{-q}{\varepsilon_s}\left[n_i\left(e^{\beta\phi_B} - e^{-\beta(\psi - \phi_B)}\right)\right.$$
$$\left. - n_i\left(e^{-\beta\phi_B} - e^{\beta(\psi - \phi_B - V_c(x))}\right)\right] \tag{2.37}$$

Using the transformation shown in Equation (2.18) and integrating from the

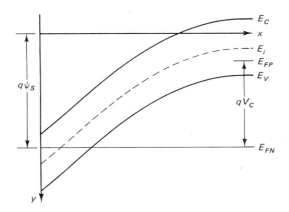

Figure 2.15 Energy band diagram illustrating the split in the Fermi energies caused by an applied voltage.

bulk toward the surface gives the electric field as

$$E = -\frac{\partial \psi}{\partial y} = \pm \frac{\sqrt{2}}{\beta L_D} F(\psi, V_c(x))$$ (2.38)

where

$$F\left[(\psi, V_c(x))\right]$$
$$= \left[e^{-\beta\psi} + \beta\psi - 1 + e^{-\beta(2\phi_B + V_c(x))}\left(e^{\beta\psi} - \beta\psi e^{\beta V_c(x)} - 1\right)\right]^{1/2}$$ (2.39)

The total charge within the inversion layer per unit area is

$$Q_n = q \int_0^{y_i} n(y)\, dy$$ (2.40)

where y_i is the depth of the inversion layer. Using a simple transformation, this equation may be expressed as

$$Q_n = -q \int_{\psi_s}^{\phi_B} \frac{n(\psi)}{E}\, d\psi$$ (2.41)

Unfortunately, as in Section 2.1, neither the electrostatic potential nor the total charge can be expressed explicitly in closed form as a function of distance. For example, integrating (2.38) gives

$$\frac{y}{L_D} = \int_\psi^{\psi_s} \frac{\beta}{\sqrt{2}\, F(\psi, V_c(x))}\, d\psi$$ (2.42)

Equation (2.42) is not integrable in closed form, and therefore numerical techniques must be used to obtain ψ as a function of y. Once ψ as a function of y is obtained, E and ρ as a function of position may be obtained. Figures

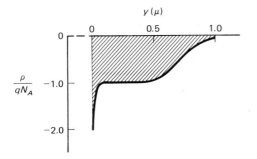

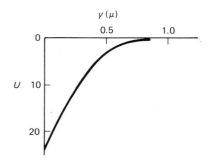

Figure 2.16 Normalized charge density at the onset of inversion as a function of position in the semiconductor (after Pierret [5]).

Figure 2.17 Normalized electrostatic potential at the onset of inversion as a function of position into the semiconductor (after Pierret [5]).

2.16 and 2.17 illustrate how ρ and U, where U is the normalized electrostatic potential, vary with position.

The total current in the MOSFET may be obtained by integrating the incremental channel conductance, $\mu_n W Q_n$, from source to drain. This may be expressed as

$$I_D = -\frac{W\mu_n q\beta_{n_i}^2 L_D}{L\sqrt{2}\,N_A} \int_0^{V_{DS}} \int_{\phi_B}^{\psi_s} \frac{e^{\beta(\psi - V_c)}}{F(\psi, V_c)} d\psi \, dV_c \qquad (2.43)$$

While (2.38), (2.41), and (2.43) are accurate for large geometry devices, they are complex and obscure a clear picture of device operation. A much simpler, yet not as accurate, expression for the potential, total charge, and current may be obtained from the following charge control models.

2.3.1 Subthreshold Current

Most classical analyses assume zero current for $V_{GS} \leq V_T$. This is not true for small or large geometry MOSFETs. While with large devices this current can often be neglected, with small devices this current can be significant. The subthreshold current arises when the surface potential is between $\phi_B \leq \psi_s \leq 2\phi_B$. This range of operation is called weak inversion. The minority carrier concentration in the region near the surface is equal to the intrinsic carrier concentration for $\psi_s = \phi_B$, and equal to the magnitude of the majority carrier concentration for $\psi_s = 2\phi_B$. For ψ_s less than $2\phi_B$, the current flow is almost exclusively by diffusion, but as ψ_s approaches $2\phi_B$, a component of drift current appears.

Approximating the current flow in the subthreshold region entirely by diffusion,

$$I_D = -qAD_n\frac{\partial n}{\partial x} \qquad (2.44)$$

where A is the cross-sectional area the current flows through, and D_n is the electron diffusion constant. Since the drain current is constant along the channel, (2.44) may be solved to yield

$$I_D = qAD_n\left[\frac{n(s) - n(d)}{L}\right] \tag{2.45}$$

where $n(s)$ is the electron concentration at the source-channel edge, and $n(d)$ is the concentration evaluated at the channel-drain edge. These concentrations can be expressed as

$$n(s) = n_i e^{\beta(\psi_s - \phi_B)} \tag{2.46}$$

and

$$n(d) = n_i e^{\beta(\psi_s - \phi_B - V_{DS})} \tag{2.47}$$

The area A through which the current flows is the width of the device W times the depth of the region y_c. The effective channel width will be defined in more detail in Section 2.5.2.3, but for now it can be considered to be the width of the gate electrode. The depth of the region in which the current flows can be defined as the distance for the surface potential to decrease by $1/\beta$, or 25 mV at room temperature. Therefore, y_c can be defined as

$$y_c = \frac{\beta}{E_s} \tag{2.48}$$

where the electric field at the surface is

$$E_s = -Q_B/\varepsilon_s = \sqrt{2qN_A\psi_s/\varepsilon_s} \tag{2.49}$$

with Q_B being the bulk charge. The cross sectional area can now be expressed as

$$A = \frac{W\beta}{\sqrt{2qN_A\psi_s/\varepsilon_s}} \tag{2.50}$$

Substituting (2.50) into (2.45) gives the subthreshold current for a long channel, wide MOSFET as

$$I_D = \frac{qD_n\beta n_i e^{\beta(\psi_s - \phi_B)}(1 - e^{-\beta V_{DS}})}{\sqrt{2qN_A\psi_s/\varepsilon_s}} \tag{2.51}$$

Two important characteristics of the subthreshold current are observed. First, the current is exponentially dependent on ψ_s. Figure 2.18 shows a plot of the log of the subthreshold current versus V_{GS}. V_{GS} is related to ψ_s through the voltage drop across the oxide. Notice that the curve is linear until the device starts to turn on. The second point to be observed is that for $V_{DS} > 100$ mV, the negative exponential of (2.51) rapidly becomes very small and the drain voltage has little or no effect on the subthreshold current.

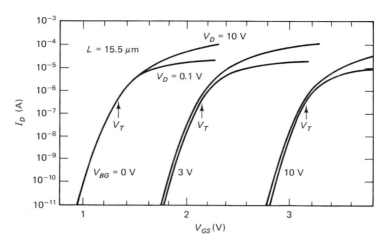

Figure 2.18 Subthreshold current versus V_{GS} (after Troutman [6], ©1974, IEEE).

2.3.2 Linear Operation

A number of formulations have been developed to simulate the linear mode of operation. We will start from the simplest and advance to a more complex and accurate expression.

The simplest description of the MOSFET is to consider the carriers as particles traveling from the source to the drain with a constant velocity. The time required to traverse the channel, L, is

$$\tau = \frac{L}{v} \tag{2.52}$$

where v is the carrier velocity. The velocity is related to the electric field, E, by the mobility

$$v = \mu E \tag{2.53}$$

Approximating the voltage drop from the source to drain to be linear

$$E = \frac{V_{DS}}{L} \tag{2.54}$$

and hence

$$\tau = \frac{L^2}{\mu E} \tag{2.55}$$

Equation (2.55) allows us to make a few important observations. To increase the switching speed of the MOSFET the channel length should be reduced. Furthermore, the electric field should be increased and the mobility needs to be increased or at least made as large as possible. As we shall see in Section 2.5, today's small devices use both of these concepts to increase device speed.

The current is calculated by dividing the total charge in the channel by the transit time. The inversion charge can be approximated as being induced by the gate voltage, once V_{GS} is greater than the threshold voltage. This concept explicitly neglects any subthreshold current. Using Gauss's law

$$Q_n = -C_{ox}(V_{GS} - V_T)WL \qquad (2.56)$$

where C_{ox} is the oxide capacitance per unit area. Hence, the current in the device is

$$I_{DS} = -\frac{Q_n}{\tau} \qquad (2.57)$$

or

$$I_{DS} = \mu C_{ox}\frac{W}{L}(V_{GS} - V_T)V_{DS} \qquad (2.58)$$

While this expression is very elementary, some important observations can be made. Increased current drive can be obtained by reducing the channel length or the threshold voltage, and by increasing the width or the gate and drain voltages. Equation (2.58) also allows the RC charging time to be calculated. Assuming we are driving an identical device, the charging time is

$$\tau_{RC} = \frac{V_{DS}}{I_{DS}}C_{ox} \qquad (2.59)$$

or

$$\tau_{RC} = \frac{L^2}{\mu C_{ox}(V_{GS} - V_T)} \qquad (2.60)$$

This once again points out that short channel lengths, wide gate widths, and large overdrive, i.e., $(V_{GS} - V_T)$, are required for fast circuits.

These simple expressions are very first order and rapidly become invalid. For example, (2.58) is valid only in the linear mode of operation. One reason this expression fails is the assumption that the electric field is constant from source to drain which is incorrect for even moderate drain voltages.

A more accurate, yet more complex expression for the static output curves can be derived. The current density can be written as

$$J_n = q\mu_n nE + qD_n\nabla n \qquad (2.61)$$

In the linear region, the current flow is mostly by drift. Hence, (2.61) may be expressed as

$$J_n = -q\mu_n n\frac{dV}{dx} \qquad (2.62)$$

Assuming that no generation or recombination occurs, and that steady-state conditions exist, the current flowing through any cross-section in the channel must equal the drain current. Integrating (2.62),

$$I_D = \int_0^{y_i} \int_0^W J_n \, dz \, dy \tag{2.63}$$

$$= -qW \int_0^{y_i} \mu_n n \frac{dV}{dx} \, dy \tag{2.64}$$

Considering the inversion layer as a thin, highly conductive layer allows us to assume dV/dx is constant in y. The mobility may be considered either as constant or to be an effective mobility that may be defined and removed from the integral. The equation to be integrated is now

$$I_D = -W \frac{dV}{dx} \mu_n \int_0^{y_i} qn \, dy \tag{2.65}$$

Integrating in the depth direction gives the total charge Q_n. Hence

$$I_D = -W \mu_n Q_n \frac{dV}{dx} \tag{2.66}$$

Integrating along the channel length direction, x, and noting that current continuity requires I_D to be independent of x, gives

$$I_D \int_0^L dx = -\int_0^{V_{DS}} W \mu_n Q_n \, dV \tag{2.67}$$

and

$$I_D = -\frac{W \mu_n}{L} \int_0^{V_{DS}} Q_n \, dV \tag{2.68}$$

The total charge induced in the semiconductor per unit area, Q_s, at some point x in the channel is

$$Q_s(x) = [-V_{GS} + \psi_s(x)] C_{\text{ox}} \tag{2.69}$$

The charge in the inversion layer is simply

$$Q_n(x) = Q_s(x) - Q_B(x) \tag{2.70}$$

$$= [-V_{GS} + \psi_s(x)] C_{\text{ox}} - Q_B(x) \tag{2.71}$$

The bulk charge per unit area may be expressed as

$$Q_B = -q N_A W_D \tag{2.72}$$

$$= -\sqrt{2 \varepsilon_s q N_A (V(x) + 2\phi_B)} \tag{2.73}$$

Substituting (2.73) into (2.71) gives

$$Q_n(x) = -(V_{GS} - V(x) - 2\phi_B) C_{\text{ox}}$$
$$+ \sqrt{2 \varepsilon_s q N_A (V(x) + 2\phi_B)} \tag{2.74}$$

Integrating (2.68) using (2.74) gives the static output equation as

$$I_D = \frac{W}{L}\mu_n C_{ox}\left\{\left[\left(V_{GS} - 2\phi_B - \frac{V_{DS}}{2}\right)V_{DS}\right]\right.$$
$$\left. - \frac{2}{3}\frac{\sqrt{2\varepsilon_s qN_A}}{C_{ox}}\left[(V_{DS} + 2\phi_B)^{3/2} - (2\phi_B)^{3/2}\right]\right\} \tag{2.75}$$

Equation (2.75) will simulate the MOSFET in both the linear region and in the approach to saturation. For small V_{DS}, (2.75) reduces to

$$I_D = \frac{W}{L}\mu_n C_{ox}\left[(V_{GS} - V_T)V_{DS} - \frac{V_{DS}^2}{2}\right] \tag{2.76}$$

where V_T is defined as

$$V_T = 2\phi_B + \frac{1}{C_{ox}}\sqrt{2\varepsilon_s qN_A(2\phi_B)} \tag{2.77}$$

Notice the additional quadratic term in Equation (2.76) which differs from the simpler form of Equation (2.58). This quadratic term will reduce the slope of the $I_D - V_{DS}$ curve at large V_{DS}.

2.3.3 Saturation Region

Equation (2.75) is not valid in the saturation region. Once the inversion layer has collapsed in the drain region, (2.71) used to obtain (2.75) is not valid. If we approximate the drain voltage required to cause the inversion region to pinch-off at the drain end of the channel as

$$V_{DS\,sat} = V_{GS} - V_T \tag{2.78}$$

(2.76) may be rewritten as

$$I_D = \mu_n C_{ox}\frac{W}{2L}(V_{GS} - V_T)^2 \tag{2.79}$$

We observe that the drain current is independent of the drain voltage and has a square law dependence upon the gate voltage. As we shall see in Section 2.4, neither of these characteristics are valid for a small MOSFET.

A more exact expression for the saturated drain voltage may be obtained from (2.74) by solving for $V(L)$, defined as the saturated drain voltage, with $Q_n(L) = 0$. $V_{DS\,sat}$ obtained from this equation is

$$V_{DS\,sat} = V_{GS} - 2\phi_B + K^2\left(1 - \sqrt{1 + 2V_{GS}/K^2}\right) \tag{2.80}$$

where

$$K = \sqrt{\varepsilon_s qN_A/C_{ox}} \tag{2.81}$$

This gives a saturation current of

$$I_D = \frac{W}{6L} \mu_n C_{\text{ox}} \left[(V_{DS\,\text{sat}} + 2\phi_B)^2 \right.$$

$$\left. + V_{GS}(V_{DS\,\text{sat}} + 2\phi_B) - 12\phi_B\left(V_{GS} - \phi_B - 4/3K\sqrt{\phi_B}\right) \right] \tag{2.82}$$

2.4 MOSFET PARAMETERS

Various terminal measurements are used to characterize the behavior of a MOSFET. While in large devices these measurements are straightforward and the device parameters extracted from the measurements are thought to be unique, this is not the case as devices are reduced in size. The interpretation of the MOSFET parameters can become ambiguous and at times erroneous in small devices. Care must always be used with their application.

2.4.1 Mobility

The carrier mobilities of electrons and holes, μ_n and μ_p, are a measure of the ease of motion of the electrons and holes within the semiconductor crystal. In the bulk of the semiconductor, far away from any interface, the carrier mobility is determined primarily by lattice scattering and ionized impurity scattering. This results in $\mu_n = 1350$ cm^2/V-s and $\mu_p = 480$ cm^2/V-s in silicon. These are bulk mobility values and while some devices, such as a buried channel device, can take advantage of these values, most structures have carriers flowing near interfaces. The interface or surface mobility is considerably less than the bulk mobility and is in the range of 300 cm^2/V-s to 700 cm^2/V-s for electrons and 100 cm^2/V-s to 300 cm^2/V-s for holes. This reduction results from carriers being constrained to the thin inversion layer. The electron to hole mobility ratio is approximately 2 to 3. The electron mobility has been studied, both experimentally and theoretically, for a great many years. It has been found from these measurements that the mobility scales with an effective field in the semiconductor. This field is related to the bulk depletion charge and to the inversion charge. An increase in the effective normal field, due to an increase in either the depletion charge or the inversion charge, causes the carriers to be drawn closer to the interface and thus to suffer stronger scattering.

The mobility value is measured from the slope of the I_D versus V_{GS} curve at low gate and drain voltages. At higher gate voltages, the mobility further decreases. This results from the carrier being attracted closer to the interface causing increased surface scattering. The consequence of this reduction in mobility is reduced drive current and switching speed.

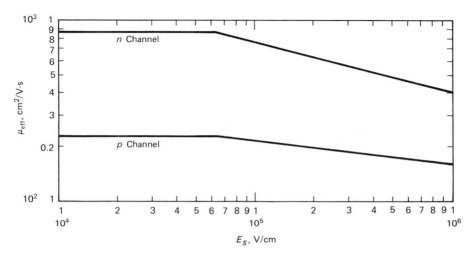

Figure 2.19 Effective mobility versus the gate field (after Ong [7]).

Figure 2.19 is a plot of the effective mobility versus the gate field. This effective mobility can be modeled as

$$\mu_{eff} = \frac{\mu_o}{1 + \Theta(V_{GS} - V_T)} \tag{2.83}$$

where Θ is the field reduction coefficient. Plotting $1/\mu_{eff}$ versus $V_{GS} - V_T$, Figure 2.20, and fitting a straight line to the data points allows μ_o and Θ to be determined.

In actual fact, the form of (2.83) is not correct, at least in terms of a physically understood theory. However, it is very useful for design, does not differ from the observed mobility variation, and fits well into the models. We

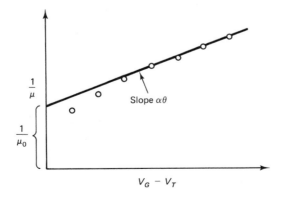

Figure 2.20 Determination of μ_o and Θ (after Ong [7]).

would like to have a better form though. At least three different scattering mechanisms have been proposed to account for the decreasing mobility in the channel carriers. These are: bulk and interface phonons, coulomb scattering due to the charge centers in or near the surface, and surface-roughness scattering. In general, the coulomb scattering due to the charge centers scatter by a screened potential which is ineffective at high carrier densities and temperatures. On the other hand, it has generally been felt that surface-roughness scattering was a significant contributor to the reduced mobility. However, we now know from direct measurements of the interface roughness parameters by high-resolution lattice-plane imaging techniques that the limiting mobility due to this mechanism is far too high to contribute much at normal effective fields. Moreover, the dependence of this mobility limiting mechanism goes as $1/E_{eff}^2$, which is much too rapid to fit the data in Figure 2.19. Consequently, surface-roughness scattering is found to be ineffective in determining the inversion layer mobility except in the very-high-normal field cases.

This then leaves us with only the contributions of bulk and interface phonons to the inversion layer mobility in strong inversion. We shall introduce an effective projection technique for estimating the role that scattering by bulk phonons will have on the inversion layer electrons. This technique scales the bulk lattice limited mobility by a factor given by the ratio of the inversion layer thickness to the unconstrained electron wavelength. The results of this process indicate that the normal bulk phonon scattering processes, when projected into the quantized inversion layer, have the proper size and effective field dependence to largely explain the mobility variations of the electrons. The contribution of the interface acoustic modes, essentially the scattering from interface Rayleigh waves, has the same field dependence as the bulk modes and contributes about 10% to the total scattering. This approach predicts a power law variation for the mobility on the effective normal field.

If we compare the quasi-two-dimensional scattering probabilities of each of the various phonon scattering processes with their three-dimensional equivalents, we are struck with an amazing fact. The quasi-two-dimensional scattering rate differs from its three-dimensional counterpart by just the factor

$$2\pi/k_{eff}y_{eff} \tag{2.84}$$

where k_{eff} is an effective value of the wavefunction in the final state of the scattering process and y_{eff} is the effective (average) thickness of the inversion layer. The former will involve the change in momentum due to the emission or absorption of a phonon, effects which tend to balance out in the equilibrium case. Thus, we may approximate (2.84) by the factor λ/w, where we have written w for the quantity y_{eff}. Thus, we may introduce this into the mobility, since it enters each scattering mechanism equally. Then, we can write

$$\mu_{2D} = \mu_{3D}(\lambda/w) \tag{2.85}$$

It remains now to determine the latter quantities.

In general, the thickness of the inversion layer can be found by assuming a simple model of the inversion potential. Here, we use the triangular well approximation, in which the surface-normal field is constant and equal to

$$E_{eff} = q\left[N_{depl} + N_{inv}/2\right]\epsilon_s \qquad (2.86)$$

The wave functions for this field (triangular potential) are Airy functions, and the lowest subband is given by the energy

$$E_o = \left(h^2/2m_3\right)^{1/3}\left(9\pi qE_{eff}/8\right)^{2/3} \qquad (2.87)$$

and the effective width of the inversion layer is just

$$w = E_o/qE_{eff} = \left(h^2/2m_3qE_{eff}\right)^{1/3}\left(9\pi/8\right)^{2/3} \qquad (2.88)$$

The electron wavelength is just $\lambda = h/(m_1 v)^{1/2}$ which, when averaged over the Maxwellian distribution function (to get the average momentum of the distribution), leads us to

$$\mu_{2D} = \mu_{3D}\left(E_c/_{eff}\right)^{1/3} \qquad (2.89)$$

where

$$E_c = \left(4/\pi\right)^3\left(2m_1kT/\pi h^2\right)^{3/2}\left(h^2\pi/4m_3q\right) \qquad (2.90)$$

Here, we have used m_3 as the mass normal to the interface and m_1 as the mass in the current flow direction along the interface (these are different due to the anisotropic band structure of Si in the quantizing effective field normal to the interface).

We note that this leads to a negative cube-root dependence of the surface mobility on the effective field. Substituting the values for the constants in (2.90) gives $E_c = 2.48 \times 10^4$ V/cm at room temperature. Additional scattering at the interface from acoustic modes arises from the possibility of Rayleigh waves at the interface. This scattering rate has been calculated by several workers [8, 9], and is beyond the treatment here. The result, however, is that

$$\mu_{SA} = qh^3\rho v_s^2 w/\lambda E_1^2 m_1^2 kT \qquad (2.91)$$

where λE_1^2 is the product of the new overlap integral and the deformation potential for the interface modes, ρ is the mass density of Si, and v_s is the velocity of sound in Si. We note that this mobility also varies as the negative cube root of the effective field, through the dependence upon w. The estimate is that this scattering is coupled through an effective potential (corrected for λ) of $E_1 = 4.2$ eV. In this case, the mobility given by the surface scattering is 1900 cm²/V-s at an effective field of 8.7×10^5 V/cm. Combining this with the previous values gives a new value for the three-dimensional mobility of 1075 cm²/V-s. This curve is shown in Figure 2.21, with the data for comparison. The surface-roughness scattering limit is also shown, and it is apparent that it does not explain the data.

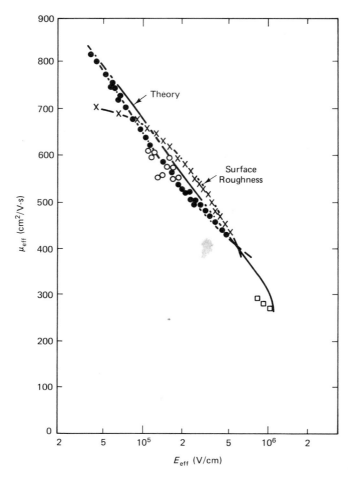

Figure 2.21 Comparison of the theoretical mobility and a variety of experimental measurements (after Ferry [10]).

2.4.2 Threshold Voltage

The threshold voltage, also called the turn-on voltage, V_T, has already been used in the classical current expression. The threshold voltage is related to the switching speed and the subthreshold leakage current and hence is a very important parameter. We will derive the threshold voltage by first assuming the length of the channel is much greater than the source or drain junction depletion depths, and the width is greater than the depth of the gate induced channel depletion region. Devices with $L \geq 3 \ \mu$m and $W \geq 4 \ \mu$m can typically be considered large. As we shall see in Section 2.5.2, for lengths and widths smaller than these values, significant variation in V_T with geometry

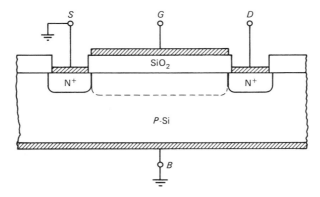

Figure 2.22 Assumed rectangular shaped depletion region.

occur. One also must assume that (1) the inversion region is basically created at $V_{GS} = V_T$ and (2) that current starts to flow at this gate voltage.

For a large geometry MOSFET, a one-dimensional model into the substrate is sufficient to derive V_T. This implies that the built-in depletion region at the source and drain can be neglected. The assumed shape of the gate-induced depletion region is illustrated in Figure 2.22. Charge neutrality in the region bounded by the gate electrode and the semiconductor bulk requires that

$$Q_G + Q_f - (Q_n + Q_B) = 0 \qquad (2.92)$$

where Q_G is the gate charge, Q_f is the fixed charge in the oxide, Q_n is the inversion layer charge and Q_B is the bulk charge. At $V_{GS} = V_T$, the inversion layer is just being created so we can approximate $Q_n < Q_B$ (and therefore neglect Q_n). Applying Gauss's law, the following voltage equation may be written

$$V_{GS} = V_{FB} + \psi_s + Q_B/(C_{ox}WL) \qquad (2.93)$$

At strong inversion, the surface potential is approximately $2\phi_B$, and the threshold voltage is therefore defined as the gate voltage required for $\psi_s = 2\phi_B$. The total bulk charge, Q_B, may be expressed as

$$Q_B = qN_A W_D WL \qquad (2.94)$$

Substituting (2.94) into (2.93) gives the classical threshold voltage expression

$$V_T = V_{FB} + 2\phi_B + \frac{qN_A W_D}{C_{ox}} \qquad (2.95)$$

Equation (2.95) is valid only for uniform substrate doping. A substrate bias may be included by simply modifying (2.73). A substrate bias will cause the depletion depth to increase and hence increase V_T. This equation also indicates that V_T is independent of device length or width. This is definitely incorrect in small devices as we show below.

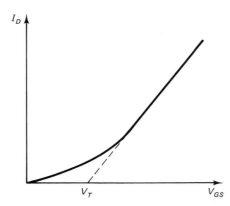

Figure 2.23 Method to determine threshold voltage.

The threshold voltage can be measured by a number of experimental methods. Each method unfortunately can give a slightly different value for V_T, so one must be careful in comparison of data with theory. The most popular experimental method used to determine V_T is to extrapolate the I_D versus V_{GS} curve to zero I_D for a low applied drain voltage (50 mV to 100 mV range), as shown in Figure 2.23. The V_{GS} intercept is defined as V_T. However, as may be seen from (2.76), the intercept also depends upon V_{DS}, so V_T should be reduced by $V_{DS}/2$. This 25 mV to 50 mV correction is normally neglected.

Closely related to the above method is the $\sqrt{I_D}$ measurement, in which the square root of I_D is plotted as a function of the gate voltage, with the device in saturation. A simple method to force the device into saturation is to tie the gate and drain terminals together. The curve is again extrapolated to zero I_D in order to define V_T. A problem with this method is that at large drain current, threshold voltage modulation with V_{DS} can occur. This will be discussed in more detail in Section 2.5.2.

Other methods to measure or calculate V_T exist. One method that is easy to automate is to define V_T as the gate voltage required for a drain current of 1 μA. The obvious problem with this method is it does not account for different W/L ratios. If the current is normalized to remove device size, the method does have merit. For numerical simulations, V_T is typically defined as the gate voltage required for the minimum of the surface potential in the source region to equal $2\phi_B$. A continuing problem has been to relate the V_T obtained from numerical device simulation to the experimental V_T. Since the definition of V_T is rather ambiguous and is becoming less exact as device size is reduced, simulations which indicate trends rather than exact values of V_T are probably more useful.

2.4.3 Transconductance

Transconductance, g_m commonly referred to as device gain, is directly related to circuit speed and needs to be maximized. Transconductance is defined as

$$g_m \triangleq \frac{\partial I_D}{\partial V_{GS}}\bigg|_{V_{DS} = \text{constant}} \tag{2.96}$$

In the linear region, for a large MOSFET,

$$g_m = \frac{W}{L}\mu C_{ox}V_{DS} \tag{2.97}$$

and in the saturated region

$$g_m = \frac{W}{L}\mu C_{ox}(V_{GS} - V_T) \tag{2.98}$$

These equations show that g_m is increased by reducing the channel length, threshold voltage, or oxide thickness, or increasing device width or gate voltage. These parameters, though, cannot be changed arbitrarily since they also depend upon a multitude of process factors and constraints.

2.4.4 Channel Conductance

Channel conductance, g_D, is the inverse of the channel resistance. When the device is in biased in the linear region of operation, it is important for the channel resistance to be as low as possible, hence g_D should be as large as possible. When the device is saturated, the channel resistance should be as large as possible, hence g_D should be small.

The channel conductance is defined as

$$g_D = \frac{\partial I_D}{\partial V_{DS}}\bigg|_{V_{GS} = \text{constant}} \tag{2.99}$$

For the classical large geometry MOSFET in the linear region

$$g_D = \frac{W}{L}\mu C_{ox}(V_{GS} - V_T) \tag{2.100}$$

and in the saturated region

$$g_D = 0 \tag{2.101}$$

The extreme simplicity of (2.79) is responsible for such a small saturated conductance. A more accurate calculation of g_D in the saturated region obtained from (2.82) give

$$g_D = \frac{\mu W C_{ox}\sqrt{2\varepsilon_s/qN_A}}{12\left[L\sqrt{V_D - V_{DS\text{sat}}} - \sqrt{2\varepsilon_s/qN_A}\,(V_D - V_{DS\text{sat}})\right]}$$
$$\times\left[(V_{DS\text{sat}} + 2\phi_B)^2 + V_{GS}(V_{DS\text{sat}} + 2\phi_B)\right.$$
$$\left. - 12\phi_B\left(V_{GS} - \phi_B - 4/3K\sqrt{\phi_B}\right)\right] \tag{2.102}$$

2.4.5 Swing

Measurement of the drain current in the subthreshold region provides a measure of how fast a device can be turned on or off. A device is considered off when the current has dropped an order of magnitude below its level at V_T. Swing, S, has been defined as the variation in the gate voltage in subthreshold required to reduce the drain current by one decade. By this definition,

$$S \triangleq \ln 10 \frac{dV_{GS}}{d(\ln I_D)}$$

(2.103)

Defining the depletion capacitance as

$$C_D = \frac{\partial Q_B}{\partial \psi_s}$$

(2.104)

the swing can be shown to be

$$S = \frac{kT}{q} \ln 10 \left(1 + \frac{C_D}{C_{ox}}\right)$$

(2.105)

From equation (2.105), it is observed that a minimum swing of 57.5 mV is required to turn off an ideal MOSFET. Swing can be reduced by decreasing the oxide thickness or substrate doping, or by the application of a substrate bias. In practice, swings in the range of 80 mV to 90 mV are quite common.

2.5 SMALL-GEOMETRY EFFECTS

The scaling down of MOS device size has reduced channel lengths from 25 μm to hundreds of nanometers. This reduction in device size has allowed increased circuit speed and increased circuit density. As these devices are scaled, previously neglected second-order effects such as threshold voltage variation with device size, subthreshold current modulated by drain voltage, velocity saturation, and hot carriers start dominating device behavior. This section will discuss these effects.

2.5.1 Device Scaling

The scaling down or shrinking of device size has been extensively used over the last decade to enhance device and circuit performance. This enhanced performance includes faster switching speed, lower power dissipation and smaller device and circuit area. The initial scaling concept [11], the constant-field scaling law, keeps the electric field in the channel constant as the device is scaled. This is obtained by reducing all geometries and voltages by a scaling factor α. The doping concentration is increased by α so the junction depletion

TABLE 2.1   Scaled Parameters and Their Effects (after Prince [12]).

Parameter	Scaling Factor
Device dimension-T_{ox}, L, W	$1/\alpha$
Doping concentration N_A	α
Voltage V	$1/\alpha$
Current I	$1/\alpha$
Logic gate area	$1/\alpha^2$
Depletion and oxide capacitance ($\varepsilon A/T$)	$1/\alpha$
Delay time ($R_{on}C = T_D$)	$1/\alpha$
DC power dissipation/gate($V \cdot I$)	$1/\alpha^2$
Chip DC power density ($V \cdot I/A$)	1
Power-delay product	$1/\alpha^3$
Frequency-dependent power dissipation (CV^2/T_D)	$1/\alpha^2$
Chip frequency-dependent power dissipation ($CV^2/T_D)/A$	1
Interconnection line resistance ($R_L = \rho L/WT$)	α
Normalized interconnection line voltage drop (IR/V)	α
Interconnection line response time ($R_L \cdot C_L$)	1
Interconnection line current density (I/A)	α
Contact resistance (R_C)	α^2
Contact voltage drop (V_C)	α
Normalized contact voltage drop (V_C/V)	α^2
Normalized line response time ($R_L \cdot C_L/T_D$)	α

depth is reduced by approximately α. The objective of keeping the electric field constant is to maintain large-geometry device behavior even in small-geometry devices. Scaling reduces the current drive and switching delay by α, and the power dissipation by α^2. Table 2.1 lists the scaled parameters and their effects.

Not all of the effects of scaling are beneficial. Notice in Table 2.1 that the interconnect resistance increases with scaling. Hence, the RC time constant will remain constant as the interconnect length, width, and thickness are scaled. Historically though, while chip size on specific products has been reduced as components are scaled to increase yields, designers tend to expand circuits to take advantage of available chip area. The increase in dynamic memories from 64K bit to 4M bit illustrates this point. This can result in the worst-case interconnect length staying constant and the RC time constant increasing by α or, in some cases, by α^2. The *average* interconnect length in properly designed VLSI and ULSI circuits can be shown to be independent of the number of gates on a chip. We discuss this further, along with the theoretical basis, in Chapter 5. Furthermore, parasitic capacitance does not continue to scale, but can actually start increasing for design rules less than 1 μm. Also, other device characteristics such as the swing and the built-in potential do not scale.

These deviations, as well as non-ideal devices, reduce the actual circuit performance predicted by the constant-field scaling law. This has prompted

TABLE 2.2   The Constant-Voltage and Quasi-Constant-Voltage Scaling Laws (After Chatterjee *et al.* [13]).

Scaling Law	Constant-Voltage	Quasi-Constant-Voltage
Dimensions (α)	α	α
Gate oxide (α_o)	$\sqrt{\alpha}$	α
Doping (α_N)	α	α
Voltage (α_V)	1	$\sqrt{\alpha}$

other scaling laws to be introduced to either enhance a particular device characteristic, such as switching speed, or to achieve other design goals. A constant-voltage scaling law has been developed [13] to keep circuit supply voltages compatible with other logic families (e.g., 5 volts). Problems resulting from the large electric fields limit this approach. A more practical approach is the quasi-constant-voltage scaling law [13]. The quasi-constant-voltage law does not scale the supply voltage as rapidly as the constant-field scaling law. These scaling laws are listed in Table 2.2. In practice the device dimensions and supply voltages are reduced, but not by a fixed constant. The requirements of the circuit and the available fabrication process dictate these values.

Several experimental measurements have indicated scaling devices past certain dimensions result in no increase in performance. Available current drive in NMOS has been seen to peak at channel lengths of $L = 0.4$ μm to 0.5 μm, and a similar effect in PMOS has been observed to occur at $L = 0.3$ μm. While individual device performance may peak at these values (different device structures can change these numbers), increases in density give continued motivation for scaling. Significant increase in system performance is still achieved if the number of chips in a design can be reduced by combining circuits on a single chip. As discussed in Chapter 5, off-chip communications is the real speed killer.

2.5.2 Threshold Voltage Variations

2.5.2.1 Nonuniform doping.   The threshold voltage derivation for the large-geometry MOSFET assumed uniform doping. In many cases this is not a realistic assumption. In fact, nonuniform doping offers an excellent opportunity to modify the electrical behavior of the MOSFET. Shallow doping can effectively shift the flatband voltage and therefore V_T without a reduction in the gate-induced depletion region. This allows the threshold voltage to be increased without the resultant increase in substrate capacitance. A deep implant can reduce punch-through, the merging of the source and drain depletion region in the bulk. A retrograde implant, where the doping peak is below the surface, allows the threshold voltage to be set by the total charge in the depletion region while reducing the surface concentration. A reduction in the surface concentration will reduce impurity scattering and hence improve mobility.

To derive the threshold voltage shift resulting from nonuniform doping, we will transform a nonuniform doping profile, Figure 2.24a, into a uniformly doped substrate with the same depletion depth as the original structure, Figure 2.24b. A virtual charge sheet located in the semiconductor must also be added as shown in Figure 2.24c to satisfy charge conservation. The equivalent doping level, Ne, is

$$N_e = \frac{2\varepsilon_s \psi_s}{q W_D^2} \tag{2.106}$$

The location of the virtual charge and its magnitude is obtained by calculating the field and potential in the original and the equivalent doped structure.

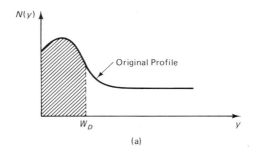

(a)

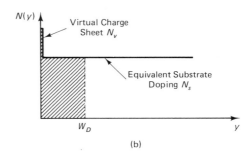

(b)

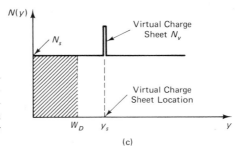

(c)

Figure 2.24 Concept of doping transformation. (a) Original profile. (b) Transformed structure with charge conservation. (c) Transformed structure with charge and energy conservation (after Ratnam and Salama [14], ©1984, IEEE).

For the nonuniformed doped structure,

$$E(y) = E(W_D) + \frac{q}{\varepsilon_s} \int_y^{W_D} N(y)\, dy \tag{2.107}$$

and

$$\psi(y) = \psi(W_D) + W_D E(W_D) - yE(W_D) + \frac{q}{\varepsilon_s} \int_y^{W_D} yN(y)\, dy \tag{2.108}$$

$E(W_D)$ and $\psi(W_D)$ represent the built-in field and potential at the depletion edge due to the doping gradient in the nonuniformly doped substrate.

For the equivalent uniformed doped substrate,

$$Ee(y) = \frac{q}{\varepsilon_s} N_e(W_D - y) \tag{2.109}$$

and

$$\psi e(y) = \frac{q}{2\varepsilon_s} N_e(W_D^2 - y^2) \tag{2.110}$$

The magnitude of the charge sheet is given by

$$N_v = \frac{\varepsilon_s}{q}[E(o) - Ee(o)] \tag{2.111}$$

The position of the charge sheet is y_s from the SiO–Si interface given by

$$y_s = \frac{\left[\int_0^{W_D} E^2(y)\, dy - \int_0^{W_D} Ee^2(y)\, dy \right]}{[E(o) - Ee(o)]} \tag{2.112}$$

Figure 2.25a is a plot into the substrate of a realistic doping profile of a PMOS device and an approximate piece-wise linear fit. Figure 2.25b illustrates the calculated N_e, N_v, and y_s as a function of W_D. N_e and N_v increase with increasing W_D and saturate when the depletion edge moves into the uniformly doped bulk region. The location of the sheet of virtual charge, y_s, decreases with increasing depletion depth until it reaches a minimum y_{sm} at W_{Dm}. The transformation is incorrect for $W_D > W_{Dm}$. For $W_D \geq W_{Dm}$, the following approximations can be applied

$$N_e \simeq N_{em} \tag{2.113}$$

$$N_v \simeq N_{vm} \tag{2.114}$$

and

$$y_s \simeq y_{sm} \tag{2.115}$$

where N_{em}, N_{vm} and y_{sm} are the value of N_e, N_v and y_s at $y = W_{Dm}$ [14].

The implant causing the nonuniformly doped substrate is considered shallow if $\psi(y_{sm}) \leq 2\phi_B$, where ϕ_B is calculated at the depletion region edge.

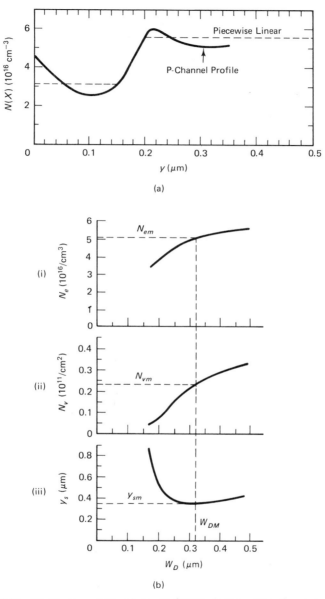

Figure 2.25 (a) Doping profile of n-well CMOS devices. Also shown are the piecewise linear approximations used for transformation. (b) The doping transformation parameters for a p-channel device. (i) The equivalent substrate doping. (ii) The virtual charge value. (iii) The location of virtual charge (after Ratnam and Salama [14], ©1984, IEEE).

For a shallow implant, the threshold voltage is

$$V_T = V_{FB} + 2\phi_B + \frac{qN_{vm}}{C_{ox}} + \frac{1}{C_{ox}}\sqrt{2\varepsilon_s qN_{em}(2\phi_B + V_{BG})} \qquad (2.116)$$

A shallow implant effectively only shifts the flatband voltage by qN_{vm}/C_{ox}. Experimentally, measured V_T versus $\sqrt{(2\phi_B + V_{BG})}$ gives a simple linear relationship.

Implants are considered deep when $\psi(y_{sm}) \geq 2\phi_B$. For deep implants, the threshold voltage expression depends on the backgate bias. For $(2\phi_B + V_{BG}) \leq \psi(y_{sm})$,

$$V_T = V_{FB} + 2\phi_B + \frac{qN_v}{C_t} + \frac{1}{C_{ox}}\sqrt{2\varepsilon_s qN_e(2\phi_B + V_{BG})} \qquad (2.117)$$

here N_e, N_v, are computed at $\psi_s = 2\phi_B + V_{BG}$ and $C_t = (C_{ox}C_g)/(C_{ox} + C_g)$ with $C_g = \frac{\varepsilon_s}{W_D}$. Experimentally measured V_T versus $\sqrt{(2\phi_B + V_{BG})}$ does not give a linear relationship since N_e and N_v vary with ψ_s.

For $(2\phi_B + V_{BG}) > \psi(y_{sm})$, the depletion region has expanded out of the implant and the implant acts like a sheet of charge N_{vm} at W_{Dm}. For this case, the threshold voltage is

$$V_T = V_{FB} + 2\phi_B + \frac{qN_{vm}}{C_t} + \frac{1}{C_{ox}}\sqrt{2\varepsilon_s qN_{em}(2\phi_B + V_{BG})} \qquad (2.118)$$

where N_{em}, N_{vm}, and C_t are computed at $\psi(y_{sm})$. This expression gives a linear V_T versus $\sqrt{(2\phi_B + V_{BG})}$ relationship [14].

2.5.2.2 The Short-Channel Effect.

Experimental measurements of the threshold voltage, V_T, has shown that as channel length is reduced, the threshold voltage decreases. This is not predicted by the classical V_T expression, (2.95). This reduction becomes noticeable when the channel length is of the same order of magnitude as the source-substrate or drain-substrate depletion depths. Typically, for channel lengths less than 3 μm this effect is observed.

The derivation of the classical threshold voltage, Section 2.4.2, required a number of approximations. One dealt with the shape of the depletion region charge that terminated the gate field. It was assumed that the depletion region was a rectangular shaped volume. This approximation neglects the charge near the source and drain junctions that terminate the built-in fields from the source and drain. In fact, these depletion regions overlap and this charge sharing reduces the total amount of depleted charge in the substrate that is available to terminate the gate field. Therefore, the bulk charge term in (2.93) is reduced and V_T will decrease.

Figure 2.26 illustrates this charge sharing. The depletion charge linked to the gate is in a trapezoidal area of depth W_D, length L at the surface, and

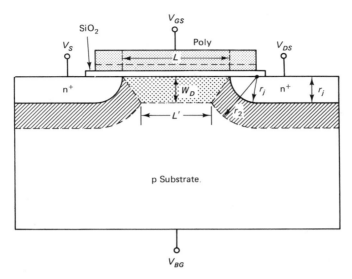

Figure 2.26   Charge sharing with source and drain.

length L' at the bottom of the depletion region. The charge in this trapezoid area integrated over the width is

$$Q_{BT} = qW_D WN_A \left[\frac{L + L'}{2} \right] \qquad (2.119)$$

By approximating the built-in potential of the junctions and the substrate to be equal, r_2 as defined in Figure 2.26 may be expressed as

$$r_2 = r_j + W_D \qquad (2.120)$$

where r_j is the radius of curvature of the source and drain junctions. The ratio of the charge in the trapezoidal region to the total bulk depletion charge can be shown to be [15]

$$\frac{Q_{BT}}{Q_B} = 1 - \frac{r_j}{L} \left(\sqrt{1 + \frac{2W_D}{r_j}} - 1 \right) \qquad (2.121)$$

This allows the V_T for a short-channel MOSFET to be expressed as

$$V_T = V_{FB} + 2\phi_B + \frac{qN_A W_D}{C_{ox}} \left[1 - \left(\sqrt{\left(1 + \frac{2W_D}{r_j} \right)} - 1 \right) \frac{r_j}{L} \right] \qquad (2.122)$$

Figure 2.27 shows (2.122) as a function of L for various doping concentrations. Being able to predict such a variation in V_T is important. As devices are scaled, the variations in V_T caused by normal process variations in channel length can cause wide variations in circuit performance. A limitation

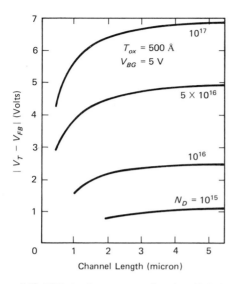

Figure 2.27 Threshold voltage versus channel length for various doping concentrations (after Prince [12]).

of (2.122) is the assumption implicit in the derivation that the source and drain depletion regions are similar. This is only true for very low V_D.

For non-negligible drain voltages, and for an applied backgate bias V_{BG}, the drain depletion depth may be expressed as

$$W_D = \sqrt{\frac{2\varepsilon_s}{qN_A}(V_{Bi} + V_{BG} + V_{DS})} \qquad (2.123)$$

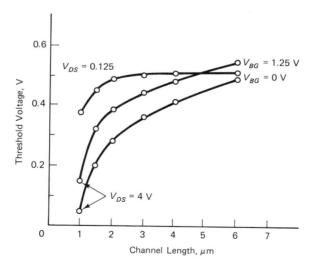

Figure 2.28 The variation in the threshold voltage for different V_{DS} (after Fichtner and Potzl [17]).

Splitting the charge sharing into a source-gate region and a drain-gate region, (2.122) can be modified to be [16]

$$V_T = V_{FB} + 2\phi_B$$

$$+ \frac{qN_A W_D}{C_{ox}}\left[1 - \frac{r_j}{2L}\left(\sqrt{1 - \frac{2W_D}{r_j}} - 1\right) - \frac{r_j}{2L}\left(\sqrt{1 + \frac{2W_S}{r_j}} - 1\right)\right]$$

$$(2.124)$$

This equation includes the reduction in V_T as the drain voltage is increased. Figure 2.28 illustrates the effect of a drain and substrate voltage on the threshold voltage.

2.5.2.3 The Narrow and Inverse Narrow-Width Effect.   Device width has an important effect on device behavior. For increased current drive, and hence circuit speed, a large width is required. But, to realize the area squared increase in density available through scaling device dimensions, the channel width must also be reduced.

A MOSFET is considered narrow if the channel width, the distance between the isolation oxides, is of the same order of magnitude as the depth of the gate induced channel depletion region. For typical doping profiles, widths of 4 μm or less can be considered narrow. Narrow widths have been found to have a significant effect on device behavior.

The narrow-width effect is the *increase* in the threshold voltage as the channel width is reduced. The previously shown width cross-section, Figure 2.12, illustrates a simplified model of a MOSFET with a non-recessed isolation oxide. This isolation oxide is used to increase V_T in the side regions in order to isolate a device from its neighbors. Also, the region under the thick oxide is heavily doped to further increase V_T.

For the non-recessed oxide structure, the increase in the threshold voltage, as width is reduced, can be explained as follows. As the depletion region edge approaches the edge of the device, it makes a transition from the deep depletion under the gate to the shallow depletion region under the thick oxide. This transition region is shown in Figure 2.29. Notice that this transition is not abrupt as is assumed in the classical V_T derivation, but allows a pocket of charge to exist to terminate the gate field. For wide widths, the size of this extra charge relative to the bulk charge is small and can be neglected. But, as the width is reduced, this ratio increases and becomes significant. This extra charge increases the bulk charge and causes V_T to increase. Also, since the electrical channel width in structures with a non-recessed isolation oxide can spread out under the field oxide, the effective electrical channel width can be larger than the oxide defined device width.

A closed form expression for the narrow-width effect can be derived by adding this extra charge to the bulk depletion charge in the classical V_T

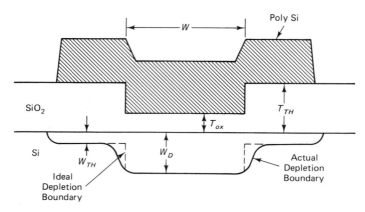

Figure 2.29 MOS width cross section showing actual and ideal depletion shapes.

expression. The amount of this extra depletion charge is [18]

$$\frac{\delta q}{2} N_A W_D^2 L \tag{2.125}$$

where δ is a fitting parameter to account for the shape of the transition region. The charge on both sides of the width contribute an additional voltage to the threshold voltage of

$$V_{\Delta Q} = \frac{\delta q N_A W_D^2}{C_{ox} W} \tag{2.126}$$

Therefore, for a narrow-width MOSFET with uniform doping, V_T is

$$V_T = V_{FB} + 2\phi_B + \frac{q N_A}{C_{ox}}\left[W_D + \frac{\delta W_D^2}{W}\right] \tag{2.127}$$

Figure 2.30 illustrates (2.127) as a function of W for various doping concentrations.

As mentioned above, in order to further increase the threshold voltage in the thick field oxide region, a heavily doped region, called a channel stop, is introduced under the thick oxide. During high-temperature processing steps, this doping will encroach into the channel, further increasing the density of the bulk depletion charge in the region near the sides. Combined with this doping encroachment, some fabrication processes causing a tapering of the thick to the thin oxide, as shown in Figure 2.31. This tapering causes a structure that looks like a bird's beak and has been given that name. The extra charge stored under this oxide structure further raises V_T [19]. Also, notice how the "bird's beak" increases the required distance between devices and therefore wastes space.

To eliminate the wasted distance between devices, a new isolation oxide structure was developed. This structure, as shown in Figure 2.32, is termed

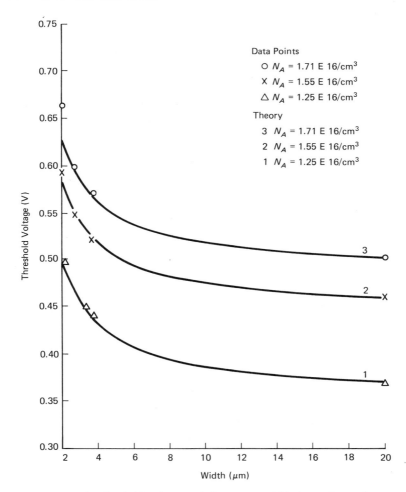

Figure 2.30 The threshold voltage variation versus width for various substrate doping concentrations.

fully-recessed or trench. Besides allowing very high packing density, it behaves different electrically from the non-recessed and semi-recessed structure. Also shown in Figure 2.32 are the gate field lines. Gate overlap causes fringing field lines which terminate on the sidewall of the oxide rather than under the thick oxide. This increases the concentration of field lines near the edges and acts to deplete the side regions at a smaller V_{GS} than required in the middle of the channel. Hence, side channels are created at a smaller gate voltage, so the threshold voltage is effectively reduced. The *decrease* in V_T, as the width is reduced, has been termed the inverse narrow-width effect.

Figure 2.33 illustrates the surface potential of a MOSFET with fully recessed isolation oxides. Notice the enhanced potentials at the edges of the

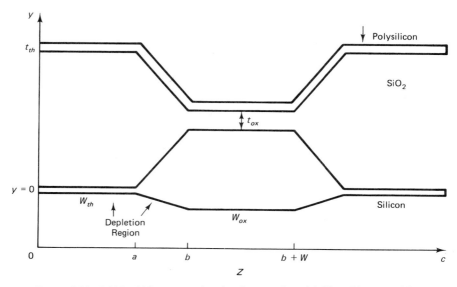

Figure 2.31 MOS width cross section showing tapering of field to thin gate oxide.

channel. This is caused by fringing gate fields terminating on the sidewalls of the channel. The gate capacitance used in (2.95) normally is considered ideal and its capacitance is calculated using the parallel-plate approximation. For the device used in Figure 2.32, the fringing fields neglected by the parallel-plate approximation are significant and must be included in C_{ox}. We model the total gate capacitance, C_g, as a gate capacitor in parallel with two sidewall capacitors. The interface charge along both the thin and the field oxide-silicon

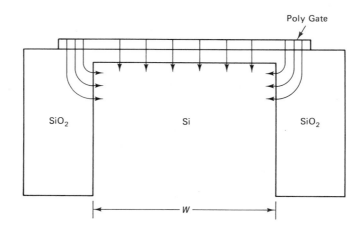

Figure 2.32 MOS width cross section with fully-recessed isolation oxide.

Potential

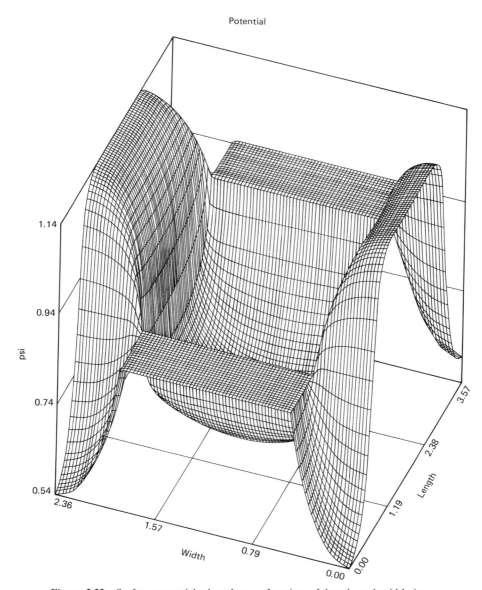

Figure 2.33 Surface potential plotted as a function of length and width in a small-geometry MOSFET.

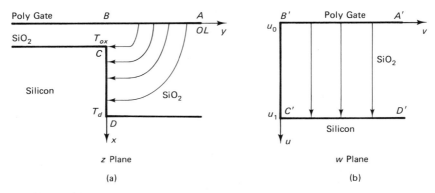

Figure 2.34 (a) Sidewall. (b) Transformed into parallel plate configuration (after Akers [20]).

boundary is considered uniform and constant. Hence the total gate capacitance is

$$C_g = C_{ox}(WL) + 2C_f \qquad (2.128)$$

where C_f is the fringing capacitance.

Consider the long channel narrow-width MOSFET case. Figure 2.34a illustrates one side of the channel. The gate electrode overlaps the recessed oxide by OL. The thin oxide has a thickness of T_{ox}, and the field oxide has a thickness of T_d. While the potential in the inversion layer along the sidewall is constant, the potential will drop to the substrate potential after the inversion layer collapses. Since the inversion capacitance is larger than the depletion capacitance, we approximate the potential along the complete depth of the sidewall to be constant and derive and use the inversion capacitance for this structure. This assumption will cause the fringing capacitance, C_f, to be overestimated. The structure in Figure 2.34(a) is transformed into the structure in Figure 2.34(b) by the transformation

$$z = \sin(\pi w/2) \qquad (2.129)$$

where z and w represent complex planes. In the w plane, C_f is obtained from the parallel-plate formula as

$$C_f = \varepsilon_{ox} A / (u_o - u_1) \qquad (2.130)$$

where A is the plate area in the w plane.

Realizing the fringing field component cannot extend past T_d, C_f in the original z plane is

$$C_f = (2\varepsilon_{ox}L/\pi)\ln\left(\left(\sqrt{(T_d/T_{ox})^2 - 1}\right) + T_d/T_{ox}\right) \qquad (2.131)$$

The argument of the natural logarithm can be simplified to give

$$C_f = (2\varepsilon_{ox}L/\pi)\ln(2T_d/T_{ox}) \qquad (2.132)$$

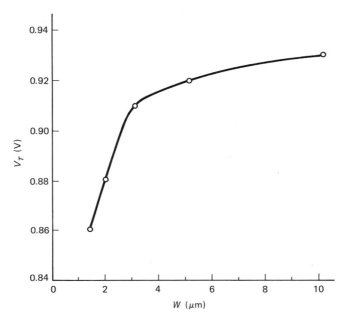

Figure 2.35 Threshold voltage versus W for a fully-recessed isolation oxide structure.

Therefore the total gate capacitance can be expressed as

$$C_g = C_{ox}(WL) + (4\varepsilon_{ox}L/\pi)\ln(2T_d/T_{ox}) \tag{2.133}$$

or

$$C_g = C_{ox}(WL)(1 + F/W) \tag{2.134}$$

where the fringing factor F is

$$F = (4T_{ox}/\pi)\ln(2T_d/T_{ox}) \tag{2.135}$$

Hence the threshold voltage for a long channel narrow-width NMOS device is

$$V_T = V_{FB} + 2\phi_b + \frac{qN_aW_D}{C_{ox}}\left(\frac{W}{W+F}\right) \tag{2.136}$$

Figure 2.35 illustrates V_T as a function of W for a device with a fully-recessed oxide. In summary, for a non-recessed oxide, or a semi-recessed oxide with doping encroachment, V_T increases with decreasing width. For a fully-recessed oxide, V_T is reduced as the width is reduced.

2.5.2.4 Small-Geometry Effect.

While a long, narrow device is useful to explain the narrow and inverse narrow-width effects, it is not a very practical device structure. The length and width simultaneously need to be reduced. This new, small-geometry structure exhibits not only the effects of short-channels and narrow-widths, but a coupling of these effects. For this new small-geometry MOSFET, the mere addition of the short-channel effect and the narrow-width effect does not accurately predict V_T.

A small-geometry MOSFET will be defined as the superposition of the definition used to define short and narrow devices. For example, a device with a W/L ratio of 4 μm/3 μm could be considered small. A three-dimensional approximation of the bulk charge can be obtained by integrating the length cross-section developed from Figure 2.26 over the complete width depletion region. The length cross-sectional area is

$$\left[1 - \left(\sqrt{1 + \frac{2W_D}{r_j}} - 1\right)\frac{r_j}{L}\right]LW_D \qquad (2.137)$$

Integrating (2.137) over the width distance of $W + \delta W_D$, where δW_D accounts for the extension of the depletion region on both sides of the channel, gives the total volume depletion charge.

This calculation gives the total depletion charge as

$$qN_A\left[1 - \left(\sqrt{1 + \frac{2W_D}{r_j}} - 1\right)\left(\frac{r_j}{L} + \frac{2W_D r_j}{WL}\right) + \frac{2W_D}{W}\right]LWW_D \qquad (2.138)$$

Therefore, the threshold voltage expression for a small-geometry MOSFET with a nonrecessed isolation oxide is

$$V_T = V_{FB} + 2\phi_B$$

$$+ \frac{qN_AW_D}{C_{ox}}\left[1 - \left(\sqrt{1 + \frac{2W_D}{r_j}} - 1\right)\left(\frac{r_j}{L} + \frac{2W_D r_j}{WL}\right) + \frac{2W_D}{W}\right] \qquad (2.139)$$

Notice the $2W_D r_j/WL$ term. This term represents coupling between the length and width depletion regions.

Figure 2.36 shows experimental values of V_T as a function of L for a 2 μm and 3 μm wide device. This data is compared with (2.139). Clearly, the variation of V_T with length and width is significant and must be considered in the design of small devices.

The small-geometry threshold voltage expression for an n-channel MOSFET with a fully recessed isolation oxide is

$$V_T = V_{FB} + 2\phi_B + (qN_AW_D/C_{ox})$$

$$\times \left[1 - \left(\sqrt{1 + 2W_d/r_j} - 1\right)(r_j/L)\right][W/(W + F)] \qquad (2.140)$$

Figure 2.37 is a comparison of PMOS threshold voltage data from three

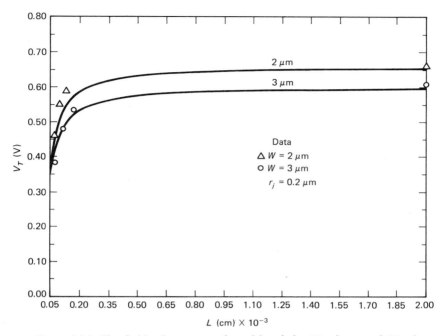

Figure 2.36 Threshold voltage versus channel length for $W = 2$ μm and $W = 3$ μm.

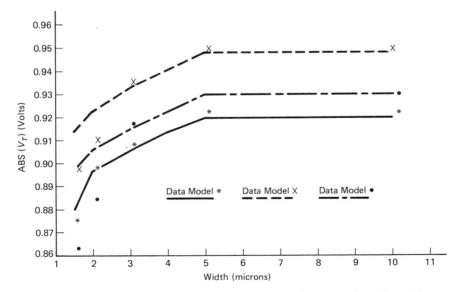

Figure 2.37 Comparison of PMOS threshold voltage data (symbols) with model (lines).

different die with (2.140). The appropriate signs were changed in (2.140) for PMOS. Below 3 μm, the model overestimates the threshold voltage. While the exact cause for this is unknown, it could result from confinement of the depletion region in the narrow-widths and the interaction of adjacent sidewall depletion regions. It could also indicate a more accurate capacitance expression is needed which takes into account possible nonuniform variation in the interface charge at the channel edges and along the sidewalls and in the variation in the potential along the sidewalls.

2.5.3 Current Formulations

Scaling the channel length, while keeping all other parameters constant, should increase the current by the scaling factor. As we shall show, the current does increase as the channel length is reduced, however, it does not increase as rapidly as predicted. This results from the onset of second-order effects, which become dominant. In this section, the second-order effects which produce major changes in device current-voltage characteristics will be discussed.

2.5.3.1 Subthreshold Current in Short-Channel MOSFETs.   While the subthreshold current for a large geometry MOSFET can in many cases be neglected, this current is critical in a short-channel device. The magnitude of the subthreshold current determines the standby power dissipation, which is important in low power battery operation, the switching speed, and the refresh time for dynamic memories and circuits.

In Section 2.3.1, the subthreshold current for a large MOSFET was derived. The resulting model showed that for $V_{DS} \geq \dfrac{4kT}{q}$, the current was independent of the drain voltage. In a short device, this is no longer the case. The subthreshold current has been found to increase with increasing drain voltage.

The reason this current varies with V_{DS} can be explained as follows. When two reversed-biased junctions are in the vicinity of one another, one of the junctions creates a field pattern that lowers the potential barrier separating the two junctions. If this barrier lowering is large enough, the neighboring junction can inject current. In a MOSFET, if the drain junction is sufficiently close to the source junction for its fields resulting from the drain voltage to lower the source barrier, current will flow. This barrier lowering is termed drain induced barrier lowering (DIBL) [21].

Figure 2.38 illustrates the surface potential in the region between the source and the drain. The channel current is basically controlled by emission over the potential barrier near the source. For curve A, the long channel case, the peak of the surface potential distribution is constant and extends over most of the channel. As the channel length is reduced, curve B, this peak is

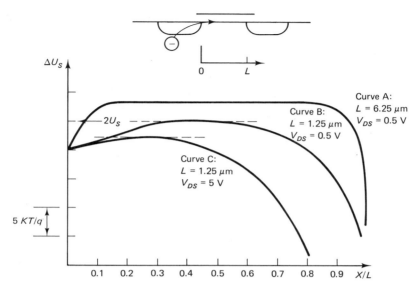

Figure 2.38 Surface potential for a constant gate voltage (after Troutman [21], ©1979, IEEE).

reduced and is constant only over a small part of the channel. Since the peak potential has been reduced, the subthreshold current will increase. If the drain voltage is increased, curve C, the peak is further reduced and the region of constant potential is also reduced.

DIBL is caused by two effects. First, for $V_{DS} = 0$, the physical distance between the source and drain depletion regions may be inadequate to accommodate the complete depletion widths of each junction. This will cause the barrier between the two junctions to be reduced and is termed the proximity effect. Secondly, for $V_{DS} > 0$, the drain field lines penetrate further into the source region, which further reduces the barrier [21].

To model DIBL with a simple analytical expression, we assume *a priori* the shape of the source and drain depletion regions in a short device under applied bias. We also must assume the manner in which the gate induced depletion region merges with the other two depletion regions. Using such an approach allows the subthreshold current in a short-channel device to be expressed as [7]

$$I = \frac{qWy_cDn_i e^{-q\phi_B/kT}e^{q\psi_s/kT}}{L - \sqrt{\dfrac{2\varepsilon_s}{qN_A}(V_{DS} - V_{Bi} - \psi_s)} - \sqrt{\dfrac{2\varepsilon_s}{qN_A}(V_{Bi} - \psi_s)} + 2\sqrt{\dfrac{\varepsilon_s kT}{q^2 N_A}}}$$

$$(2.141)$$

The surface potential, ψ_s, is related to the gate voltage, V_G, by

$$\psi_s = V_G - V_{FB} - \frac{a^2}{2\beta}\left\{\left\{1 + \frac{4}{a^2}(\beta V_G - \beta V_{FB} - 1)\right\}^{1/2} - 1\right\} \qquad (2.142)$$

2.5.3.2 Linear and Saturated Current in Short-Channel MOSFETs.

As the channel length is reduced, significant changes in the linear and saturated current expressions occur. The linear and saturated current expressions for a long channel MOSFET were given in (2.76) and (2.79), but are repeated here for convenience. In the linear region,

$$I_{DS} = \mu C_{ox}\frac{W}{L}\left[(V_{GS} - V_T)V_{DS} - \frac{V_{DS}^2}{2}\right] \qquad (2.143)$$

and in the saturated region,

$$I_{DS\,sat} = \mu C_{ox}\frac{W}{2L}(V_{GS} - V_T)^2 \qquad (2.144)$$

These equations will be progressively modified to account for short-channel effects.

The first short-channel characteristic observed is channel length modulation. For a long channel MOSFET, we assumed the saturated drain current was independent of drain voltage. In fact, there is some modulation of $I_{DS\,sat}$ with drain voltage. As discussed in Section 2.3.3, for $V_{DS} > V_{DS\,sat}$, the pinch-off point, more properly described as the end of the ohmic channel, moves toward the source. The saturated current, as calculated by (2.144) is determined in part by this ohmic channel length. For a long device, the distance between the source and drain, L, and the ohmic channel length, L', is negligible. But, as the channel length is reduced, this difference can be significant. Equation (2.144) then should have L replaced by L'. Then, as V_{DS} is increased, $I_{DS\,sat}$ will increase as shown in Figure 2.39.

A simple one-dimensional physical model with which to calculate L' is the abrupt junction approximation. Here, L' may be expressed as

$$L' = L - \sqrt{\frac{2\varepsilon_s}{qN_A}(V_{DS} - V_{DS\,sat})} \qquad (2.145)$$

This expression is accurate only if the oxide thickness is much less than the depth of the gate induced depletion region. If this is not the case, a more exact two-dimensional solution is required. In fact, under most practical conditions, (2.145) is just not sufficiently accurate to simulate this effect. An empirical method which uses a curve fitting parameter, called the channel length modulation factor, λ, is more often used. This parameter is easy to determine experimentally. The saturated current may then be expressed as

$$I_{D\,sat} = \frac{\mu C_{ox}W}{2L}(V_{GS} - V_T)^2[1 + \lambda(V_{DS} - V_{DS\,sat})] \qquad (2.146)$$

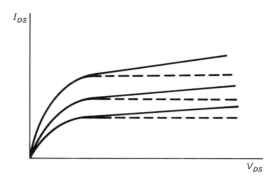

Figure 2.39 Static output curves with channel length modulation (solid) and without channel length modulation (dashed).

As discussed in Section 2.5.2, the threshold voltage is reduced as V_{DS} is increased. This effect causes enhanced drain current with increasing V_{DS}. It is usually recognized as the upward curving of the current in the saturation region. This can be included in (2.146) by using a short-channel expression for V_T.

The next two short-channel effects and their fitting parameters, α' and γ, are intermixed and will be discussed together. First, α', is defined as the ratio of the mobilities for the linear region to that for the saturated region, and can be expressed as [22]

$$\alpha' = \alpha + \gamma(V_{GS} - V_T) \qquad (2.147)$$

where α is the same ratio as α', except for a long channel device. The parameter γ is the velocity saturation factor. Since the linear mobility is larger than the saturated mobility, α and α' are greater than one. This causes the transconductance in the linear region to increase. More importantly, α' will cause the drain current to saturate at a drain voltage less than the classical drain saturation voltage of $(V_{GS} - V_T)$. This new short-channel saturation voltage is expressed as

$$V_{DSsat} = (V_{GS} - V_T)/\alpha' \qquad (2.148)$$

In the discussion of mobility in Section 2.4.1, it was assumed that as the electric field in the lateral direction is increased, the carrier velocity also increased. This is correct until the electric field reaches approximately 1×10^4 V/cm for electrons or 2×10^4 V/cm for holes. At these high field values, the carrier velocities saturate. For a short-channel MOSFET, with a non-scaled supply voltage, this field magnitude can be reached in the center of the channel. Once velocity saturation has occurred, the current will also saturate. Hence, the saturation voltage for a short device is no longer the voltage required to cause pinch-off, but a smaller voltage.

These short-channel parameters can be included into the current formulation to give [22]

$$I_D(\text{linear}) = \mu C_{\text{ox}} \frac{W}{L} \alpha' \left((V_{GS} - V_T)V_{DS} - \alpha' \frac{V_{DS}^2}{2} \right) \tag{2.149}$$

$$\text{if } V_{DS} < (V_{GS} - V_T)/\alpha' \tag{2.150}$$

and

$$I_{DS\text{sat}} = \mu \frac{C_{\text{ox}}}{2L} W(V_{GS} - V_T)^2 \left[1 + \lambda \left(\frac{\alpha}{\alpha'} \right)^2 (V_{DS} - V_{D\text{sat}}) \right] \tag{2.151}$$

$$\text{if } V_{DS} \geq (V_{GS} - V_T)/\alpha' \tag{2.152}$$

Figure 2.40 illustrates the addition of the parameter V_T, λ, γ and α' to the I–V curve.

As previously discussed in Section 2.4.1, the vertical oxide field can also cause a reduction in the mobility. This reduction was characterized by a mobility degradation factor θ. Modifying the low field mobility term in (2.149) and (2.151) gives

$$I_{D(\text{linear})} = \mu_o C_{\text{ox}} \frac{W}{L} \alpha' \left[\frac{(V_{GS} - V_T)V_{DS} - \alpha'V_{DS}^2/2}{1 + \theta(V_{GS} - V_T)} \right] \tag{2.153}$$

and

$$I_{DS\text{sat}} = \mu_o C_{\text{ox}} \frac{W}{2L} \frac{(V_{GS} - V_T)^2 \left[1 + \lambda \left(\frac{\alpha}{\alpha'} \right)^2 (V_{DS} - V_{DS\text{sat}}) \right]}{1 + \theta(V_{GS} - V_T)} \tag{2.154}$$

When the channel length is scaled, the gate oxide thickness is also scaled, as described by the constant field scaling law. Eventually, the oxide thickness

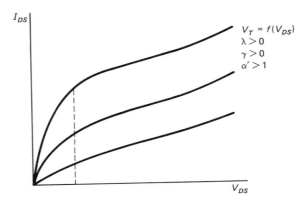

Figure 2.40 Influence of short-channel parameters V_T, λ, γ, and α' on IV characteristics of an ideal MOSFET (after Duuvnry [22]).

becomes comparable to the thickness of the inversion layer, 30 Å to 200 Å. Once this occurs, the voltage drop across the inversion layer begins to become comparable to the voltage drop across the oxide. This causes the effective capacitance to be the series connection of the gate capacitance and the capacitance of the inversion layer. For oxide thickness of 100 Å or less, C_{ox} should be replaced with C_{eff} where

$$\frac{1}{C_{eff}} = \frac{1}{C_{ox}} + \frac{1}{C_{inv}} \qquad (2.155)$$

where $C_{inv} = \dfrac{\varepsilon_{si}}{\chi_{av}}$ and χ_{av} is the average thickness of the inversion layer, which may be approximated as [23]

$$\chi_{av} = 1.85 \times 10^{-9}\left(Q_B + \tfrac{1}{3}Q_n\right)^{-1/3} \qquad (2.156)$$

This saturation of C_{eff} as t_{ox} is reduced results in a degradation of the transconductance.

The last short-channel effect to be discussed is the effect of the source and drain series resistance. This intrinsic parasitic resistance has a serious effect on device current and gain. This resistance arises from the resistance of the source and drain junction and the contact resistance of the aluminum or silicide and the junction. An exact expression for this resistance is difficult to obtain in closed form due to the distributed contact resistance and current crowding. Using a simple lumped parameter model as illustrated in Figure 2.41, and neglecting the voltage drop in the source-gate loop, the current in the linear region can be shown to be,

$$I_D = \frac{\mu C_{ox}(W/L)(V_{GS} - V_T)V_{DS}}{1 + \mu C_{ox}(W/L)(V_{GS} - V_T)(R_D + R_S)} \qquad (2.157)$$

where V'_{DS} is the drain to ground voltage, and R_D and R_S are the lumped drain and source resistances.

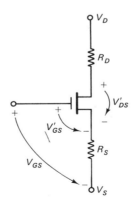

Figure 2.41 Lumped parameter MOSFET model including source and drain resistance.

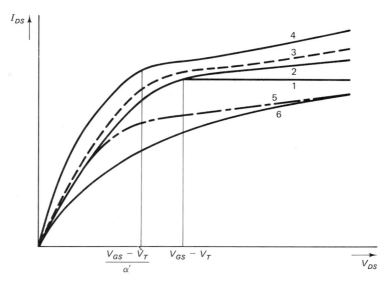

Figure 2.42 Influence of all discussed short-channel parameters on IV characteristics of an ideal MOSFET (after Duuvnry [22]). (1) Ideal curve. (2) Addition of λ. (3) Addition of $V_T = f(V_{DS})$. (4) Addition of α' and γ. (5) Addition of Θ. (6) Addition of series resistance.

Figure 2.42 illustrates the addition of λ, V_T as a function of V_{DS} and L, α' and γ, θ, and source and drain resistance to the ideal static curve. In summary, short-channel effects have reduced the expected current gain and introduced significant variation in the saturated current with V_{DS}.

2.5.3.3 Current in Small-Geometry MOSFETs.

As the width direction is reduced to increase circuit packing density, the current is reduced. This reduction is not just a linear scaling with W, but includes complex interactions of a three-dimensional nature. The shape of the field isolation oxide as well as the carrier type, electron or hole, has a significant effect on the device current.

In the subthreshold region, the shape of the isolation oxide is especially important. Figure 2.43 illustrates two isolation oxide structures, the semi-recessed and the fully-recessed. Figure 2.44 illustrates the surface potential as a function of isolation oxide angle, for a semi-recessed structure with no interface charge. A long channel device is used to eliminate the complex length-width coupling. Notice that for small θ, the surface potential decreases as the edge is approached, whereas for $\theta > 30°$, the surface potential actually increases. For the fully-recessed structure shown in Figure 2.45, the surface potential continuously increases. This differing behavior results from the gate fringing field lines enhancing the potential at the edge. The significance of the behavior of the surface potential at the edges is apparent when we consider the subthreshold current. It may be recalled that this current is exponentially

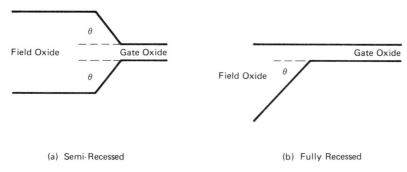

(a) Semi-Recessed   (b) Fully Recessed

Figure 2.43   (a) Semi-recessed field oxide. (b) Fully-recessed field oxide.

dependent on the surface potential. If the potential decreases upon approaching the edge, this current is reduced. But if the potential increases, the subthreshold current is enhanced, and a large increase in standby power dissipation will occur. Figure 2.46 shows the subthreshold current for the fully-recessed oxide for three device widths. As the oxide angle approaches 90°, the increase in subthreshold current is quite apparent. So far, we have neglected the effects of interface charge. Interface charge, especially along the sidewalls of the isolation oxide, will modify the surface potential. The interface charge type is usually positive and independent of the substrate type. Hence, for an NMOS device, this charge will enhance the surface potential and increase the subthreshold current. This is shown in Figure 2.47. For a PMOS device, the interface charge reduces the surface potential and hence reduces the current, as shown in Figure 2.48. Heavy doping along the sidewalls can be used to reduce this increase in current in the NMOS devices.

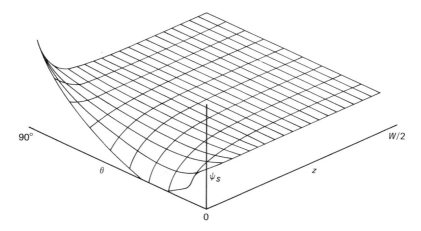

Figure 2.44 Surface potential as a function of isolation oxide angle for a semi-recessed structure without interface charge (after Sugino *et al.* [24], ©1984, IEEE).

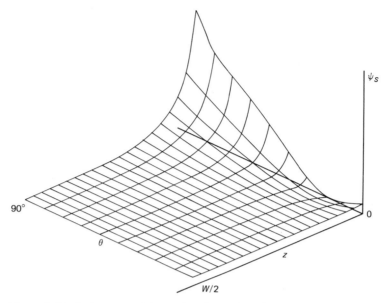

Figure 2.45 Surface potential as a function of isolation oxide angle for a fully-recessed isolation oxide structure without interface charge (after Sugino *et al* [24], ©1984, IEEE).

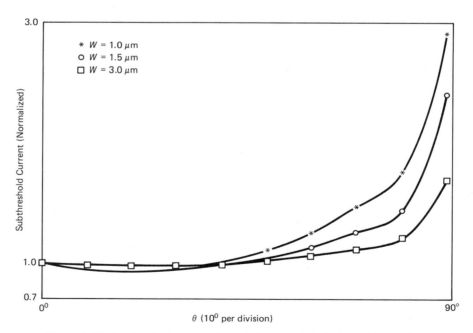

Figure 2.46 Subthreshold current for a fully-recessed isolation oxide for three device widths.

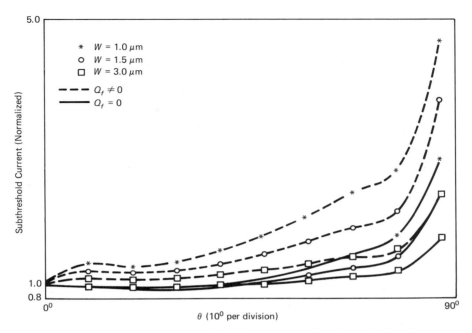

Figure 2.47 Increase in the subthreshold current resulting from the interface charge in NMOS.

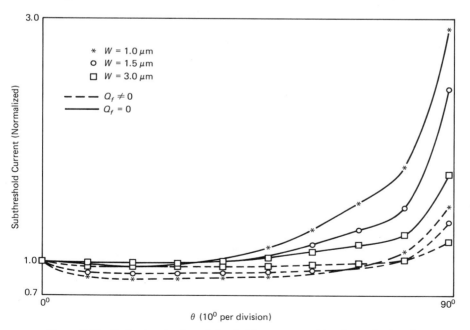

Figure 2.48 Reduction in the subthreshold current resulting from the interface charge in PMOS.

For the linear and the saturated regions, various approaches have been used to simulate the current in small-geometry MOSFETs. One approach is to modify the depletion charge to account for the short-channel and narrow-width effects. This results in the following charge balance equation

$$-C_{ox}(V_{GS} - V_{FB} - \psi_s) = Q_n + FQ_D + Q_{DL}/W \tag{2.158}$$

where F is the short-channel charge sharing factor, (2.121), and Q_{DL} accounts for the extra charge in the width direction, (2.125). Numerical methods are required to solve this transcendental equation for ψ_s.

The conducting channel can be considered to be composed of two regions, a gradual channel region operating in the linear mode and a saturated region. In the linear region, the current can be expressed as

$$I_D = W\mu \left[Q_n \frac{d\psi_s}{dy} - \frac{1}{\beta} \frac{dQ_n}{dy} \right] \tag{2.159}$$

In the saturated region, the carriers have obtained their saturated drift velocity and the current can be expressed as

$$I_D = WQ_n b v_s \tag{2.160}$$

where b is a fitting parameter. The complete details of the calculations become rather complex even for simple cases. Figure 2.49 shows the static curves generated from this method compared with experimental data.

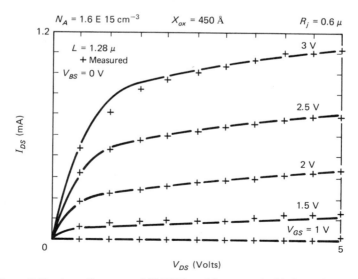

Figure 2.49 A small-geometry MOSFET model compared with data (after Guebels and Van de Wiele [25]).

2.5.3.4 NMOS versus PMOS.   Initially, PMOS was the dominant technology. The reason was simple—higher yields. The sign of the interface charge is positive. Therefore, PMOS will naturally be harder to turn on. The gate voltage first has to overcome the oxide charge before the channel can be inverted. In NMOS, the interface charge will help invert the channel. The problem in the early years of MOS was control of the interface trap charge and oxide fixed charge. The PMOS device would just be forced farther into the off state for $V_{GS} = 0$, an acceptable condition if the supply voltages used were large enough to invert the transistor and the gate oxide did not break down at this voltage. For NMOS, the variation in oxide charge could result in the device being turned on at $V_{GS} = 0$, an unacceptable condition.

As process technology improved, the oxide charge variation was brought under control. Shallow implants to control the threshold voltage, without increasing the source and drain to substrate capacitance, were also introduced. These changes allowed stable NMOS enhancement transistors to be fabricated. Therefore, the choice between NMOS and PMOS had to be reconsidered. The mobility of an electron is approximately 2–3 times as great as that of a hole. This translates into a much faster switching speed for NMOS. Hence, the change from PMOS to NMOS was made.

As circuits became larger and denser, power dissipation became a severe problem. CMOS, with its combination of NMOS and PMOS, has lower dissipation and hence started being used in those sections of a chip that dissipated large amounts of power. The high-density, low-power dissipation sections on a chip, e.g., DRAM memory cells, still could use NMOS. CMOS design does not necessarily require a one-to-one NMOS to PMOS match. Since the behavior of n and p channel devices change as they are scaled, the question of NMOS versus PMOS as the majority type of device used needs to be reconsidered as geometries are scaled into the submicron regions.

Three points need to be discussed when comparing small-geometry NMOS and PMOS. First, the approximate three-to-one mobility ratio, and hence three-to-one current drive ratio, is no longer correct. The current in a small device is determined by the saturation velocity of the carriers. Both electrons and holes have approximately the same saturation velocity of 1×10^7 cm/s. In small devices where the supply voltage is not scaled as rapidly as the dimensions, lateral fields greater than the critical electric field for velocity saturation can easily be attained. While it should be pointed out that the critical field for holes is greater than that for electrons, these field strengths still can be achieved in small devices. Therefore, the transconductance of NMOS and PMOS become comparable at small-geometries.

Second, the PMOS device has significantly larger source and drain resistance. This results from the shallow junctions required in small devices. To obtain these shallow junctions, the peak doping concentration is reduced in order to reduce the initial charge depth after ion implantation and subsequent diffusion during annealing. This causes the sheet resistance of the source and drain to increase. The contact resistivity of the metal semiconductor junction also increases as doping concentration is reduced. The difference between NMOS and PMOS arises since NMOS junctions are formed with arsenic, whereas PMOS junctions are formed with boron. Boron has a lighter mass than arsenic and a higher diffusion coefficient. This causes the boron peak surface doping concentration to be less than that for arsenic at the same equivalent junction depths. Hence, PMOS has a larger source and drain resistance than NMOS.

Finally, PMOS devices are much more resistant to problems resulting from hot carriers than NMOS. Hot carriers cause severe changes in device characteristics and present a major problem in small devices. This could be a major advantage for PMOS. Hot carriers are discussed in detail in the next section.

Which technology should be used in submicron design? The CMOS and NMOS combination probably will continue to dominate in the near term due to its enormous momentum as well as its ease in interface with TTL components.

2.6 HOT CARRIERS

For the conventional MOS structure discussed in this chapter, one needs to consider, What mechanisms will limit continued device scaling? Will certain physical mechanisms such as junction depth, reliable thin oxides, isolation techniques, and planarity limit full utilization of this technology? Will certain electrical behavior such as threshold voltage variations with geometry, sub-threshold current, transconductance degradation, device-device interactions, substrate current, low noise margins, and source and drain resistance reduce the projected performance increase of circuits designed with these structures?

Historically, devices have been scaled to improve device and circuit performance, reduce cost by allowing more die per wafer, and provide more circuit functions per chip. MOS devices with electrical channel lengths as short as 0.06 micron and as small as 0.25 micron by 0.25 micron have been fabricated and reported to be operational. The previously accepted 0.24 micron channel length limit [26] has been broken with further continued reductions predicted. Of major concern though is long term reliability. While acceptable static and dynamic characteristics have been measured, long term stability of device characteristics has yet to be demonstrated for these small devices.

To counteract mobility degradation, decreased signal to noise ratio, increased source and drain resistance, and alpha particle sensitivity as devices are scaled, supply voltages have not been reduced in strict accordance with the constant electric field scaling law is discussed in Section 2.5.1. As we have seen, a constant-voltage scaling law has been proposed. The large electric fields resulting from shrinking device dimensions, while not scaling supply voltages, cause hot carriers. Carriers can be considered to be hot when their kinetic energy is in excess of the Si–SiO$_2$ barrier of height 2.7 eV, allowing some of the carriers to surmount the barrier. Carriers can become excited when the MOSFET is biased into the saturated or channel inversion mode, or can be generated in the substrate or insulator regions. These hot carriers impose design constraints on devices, and cause long term device reliability problems.

Problems reported resulting from hot carriers include threshold voltage shift over time, transconductance degradation, avalanche induced source-drain breakdown, minority carrier current in the substrate causing discharge of memory storage nodes, majority carrier substrate current, parasitic gate currents, and reduced effectiveness of substrate backgate bias generators.

2.6.1 Generation Mechanisms of Hot Carriers

Hot carriers found in NMOS devices include hot electrons from the surface inversion channel (CHE), substrate hot electrons (SHE), and hot electrons and holes from the drain depletion region when the device is biased in saturation (AHE and AHH). Hot carrier effects in PMOS devices are not analogous to NMOS devices due to the larger ionization coefficient of holes, and the larger barrier height at the insulator interface. Hence PMOS devices have significantly fewer hot carriers. This is an important point and should be considered in circuit design. Therefore, only NMOS hot carrier problems will be discussed. Of the hot carriers found, SHE seem to be the least likely to cause problems in devices operated at the voltages used in ULSI circuits. Therefore, SHE will only be briefly discussed.

Electrons generated in the depletion region under the gate electrode are swept toward the silicon insulator interface when the gate voltage minus the flatband voltage is positive. Mobile electrons (minority carriers) in the bulk are also swept toward the interface. As the electrons are accelerated by the gate voltage toward the surface, they gain energy from the electric field. Inelastic scattering processes reduce the energy of most of the carriers and limit the number of electrons that attain energies significantly above the conduction band edge. When the electric field exceeds approximately 20 kV/cm, the electron drift velocity saturates as optical phonon emission dominates the scattering processes. Further increases in the field causes the electrons to be accelerated to a point such that a second important energy loss mechanism occurs—impact ionization. Under appropriate bias conditions, a small fraction of these electrons can gain sufficient energy to surmount the insulator barrier and be injected into the insulator. Except for this small fraction, most of the electrons are reflected back into the device.

The number of electrons that are injected into the gate oxide is determined by the emission probability. The emission probability depends in part on the barrier height at the interface. To first order this height is simply the difference in the conduction band energies of silicon and silicon dioxide. But, even under scaled operating voltages, the gate field is large enough to produce significant Schottky barrier lowering and an increase in the emission probability. Increasing the substrate doping also increases the emission probability since the fields are increased. For example, a four-fold increase in doping concentration causes the emission probability to increase over two orders of magnitude [27].

Hot carriers cause long term device stability problems. This results from the injection of electrons into the gate insulator. Since some of the carriers become trapped in the oxide, charge accumulates over time. This accumulated charge causes the flatband voltage to shift over time resulting in threshold voltage shifts. The large gate voltages needed to cause significant SHE device degradation normally do not occur on small devices.

When an NMOS device is biased into strong inversion, an n channel exists from source to drain. As electrons are attracted to the drain by a positive voltage, some of the carriers can become heated by the high electric field in the drain depletion region. If these hot electrons are scattered toward the $Si-SiO_2$ interface, with enough energy to surmount the interface barrier, they can be emitted into the insulator. This channel hot electron (CHE) emission will occur in the region where the carriers are the hottest and the gate electric field is in the direction to assist emission. For a device biased in the linear region, the region of maximum electrical field is near the drain island. As long as the device is biased in the linear region, increasing the drain voltage increases the number of electrons emitted into the insulator.

Figure 2.50 illustrates the normalized gate current versus drain voltage with the gate voltage as a parameter. The gate current, I_{GS}, caused by CHE, increases with increasing drain voltage, under linear bias conditions. This results from the drain field causing increased heating of the electrons. The injection of these electrons into the gate is assisted by the gate field. For a constant drain voltage, I_{GS} decreases as the gate voltage increases since the electric field in the longitudinal direction is decreasing as the device goes further into the linear operating region.

Device size has an important effect on CHE. Figure 2.51 is a plot of V_{DS} ($= V_{GS}$) versus channel length L, for a constant injection current. The voltage required to maintain this constant injection drops considerably as the channel length is reduced. This effective increase in emission as the channel length is reduced results from the increased electric field in the drain region, and from an increasing role of the two-dimensional nature of the fields in short-channel devices. Besides the CHE in short-channel devices being greater, the rate-of-increase in CHE with V_{DS} has been found to increase. Increasing the channel doping further increases CHE. Variations in the emission probability, caused by the fields in short-channels, can cause orders-of-magnitude increase in I_{GS}.

CHE can cause significant changes in device characteristics. A small fraction of the injected electrons can become trapped in the insulator. Once

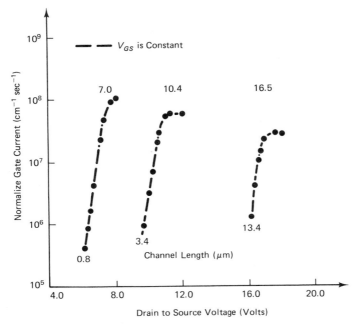

Figure 2.50 Normalized gate current versus drain voltage with gate voltage as a parameter (after Cottrell *et al.* [28], ©1979, IEEE).

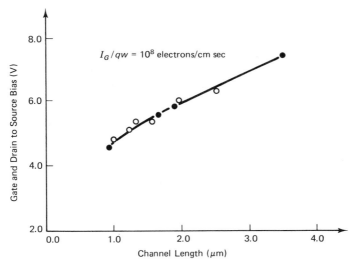

Figure 2.51 Contours of equal gate current (after Cottrell *et al.* [28], ©1979, IEEE).

the magnitude of this trapped charge becomes sufficiently large to affect the local electric field, device characteristics start to change. As this charge builds up, it starts to repel the electrons injected into the gate insulator. This is observed as a reduction in I_{GS} as a function of time. Trapped charge will also cause a variation in the threshold voltage due to a variation in the flatband voltage. This is observed as a distortion in the drain current versus gate voltage characteristics. The transconductance is also observed to degrade, a result of the trapped charge terminating the gate field. This in effect makes the channel appear electrically larger and reduces the transconductance. An interesting effect of the charge trapped over the drain region occurs when the device is operated as a pass transistor, i.e., drain and source are interchangeable. Charge gets trapped over both of the junctions. This trapped charge over the source causes significant changes in the $I - V$ characteristics, since it is located near the potential barrier minimum which controls the current flow in the device.

When the drain voltage becomes sufficiently large, weak avalanching caused by impact ionization occurs in the pinch-off region of the device. This avalanche region can generate hot holes (AHH) and hot electrons (AHE), collectively called avalanche hot carriers (AHC). Both the hot electrons and holes can be emitted into the gate insulator. The electric field determines the number and type of injected carriers. Figure 2.52 illustrates the field distribution in the channel for the saturated and linear regimes. The electric field perpendicular to the interface, E_{ox}, will attract hot holes to the gate insulator from the field reversal point, the point where the electric field from the gate to channel changes direction, to the drain. The maximum injection point will be where the longitudinal field, E_{ch}, is maximum. Electrons will be attracted to the gate insulator in the region from the source to the field reversal point. The large number of charged high energy carriers produced in AHC, and the mechanism of interface state generation result in this mode causing the greatest device degradation. Hot carrier resistance is determined by biasing the device in the AHC mode, and measuring the V_T and g_m shift over time.

2.6.2 Substrate Current

The measurement of the gate current is difficult and hence not routinely done. What can be easily measured is the substrate current, which can be up to six orders of magnitude greater than the gate current.

The substrate current is generated in the following manner. As the drain voltage is increased, the fields in the drain depletion region can become very large. At drain voltages as low as a few volts above the saturation voltage, electron and hole pairs can be created by impact ionization in the depletion region. These generated electrons can either go into the drain, causing an increase in the drain current, or be injected into the gate, causing threshold voltage stability problems. The holes are swept out of the depletion region into

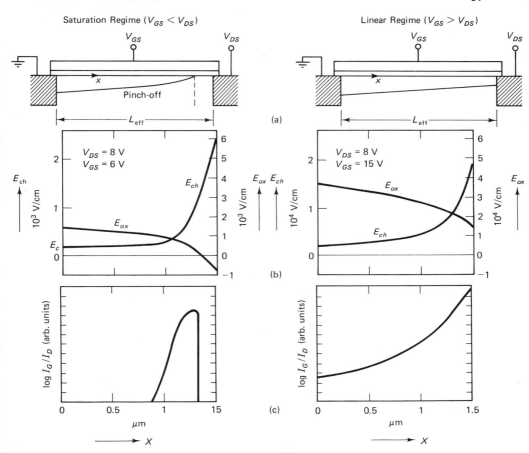

Figure 2.52 (a) A cross section of a MOS transistor with an effective channel length of 1.5 μm in two operation modes. (b) The related oxide field E_{ox} and the channel field E_{ch} in the x direction of the channel given for a fixed drain voltage $V_{DS} = 8$ V and gate voltages $V_{GS} = 6$ V and $V_{GS} = 15$ V, respectively. (c) The electronic gate current density I_G normalized to the drain current I_D as a function of the distance x in both the saturation and linear regime (after Besch et al. [29]), ©1982, IEEE).

the bulk. These holes are then collected at the substrate contact and constitute the measured substrate current. The substrate current flowing in the bulk will generate a voltage which acts to debias the source–bulk junction. This junction can now act as an emitter in a parasitic n^+(source)-p(substrate)-n^+(drain) transistor. Continued debiasing can produce a positive feedback and drive the device into breakdown. It should be noted that this breakdown is neither simple junction breakdown or source-drain punchthrough, but an avalanche induced breakdown.

The behavior of the substrate current as a function of gate voltage is different and more serious in small devices than in large devices. In Figure

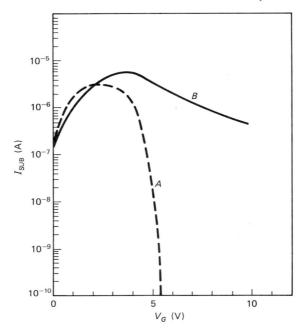

Figure 2.53 The substrate current as a function of gate voltage. (a) Simulated using classical models. (b) Experimental data from a short-channel device (after Mar *et al.* [30], ©1982, IEEE).

2.53, curve *A* is the classical substrate current shape. Curve *A* can be explained as follows. I_{SUB} initially increases for increasing V_{GS} as a result of the holes injected from the drain depletion region caused by impact ionization. As V_{GS} continues to increase the device goes from the saturation to the linear region resulting in a decrease in the electric field across the drain depletion region. As the pinch-off region (the drain depletion region near the Si–SiO$_2$ interface) is reduced, the area for impact ionization is reduced. Hence the number of electron-hole pairs are reduced and I_{SUB} is reduced. At the same time, the ionization coefficients in this region are reduced. Curve *B* is the curve observed for a short device. In short-channel devices, we do not see a significant reduction in I_{SUB} for large V_{GS}. This probably results from a positive feedback mechanism that turns on the parasitic npn transistor. The important point to be made is that the magnitude of the substrate current increases as devices are made smaller, and more hot carriers are being created.

2.6.3 Minority Carrier Current

When the electron-hole pairs are generated by impact ionization, the generated carriers are accelerated further by the field. It was first believed that these new carriers would cause further impact ionization, called secondary impact ionization, generating more carriers. For example, a hole generated by impact ionization in the depletion region, could continue being accelerated out of the depletion region causing a secondary impact ionization. Some of the electrons resulting from this impact ionization could be injected out of the depletion region and become substrate minority carriers. Calculations indicate, however, the minority carrier current resulting from secondary impact ionization should be several orders of magnitude smaller than the measured values. Another method to explain minority carrier generation is photons produced by the hot electrons. The photon travels in some cases up to 800 μm, before generating electron-hole pairs. Measurements of light in the drain region and minority carries flowing out of regions with reversed biased wells support this concept. Minority carriers can cause modulation of nearby devices and discharge storage nodes.

2.6.4 Hot Carrier Resistant Structures

Various modifications of the standard MOS structure have been developed to reduce the effects of hot carriers. These structures, shown in Figures 2.54a, 2.54b and 2.54c, have been used to reduce substrate and gate currents. All of the structures are designed to reduce the electric field in the drain region by grading the drain implant concentration. Figure 2.54a uses an As-P(n^+-n^-) double diffused drain structure. The n^+ islands are surrounded by the n^- concentration. Figure 2.54b uses a diffused phosphorous instead of As so that

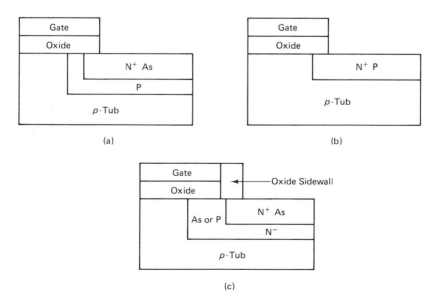

Figure 2.54 Various NMOS drain structures used to reduce hot carriers.

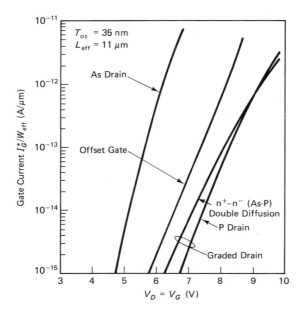

Figure 2.55 Comparison of gate currents for various kinds of MOSFET structures, each having an oxide thickness of 35 nm and an effective channel length of 1.1 μm (after Takeda *et al.* [31], ©1982, IEEE).

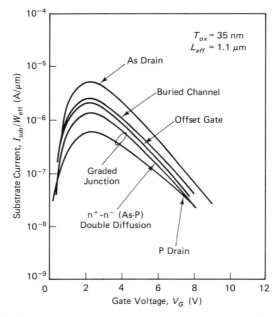

Figure 2.56 Comparison of substrate currents between various kinds of device structures as a function of V_G, with V_D as a parameter (after Takeda *et al.* [31], ©1982, IEEE).

the surface concentration will be reduced. Figure 2.54c uses an offset gate where an n^- region is introduced between the channel and the n^+ junctions. Figure 2.55 illustrates the excellent reduction in gate current, and Figure 2.56 shows the reduction in substrate current.

Graded drain junctions are obviously effective in reducing hot carrier generation. The highest applicable voltage can be raised by more than 2 volts as compared to the standard structure. There is a problem using these structures. Unless an extra mask is used, the source junction will be offset and/or graded just like the drain. This will reduce the injection efficiency of the source into the inversion layer. This will appear as an increase in source resistance and cause the transconductance to degrade. The optimum n^- region surface concentration for a transconductance degradation of no more than 25% is in the $1 \times 10^{18}/cm^3$ to $2.5 \times 10^{18}/cm^3$ range.

2.7 SUBMICRON CMOS PROCESS TECHNOLOGY

In this section we briefly discuss process development for submicron CMOS. ULSI densities have been achieved as a direct result of advances in process technology. Advances in direct-write E-beam lithography and new metallization techniques have reduced the feature sizes that can be fabricated. However, many other problems such as device isolation, planarization, and metal step coverage still must be solved.

In previous VLSI generations, simple scaling of device size, increasing die size, and using old processing techniques produced acceptable yields. However, for ULSI densities, the techniques in fabricating ultra-high-density chips require significant changes in process techniques. The fabrication of 4 M, 16 M, and 64 M density chips requires geometrics of 1 μm, .75 μm, and .5 μm, respectively. These feature sizes require an advanced fabrication process flow.

A submicron process flow demands three main characteristics: low temperature processing, low interconnect resistance, and planarity. The need for low temperature processing directly results from the desire to reduce multi-dimensional effects. ULSI devices require very shallow sources and drains. Junction depths of .1 μm are typical. Low temperature processing minimizes the lateral and vertical diffusion of dopant atoms. Research has shown high temperatures for very short times, e.g., rapid thermal annealing, can also accomplish similar results.

The second essential characteristic is low resistances. Parasitic resistances and capacitances can result in significant speed reduction in ULSI circuits. The resistance of submicron lines and contacts can be reduced by selectively growing or depositing a refractory metal on the polysilicon gate and on the source and drain. Refractory metals such as Pt, Ti, Co, and W have shown excellent reduction in polysilicon sheet resistance and source and drain contact resistance.

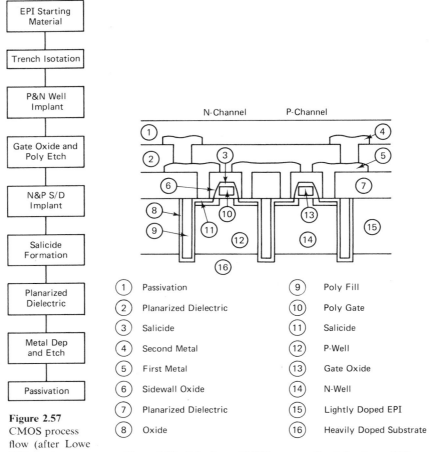

Figure 2.57
CMOS process
flow (after Lowe
[32]).

Figure 2.58   Submicron CMOS cross section (after Lowe [32]).

The third parameter which is critical for fabricating submicron structures is flatness of the surface—planarity. Planarity is needed mainly for three reasons. First, the resist must be planar so when exposed by either optical or direct write E-beam, the pattern is accurately transferred. Steps and edges make this very hard to accomplish. Second, changes in topography increase the already very hard task in focusing the exposure tool. Finally, planarity is critical to achieve good step coverage of interconnects into contacts.

Figure 2.57 lists a typical submicron CMOS process flow. The cross section of the completed structure is shown in Figure 2.58. At present, a manufacturable circuit using .25 μm drawn gates appears possible. Within a few years, circuits using .1 μm drawn geometrics may be possible. Lithography development will establish the scaling pace for devices with these geometries.

2.8 CONCLUSION

This chapter has reviewed the basic MOSFET theory and included comments on where the classical theory fails as the device is scaled. Second-order effects, and how they affect the behavior of small devices, were then discussed. While the performance of small MOSFETs is not ideal, these devices· still offer a considerable advantage by enhancing the overall performance of large systems.

In the discussion of the advantages of scaling, it was noted that driving lines off-chip were difficult due to large capacitance loads. MOSFETs do not have sufficient current drive to charge large capacitors rapidly. Large W/L ratios are required (using considerable silicon) to increase off-chip signal speed. A method to obtain fast off-chip speeds, as well as retain minimum device area, is to use small-geometry bipolar devices as output drivers. Small-geometry bipolar devices will be discussed in the next chapter.

REFERENCES

1. J. E. Lilienfeld, U.S. Patent 1,745,175 (1930).

2. D. Kahng and M. M. Atalla, *IRE Solid-State Device Res. Conf.* (Pittsburgh, PA, 1960).

3. S. M. Sze, *Physics of Semiconductor Devices*, second edition (Wiley, New York, 1981).

4. E. H. Nicollian and J. R. Brews, *MOS Physics and Technology* (Wiley, New York, 1982).

5. R. F. Pierret, *Modular Series on Solid State Devices*, *Field Effect Devices*, vol. IV (Addison-Wesley, Reading, MA, 1983).

6. R. R. Troutman, *IEEE J. Solid State Circuits*, vol. SC-9, p. 55 (1974).

7. D. G. Ong, *Modern MOS Technology* (McGraw-Hill, New York, 1984).

8. S. M. Goodnick *et al.*, *J. Vac. Sci. Technol.*, vol. 1, p. 803 (1983).

9. B. T. Moore and D. K. Ferry, *J. Vac. Sci. Technol*, vol. 17, p. 1037 (1980).

10. D. K. Ferry, *IEDM Digest*, p. 605 (1984).

11. R. H. Dennard, F. H. Gaensslen, H. Yu, V. L. Rideout, E. Bassons, and A. R. LeBlanc, *IEEE J. Solid State Circuits*, vol. SC-9, p. 256 (1974).

12. J. L. Prince, *Very Large Scale Integration*, ed. D. F. Barbe (Springer-Verlag, New York, 1980).

13. P. K. Chatterjee, W. R. Hunter, I. C. Holloway, and Y. T. Lin, *IEEE Electron Device Letters*, vol. EDL-1, p. 220 (1980).

14. P. Ratnam and C. A. Salama, *IEEE Trans. Electron Devices*, vol. ED-31, no. 9, p. 1289 (1984).

15. L. D. Yau, *Solid State Electronics*, vol. 17, p. 1059 (1974).

16. G. Taylor, *IEEE Trans. Electron Devices*, vol. ED-25, p. 337 (1978).

17. W. Fichtner and H. W. Potzl, *Int. J. Electron.*, vol. 46, p. 33 (1979).

18. L. A. Akers, *Solid State Electronics*, vol. 24, p. 621 (1981).

19. L. A. Akers, M. Beguwala, and F. Custode, *IEEE Trans. Electron Devices*, vol. ED-28, p. 1490 (1981).

20. L. A. Akers, *IEEE Electron Device Letters*, vol. EDL-7, p. 419 (1986).

21. R. R. Troutman, *IEEE Trans. Electron Devices*, vol. ED-26, no. 4, p. 461 (1979).

22. C. Duuvnry, *Circuits and Devices*, vol. 2, 6, p. 6 (1986).

23. H. Shichajo, *Solid State Electronics*, vol. 26, no. 10, p. 969 (1983).

24. M. Sugino, L. A. Akers, and J. Ford, *IEEE Trans. Electron Devices*, vol. ED-31, p. 1823 (1984).

25. P. P. Guebels and F. Van De Wiele, *Solid State Electronics*, vol. 26, no. 4, p. 267 (1983).

26. B. Hoeneisen and C. A. Mead, *Solid State Electronics*, vol. 15, p. 819 (1972).

27. T. Ning, P. Cook, R. Dennard, C. Osburn, S. Schueter, and H. Yu, *IEEE Trans. Electron Devices*, vol. ED-26, no. 4, p. 346 (1979).

28. P. Cottrell, R. Troutman, and T. Ning, *IEEE J. Solid State Circuits*, vol. SC-14, no. 2, p. 442 (1979).

29. H. Besch, J. Leburton, and G. Dorda, *IEEE Trans. Electron Devices*, vol. ED-29, no. 5, p. 913 (1982).

30. J. Mar, S. S. Li, and S. Y. Yu, *IEEE Trans. CAD of IC's and Systems*, vol. CAD-1, no. 4, (1982).

31. E. Takeda, H. Kuma, T. Toyabe, and S. Asai, *IEEE Trans. Electron Devices*, vol. ED-29, no. 4, p. 611 (1982).

32. A. T. Lowe, *Correlations*, vol. V, no. 1, p. 27 (1985).

3

SMALL-GEOMETRY BIPOLAR JUNCTION TRANSISTORS

Historically, the bipolar junction transistor (BJT) has been the workhorse of the integrated circuit industry. Since its invention in 1947, the bipolar transistor has played a key role in the development of modern semiconductor devices and integrated circuits. The fast switching speed and large current drive capability of the BJT structure combine to give it features still unmatched by other device technologies. While it is unlikely that BJTs will be used exclusively in ULSI systems, they can be used with other devices to form circuits which exploit the best features of each technology.

In this chapter, we discuss the theory and technology of small-geometry bipolar junction transistors used for high-performance digital integrated circuits. We begin with the development of a first-order theory to describe the basic device operation, followed by the inclusion of second-order and multidimensional effects which influence the behavior of small device structures. This is followed by a discussion of device parasitics and their effects on circuit performance, device scaling issues, and finally, a description of modern integrated circuit bipolar device fabrication technologies.

3.1 BJT BASICS

A cross-sectional view of a planar bipolar junction transistor, typical of the device structures used in high-performance digital integrated circuits, is shown in Figure 3.1a. High-speed performance at low currents demands that lateral dimensions be kept as small as the technology used in their fabrication will

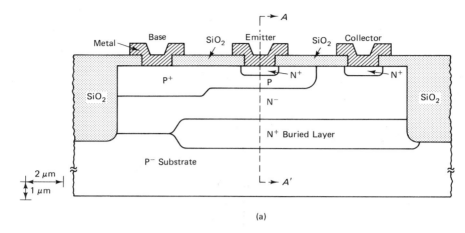

(a)

Figure 3.1(a)   Cross-sectional view of a typical NPN IC transistor.

allow. Vertical dimensions must also be kept small to minimize junction capacitances and carrier transit times. A typical doping profile is illustrated in Figure 3.1b, which shows the net dopant concentration in a one-dimensional slice (A − A′) taken through the active region of the device structure of Figure 3.1a. In normal operation, the electrical behavior of the device is determined largely by the doping profile in the emitter and base regions of the structure, and to a lesser extent, by the doping level in the N^- collector region. The purpose of the heavily-doped N^+ buried layer is to reduce the parasitic series collector resistance.

3.1.1 Intrinsic Device Structure

Even though the operation of the BJT relies on two-dimensional and three-dimensional conduction mechanisms, the basic behavior of the device can be derived from a one-dimensional model representing the intrinsic region of the device. Two-dimensional and three-dimensional effects can often be represented by parasitic circuit elements which are added to the basic one-dimensional device model.*

In those cases in which the device cannot be adequately described by one-dimensional models, two-dimensional and three-dimensional models must, of course, be used. Conditions in which multi-dimensional models are needed will be discussed later in this chapter.

---

*A classic example is emitter-current crowding (to be discussed in Section 3.3.1), which profoundly affects the terminal $I - V$ characteristics, but yet can be adequately modeled in many cases by simply adding a parasitic resistance between the intrinsic base region and the extrinsic base contact region.

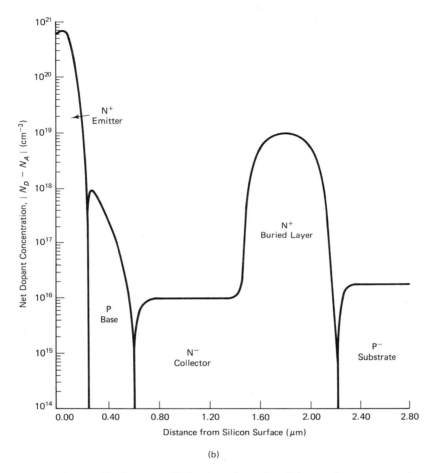

Figure 3.1(b)   Net dopant profile for the active region of the transistor structure of Figure 3.1(a).

The intrinsic transistor, shown in the upper portion of Figure 3.2, is bounded laterally by the emitter area and vertically by the distance from the silicon surface (at the emitter) to the N^-/N^+ buried layer interface in the collector region. The reason the N^+ buried layer is not included as part of the intrinsic transistor structure is that the minority carrier lifetime is much lower in the N^+ region than in the much lighter-doped N^- region. Consequently, the N^+ buried layer appears as an "infinite sink" for minority carriers arriving from the emitter. Thus, as far as the intrinsic transistor is concerned, the N^+ buried layer may be considered to be an ohmic contact. The resistance and capacitance of the buried layer can be included as part of the extrinsic (parasitic) device structure.

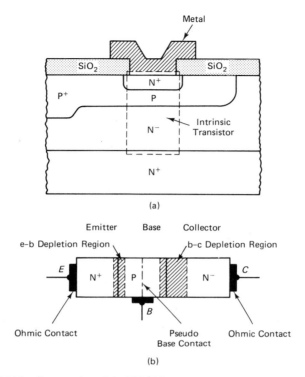

Figure 3.2(a) Cross-section of the NPN IC transistor illustrating the boundaries of the intrinsic portion of the structure. (b) One-dimensional representation of the intrinsic transistor.

3.1.2 One-Dimensional Device Model

In the lower portion of Figure 3.2 is shown a one-dimensional representation of the intrinsic transistor structure. At the boundaries of the emitter and collector regions are two ohmic contacts. In a one-dimensional model however, the base region cannot be terminated by an ohmic contact because such a contact would prevent minority carriers, which are injected into the base from the emitter, from reaching the collector. The structure would behave as two back-to-back pn junction diodes instead of a bipolar junction transistor. The problem is solved by imposing a pseudo contact boundary in the neutral base region which does not affect the minority carriers but which forces thermal equilibrium for the majority carriers at the boundary. Fortunately, the quasi-Fermi potential for majority carriers is relatively constant throughout most of the base region, so that the actual placement of the pseudo base contact boundary is not critical [1]. This contact scheme allows boundary conditions to be specified in terms of potentials appearing at the emitter, base, and collector terminals of the device.

3.1.3 Description of BJT Operation

Consider an npn transistor operating in the forward-active mode; that is, with a forward bias applied to the emitter-base junction and a reserve bias applied to the base-collector junction. In this mode of operation the principal current components are determined by the injection of mobile carriers across the emitter-base junction. The situation is illustrated schematically in the energy band diagram of Figure 3.3. Depicted is a device having the structure of Figure 3.2, the doping profile of Figure 3.1b, and being operated at a dc bias of $V_{BE} = 0.75$ volts and $V_{BC} = -1.5$ volts. The application of a forward bias to the emitter-base junction lowers the potential barrier for majority

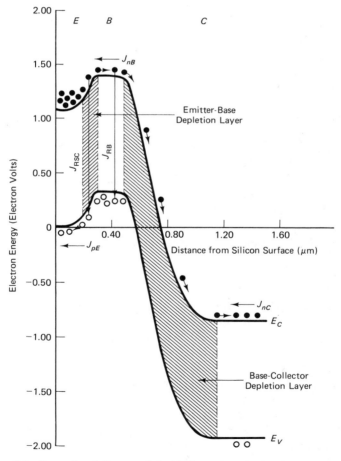

Figure 3.3 Energy band diagram of the NPN transistor having the doping profile of Figure 3.1(b) with applied biases $V_{BE} = 0.7$ volts and $V_{BC} = -1.5$ volts. Also illustrated are the principal current components.

carriers at the junction and results in an appreciable number of these carriers being injected across the junction where they add to the concentration of minority carriers already present. In the base region, the injected electrons move by a combination of drift and diffusion* toward the reverse-biased base-collector junction and give rise to a current (density) J_{nB}. Some of the injected electrons, in traversing the base, recombine with majority carriers (holes) resulting in a component of base current J_{RB}. Those electrons surviving the transit across the base are accelerated across the base-collector junction by the large electric field. Owing to the scarcity of majority carriers in the base-collector depletion layer and the fact that the electrons in this region have high velocity, there is little probability of recombination, and thus essentially all the electrons enter the collector region where they give rise to the collector current J_{nC}.

The forward bias on the emitter-base junction also results in holes being injected from the base into the emitter, giving rise to a current J_{pE}. This current is supplied by the base and its magnitude in relation to J_{nB} determines the emitter efficiency of the device. The recombination of injected holes and electrons in the emitter-base depletion layer gives rise to a third component of base current, J_{RSC}.

In Figure 3.4 we plot the electron and hole concentrations as a function of distance. These results (as well as the energy band diagram of Figure 3.3) were obtained from a one-dimensional numerical analysis using the doping profile of Figure 3.1b. Notice that most of the transistor action occurs within a distance of about 1 micron from the silicon surface. This is, of course, due to the relatively shallow junction depths which are typical of BJT structures used in modern digital integrated circuits.

3.1.4 One-Dimensional Analysis of the BJT

Analysis of the bipolar transistor entails simultaneously solving Poisson's equation and the continuity equations, and applying boundary conditions at the emitter, base, and collector contacts. In general, however, closed form analytic solutions of these equations for even the one-dimensional transistor model of Figure 3.2 are not possible without further simplifications.

The first simplification is the partitioning of the device into space-charge and quasi-neutral regions. This allows each region to be analyzed separately for the desired device parameter(s). In the space-charge regions associated with the emitter-base and base-collector junctions it is assumed that the concentration of mobile carriers is negligible in comparison with the concentration of the fixed ionized dopant atoms. While this is a good assumption for thermal equilibrium and low-level injection, other operating conditions

---

*In a transistor in which the base region is uniformly doped and operated under low-level injection conditions, the transport of minority carriers in the base would be by diffusion only.

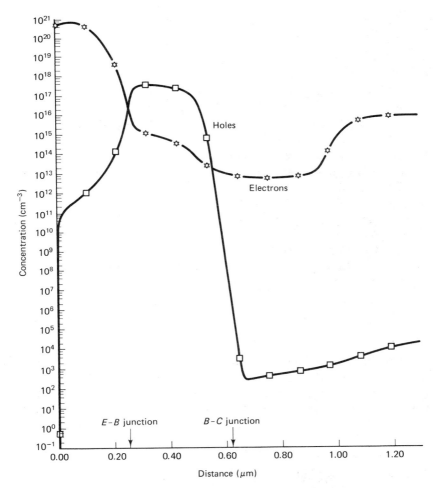

Figure 3.4 Electron and hole concentrations as a function of distance in the NPN transistor having the doping profile of Figure 3.1(b) and with applied biases of $V_{BE} = 0.7$ volts and $V_{BC} = -1.5$ volts.

which result in large quantities of mobile carriers being transported through the space-charge layers require additional considerations. For the present we will assume that the junction space-charge regions are completely depleted of mobile carriers. With this approximation, and a known doping profile, Poisson's equation can be directly solved to determine the widths of the depletion layers under given bias conditions. The quasi-neutral regions outside the depletion layers are assumed to be charge neutral. In these regions, the continuity equations are solved for the spatial and temporal distribution of mobile carriers. From these distributions, the transistor currents can be calculated. In the analysis, the following assumptions are made:

1. Doping levels are nondegenerate,
2. Low-level injection,
3. Mobilities and lifetimes in each region (emitter, base, and collector) are represented by effective average values and hence constant,
4. Dopant profiles in the emitter and collector regions are represented by effective average values, and
5. The electric field in the quasi-neutral base region is a function of only the base doping profile and can be represented by an equivalent average value which is constant.

This last assumption deserves further comment.

3.1.4.1 Equivalent base field.   Doping of the base region in modern bipolar transistors is usually accomplished by ion implantation, which gives a near Gaussian profile of impurity atoms. Thus for the base

$$N_A(x) = N_P \exp\left[-\frac{(x + R)^2}{2(\Delta R)^2} \right] \tag{3.1}$$

where R is the projected range and ΔR is the standard deviation (or straggle) of the distribution. For convenience, the coordinate system shown in Figure 3.5 is chosen. Here the neutral base region extends from the emitter-base depletion edge at $x = 0$ to the base-collector depletion edge at $x = x_B$. With

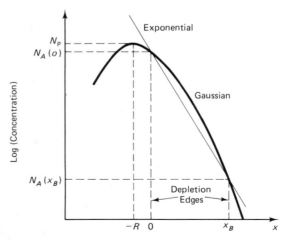

Figure 3.5   Comparison of an exponential versus a Gaussian dopant profile for the base region.

reference to the concentration at $x = 0$, (3.1) can be rewritten as

$$N_A(x) = N_A(0)\exp\left[-\frac{x(x + 2R)}{2(\Delta R)^2}\right]$$ (3.2)

The electric field in the base is found by setting the majority current (J_p) equal to zero. This gives

$$E_{Gauss} = \frac{kT}{q}\frac{1}{N_A(x)}\frac{dN_A}{dx} = -\frac{kT}{q(\Delta R)^2}(x + R)$$ (3.3)

which is seen to vary linearly with position.

Consider now an equivalent profile in which the Gaussian is approximated by an exponential of the form

$$N_A'(x) = N_A(0)\exp\left(-\frac{ax}{x_B}\right)$$ (3.4)

as illustrated in Figure 3.5 and where

$$a = \ln\left[\frac{N_A(0)}{N_A(x_B)}\right]$$

This exponential profile gives a constant field

$$E_{exp} = -\frac{kTa}{qx_B}$$ (3.5)

Equating (3.2) and (3.4) at $x = x_B$ gives

$$(\Delta R)^2 = x_B(x_B + 2R)/2a$$

and

$$E_{Gauss} = -\frac{2kTa(x + R)}{qx_B(x_B + 2R)} = \frac{2(x + R)}{(x_B + 2R)}E_{exp}$$ (3.6)

In the neutral base region the average electric field resulting from a Gaussian doping profile is

$$\langle E \rangle = \frac{1}{x_B}\int_0^{x_B}\frac{2(x + R)}{(x_B + 2R)}E_{exp}dx = E_{exp}$$ (3.7)

Thus, a Gaussian profile gives the same average electric field as an exponential profile. For our analysis we will assume that the doping in the base can be represented by an equivalent exponential profile of the form expressed in (3.4).

3.1.4.2 Nomenclature.   The one-dimensional NPN transistor structure to be analyzed is depicted in Figure 3.6. The metallurgical junction widths of the emitter, base, and collector regions are W_E, W_B, and W_C, respectively.

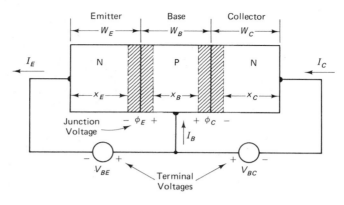

Figure 3.6 One-dimensional NPN transistor model illustrating voltage and current conventions.

The corresponding neutral region widths are X_E, X_B, and X_C. The potentials appearing across the space-charge layers associated with the emitter-base and base-collector junctions are denoted ϕ_E and ϕ_C, respectively, to differentiate them from the applied terminal voltages V_{BE} and V_{BC}. The convention chosen for the direction of the terminal currents, I_E, I_B, and I_C is that which represents the directions encountered in an actual device operating in its normal mode.

In Table 3.1 we list symbols used in the analysis to follow. Quantities which represent thermal equilibrium are identified by adding a subscript "o."

3.1.4.3 Steady-state analysis.

In the derivation of the $I - V$ characteristics of the BJT, we need to determine the distribution of minority carriers in each region (emitter, base, and collector) as a function of applied bias. Since each region differs only in dopant profile and boundary conditions, a single solution can be obtained which can then be applied to each of the three regions in the transistor.

Consider first a p-type region of arbitrary doping which has known boundary conditions at $x = 0$ and at $x = x_j$, such as illustrated in Figure 3.7.

TABLE 3.1   List of Symbols for an NPN Transistor

Parameter	Emitter	Base	Collector
Doping concentration	N_{DE}	N_{AB}	N_{DC}
Majority carrier concentration	n_{nE}	p_{pB}	n_{nC}
Minority carrier concentration	p_{nE}	n_{pB}	p_{nC}
Majority current density	J_{nE}	J_{pB}	J_{nC}
Minority carrier lifetime	τ_{pE}	τ_{nB}	τ_{pC}
Minority carrier diffusion length	L_{pE}	L_{nB}	L_{pC}
Minority carrier diffusion constant	D_{pE}	D_{nB}	D_{pC}

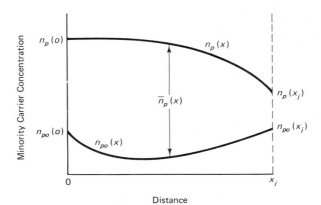

Figure 3.7 Minority carrier concentration versus distance in an arbitrarily doped p-type region. The difference between the total electron concentration, $n_p(x)$, and the thermal equilibrium concentration, $n_{po}(x)$, is the *excess* concentration, $\bar{n}_p(x)$.

The continuity equation for electrons is

$$\frac{1}{q}\frac{dJ_n}{dx} - r = 0 \tag{3.8}$$

If we assume recombination to be of the Shockley-Read-Hall type [2, 3] with recombination centers located near mid-gap, then

$$r = \frac{pn - n_i^2}{\tau_p(n + n_i) + \tau_n(p + n_i)} \tag{3.9}$$

In a p-type region of moderate doping and low-level injection such that $p \gg n$, (3.9) reduces to

$$r \approx \frac{n_p(x) - n_i^2/p_p(x)}{\tau_n} = \frac{n_p(x) - n_{po}(x)}{\tau_n} \tag{3.10}$$

Since the recombination rate depends upon the difference between the carrier concentration and its value at thermal equilibrium, it is convenient to write the continuity equation in terms of the *excess* carrier concentration, $\bar{n}_p(x)$ where

$$\bar{n}_p(x) = n_p(x) - n_{po}(x) \tag{3.11}$$

Writing the equation for electron current in terms of the excess electron concentration gives

$$J_n(x) = qD_n\left[\frac{qE}{kT}n_{po}(x) + \frac{dn_{po}}{dx} + \frac{qE}{kT}\bar{n}_p(x) + \frac{d\bar{n}_p}{dx}\right] \tag{3.12}$$

In the quasi-neutral regions of the semiconductor the electric field, E, arises from the gradient of the dopant profile (assuming low-level injection). For p-type material

$$E = \frac{kT}{q} \frac{1}{N_A(x)} \frac{dN_A}{dx} \tag{3.13}$$

Using (3.13), it is easily shown that the first two terms on the right hand side of (3.12) cancel. Thus,

$$J_n(x) = qD_n \left[\frac{qE}{kT} \bar{n}_p(x) + \frac{d\bar{n}_p}{dx} \right] \tag{3.14}$$

Combining (3.8) with (3.10), and using (3.14), yields

$$\frac{d^2\bar{n}_p}{dx^2} + \frac{qE}{kT} \frac{d\bar{n}_p}{dx} - \frac{1}{L_n^2} \bar{n}_p(x) = 0 \tag{3.15}$$

where $L_n^2 = D_n \tau_n$. The solution to (3.15) is of the form

$$\bar{n}_p(x) = C_1 \exp(m_1 x) + C_2 \exp(m_2 x) \tag{3.16}$$

where

$$m_1 = -\frac{qE}{2kT} + \lambda_n \quad \text{and} \quad m_2 = -\frac{qE}{2kT} - \lambda_n$$

with

$$\lambda_n = \sqrt{\left(\frac{qE}{2kT}\right)^2 + \left(\frac{1}{L_n}\right)^2}$$

C_1 and C_2 are constants, which are determined from the boundary conditions on $\bar{n}_p$ at $x = 0$ and $x = x_j$ as

$$\bar{n}_p(0) = C_1 + C_2 \tag{3.17a}$$

$$\bar{n}_p(x_j) = C_1 \exp(m_1 x_j) + C_2 \exp(m_2 x_j) \tag{3.17b}$$

and

$$C_1 = \frac{\bar{n}_p(x_j)\exp\left(\dfrac{qEx_j}{2kT}\right) - \bar{n}_p(0)\exp(-\lambda_n x_j)}{2\sinh(\lambda_n x_j)}$$

$$C_2 = \frac{\bar{n}_p(0)\exp(\lambda_n x_j) - \bar{n}_p(x_j)\exp\left(\dfrac{qEx_j}{2kT}\right)}{2\sinh(\lambda_n x_j)}$$

Hence,

$$\bar{n}_p(x) = \bar{n}_p(0)\sinh\left[\lambda_n(x_j - x)\right]\exp\left(-\frac{qEx}{2kT}\right)\bigg/\sinh(\lambda_n x_j)$$

$$+ \bar{n}_p(x_j)\sinh(\lambda_n x)\exp\left[\frac{qE}{2kT}(x_j - x)\right]\bigg/\sinh(\lambda_n x_j) \qquad (3.18)$$

The minority electron current, calculated from (3.14), is then

$$J_n(x) = \frac{qD_n}{\sinh(\lambda_n x_j)}\left\{\bar{n}_p(0)\exp\left(-\frac{qEx}{2kT}\right)\left(\frac{qE}{2kT}\sinh\left[\lambda_n(x_j - x)\right]\right.\right.$$

$$\left.- \lambda_n\cosh\left[\lambda_n(x_j - x)\right]\right) + \bar{n}_p(x_j)\exp\left[\frac{qE}{2kT}(x_j - x)\right]$$

$$\times \left(\frac{qE}{2kT}\sinh(\lambda_n x) + \lambda_n\cosh(\lambda_n x)\right)\bigg\} \qquad (3.19)$$

In an analogous manner, we solve the steady-state continuity equation for holes in an n-type region

$$\frac{d^2\bar{p}_n}{dx^2} - \frac{qE}{kT}\frac{d\bar{p}_n}{dx} - \frac{1}{L_p^2}\bar{p}_n(x) = 0 \qquad (3.20)$$

where

$$L_p^2 = D_p\tau_p$$

to find

$$\bar{p}_n(x) = \bar{p}_n(0)\sinh\left[\lambda_p(x_j - x)\right]\exp\left(\frac{qEx}{2kT}\right)\bigg/\sinh(\lambda_p x_j)$$

$$+ \bar{p}_n(x_j)\sinh(\lambda_p x)\exp\left[-\frac{qE}{2kT}(x_j - x)\right]\bigg/\sinh(\lambda_p x_j) \qquad (3.21)$$

with

$$\lambda_p = \sqrt{\left(\frac{qE}{2kT}\right)^2 + \left(\frac{1}{L_p}\right)^2}$$

Using

$$J_p(x) = qD_p\left[\frac{qE}{kT}\bar{p}_n(x) - \frac{d\bar{p}_n}{dx}\right] \qquad (3.22)$$

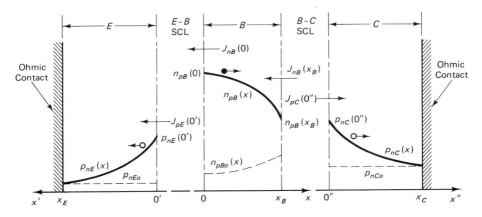

Figure 3.8 Coordinate system and current components for the emitter, base, and collector regions of an NPN transistor.

the minority hole current is

$$J_p(x) = \frac{qD_p}{\sinh(\lambda_p x_j)} \left\{ \bar{p}_n(0)\exp\left(\frac{qEx}{2kT}\right)\left(\frac{qE}{2kT}\sinh\left[\lambda_p(x_j - x)\right]\right.\right.$$

$$\left. + \lambda_p\cosh\left[\lambda_p(x_j - x)\right]\right) + \bar{p}_n(x_j)\exp\left[-\frac{qE}{2kT}(x_j - x)\right]$$

$$\times \left(\frac{qE}{2kT}\sinh(\lambda_p x) - \lambda_p\cosh(\lambda_p x)\right)\right\} \qquad (3.23)$$

3.1.4.4 Transistor currents.   If we adopt the coordinate system illustrated in Figure 3.8, then the current components associated with the neutral emitter, base, and collector regions may be calculated directly using (3.19) and (3.23).

Base Region.   The boundary conditions for the base are given by the *law-of-the-junction*:

$$\bar{n}_{pB}(0) = \frac{n_i^2}{N_{AB}(0)}\left[\exp\left(\frac{q\phi_E}{kT}\right) - 1\right] \qquad (3.24a)$$

$$\bar{n}_{pB}(x_B) = \frac{n_i^2}{N_{AB}(x_B)}\left[\exp\left(\frac{q\phi_C}{kT}\right) - 1\right] \qquad (3.24b)$$

Using (3.19), the minority current density at the depletion edge at $x = 0$

owing to injected electrons is

$$J_{nB}(0) = qD_{nB}\left\{ \bar{n}_{pB}(0)\left[\frac{qE}{2kT} - \lambda_{nB}\coth(\lambda_{nB}x_B) \right] \right.$$

$$\left. + \bar{n}_{pB}(x_B)\lambda_{nB}\exp\left(\frac{qEx_B}{2kT} \right)\operatorname{csch}(\lambda_{nB}x_B) \right\} \qquad (3.25)$$

and at the depletion edge at $x = x_B$

$$J_{nB}(x_B) = qD_{nB}\left\{ n_{pB}(x_B)\left[-\frac{qE}{2kT} + \lambda_{nB}\coth(\lambda_{nB}x_B) \right] \right.$$

$$\left. - \bar{n}_{pB}(0)\lambda_{nB}\exp\left(-\frac{qEx_B}{2kT} \right)\operatorname{csch}(\lambda_{nB}x_B) \right\} \qquad (3.26)$$

where

$$E = -\frac{kT}{qx_B}\ln\left[\frac{N_{AB}(0)}{N_{AB}(x_B)} \right] \qquad (3.27)$$

Emitter Region.   Here we represent the actual doping profile by an effective average value

$$N_{DE} = \frac{1}{x_E}\int_{0'}^{x_E}N_{DE}(x)\,dx \qquad (3.28)$$

This approximation allows us to take $E = 0$ in the quasi-neutral emitter region. The boundary condition at the depletion edge ($x = 0'$) is

$$\bar{p}_{nE}(0') = \frac{n_i^2}{N_{DE}}\left[\exp\left(\frac{q\phi_E}{kT} \right) - 1 \right] \qquad (3.29)$$

At $x = x_E$, the boundary condition is determined by the nature of the metal-semiconductor contact. If the contact is ideal (ohmic), then thermal equilibrium conditions prevail so that

$$\bar{p}_{nE}(x_E) = 0 \qquad (3.30)$$

If the contact is not ideal, then

$$qD_{pE}\left. \frac{d\bar{p}_{nE}}{dx} \right|_{x=x_E} = -qS_p\bar{p}_{nE}(x_E) \qquad (3.31)$$

where S_p is the surface recombination velocity at the metal-semiconductor interface. Using (3.23) and (3.30), the minority current density at the depletion edge at $x = 0'$ owing to injected holes is

$$J_{pE}(0') = \frac{qD_{pE}\bar{p}_{nE}(0')}{L_{pE}}\coth\left(\frac{x_E}{L_{pE}} \right) \qquad (3.32)$$

Collector Region.   In a similar fashion, we calculate

$$J_{pC}(0'') = \frac{qD_{pC}\bar{p}_{nC}(0'')}{L_{pC}} \coth\left(\frac{x_C}{L_{pC}}\right) \tag{3.33}$$

where

$$\bar{p}_{nC}(0'') = \frac{n_i^2}{N_{DC}}\left[\exp\left(\frac{q\phi_C}{kT}\right) - 1\right] \tag{3.34}$$

If recombination in the $E - B$ and $B - C$ space-charge layers (junction depletion regions) can be neglected, then the terminal currents can be determined simply by summing the minority currents at the depletion edges of the two junctions. With reference to Figures 3.6 and 3.8, we have

$$J_E = J_{pE}(0') - J_{nB}(0) \tag{3.35a}$$

$$J_C = -J_{pC}(0'') - J_{nB}(x_B) \tag{3.35b}$$

and

$$J_B = J_E - J_C \tag{3.35c}$$

The minus signs in (3.35a) and (3.35b) arise from the negative direction in the coordinate system for the emitter and the convention chosen for the direction of the terminal currents (see Figure 3.6).

In terms of the junction potentials, (3.35a) and (3.35b) can be rewritten as

$$J_E = a_{11}\left[\exp\left(\frac{q\phi_E}{kT}\right) - 1\right] - a_{12}\left[\exp\left(\frac{q\phi_C}{kT}\right) - 1\right] \tag{3.36a}$$

$$J_C = a_{21}\left[\exp\left(\frac{q\phi_E}{kT}\right) - 1\right] - a_{22}\left[\exp\left(\frac{q\phi_C}{kT}\right) - 1\right] \tag{3.36b}$$

where

$$a_{11} = \frac{D_{pE}P_{nEo}}{L_{pE}}\coth\left(\frac{x_E}{L_{pE}}\right) + qD_{nB}n_{pBo}(0)\left[\lambda_{nB}\coth(\lambda_{nB}x_B) - \frac{qE}{2kT}\right]$$

$$a_{12} = qD_{nB}n_{pBo}(x_B)\lambda_{nB}\exp\left(\frac{qEx_B}{2kT}\right)\mathrm{csch}(\lambda_{nB}x_B)$$

$$a_{21} = qD_{nB}n_{pBo}(0)\lambda_{nB}\exp\left(-\frac{qEx_B}{2kT}\right)\mathrm{csch}(\lambda_{nB}x_B)$$

$$a_{22} = \frac{qD_{pC}P_{nCo}}{L_{pC}}\coth\left(\frac{x_C}{L_{pC}}\right) + qD_{nB}n_{pBo}(x_B)\left[\lambda_{nB}\coth(\lambda_{nB}x_B) + \frac{qE}{2kT}\right]$$

As expressed in (3.36a) and (3.36b), the emitter and collector currents are given by the superposition of the currents due to the base-emitter and base-collector pn junctions. This form was originally developed by J. J. Ebers and J. L. Moll [4] and is referred to as the *Ebers-Moll model*. To express these currents in terms of the terminal potentials (V_{BE} and V_{BC}), one must take into account the resistances of the neutral emitter, base, and collector regions. Therefore,

$$\phi_E = V_{BE} - I_E R_E - I_B R_B \qquad (3.37a)$$

and

$$\phi_C = V_{BC} - I_C R_C - I_B R_B \qquad (3.37b)$$

For transistors with heavily doped, shallow emitters, the emitter resistance, R_E, can often be neglected.*

Under normal operation the collector resistance, R_C, is of little consequence since the base-collector junction is usually reversed biased ($\phi_C < 0$). Unfortunately, base resistance (R_B) cannot normally be neglected. The calculation of base resistance and its effect on device performance is discussed in Section 3.3.1.

3.1.5 Regions of Operation

Four regions of operation are possible, depending upon the polarities of the junction potentials, ϕ_E and ϕ_C. We will treat each of them in turn.

(i) *Forward Active ($\phi_E > 0$, $\phi_C < 0$).*   In this region the base-emitter junction is forward biased, which results in electrons being injected into the base region from the emitter. The base-collector junction does not inject since it is reversed biased. However, electrons arriving at this junction from the emitter see a large electric field and are accelerated through the space-charge layer of the base-collector junction where they add to the distribution of majority carriers in the quasi-neutral collector region, giving rise to a large collector current. Since the number of carriers injected into the base depends upon the base-emitter bias, the collector current is determined principally by V_{BE} rather than V_{BC}. This is the principle of the so-called *transistor action*. For $\phi_E \gg kT/q$ and $\phi_C \ll -kT/q$ we have from (3.36a) and (3.36b)

$$J_E \approx a_{11} \exp\left(\frac{q\phi_E}{kT}\right) \qquad (3.38a)$$

$$J_C \approx a_{21} \exp\left(\frac{q\phi_E}{kT}\right) \qquad (3.38b)$$

---

*Some of the newer BJT structures utilize a layer of deposited polysilicon beneath the emitter metallization to form part of the emitter. In these cases, the resistance of the polysilicon layer may not be negligible.

The forward common-base current gain is

$$\alpha_F = \frac{J_C}{J_E} = \frac{a_{21}}{a_{11}} \tag{3.39}$$

which, after substituting for the constants, gives

$$\alpha_F = \frac{\exp\left(\dfrac{-qEx_B}{2kT}\right)\operatorname{csch}(\lambda_{nB}x_B)}{\coth(\lambda_{nB}x_B) - \dfrac{qE}{2kT\lambda_{nB}} + \dfrac{D_{pE}p_{nEo}\coth(x_E/L_{pE})}{D_{nB}n_{pBo}(0)\lambda_{nB}L_{pE}}} \tag{3.40}$$

The corresponding common-emitter current gain is

$$\beta_F = \frac{J_C}{J_B} = \frac{a_{21}}{a_{11} - a_{21}} \tag{3.41}$$

Thus,

$$\beta_F = \frac{\exp\left(\dfrac{-qEx_B}{2kT}\right)\operatorname{csch}(\lambda_{nB}x_B)}{\coth(\lambda_{nB}x_B) - \dfrac{qE}{2kT\lambda_{nB}} + \dfrac{D_{pE}p_{nEo}\coth(x_E/L_{pE})}{D_{nB}n_{pBo}(0)\lambda_{nB}} - \exp\left(\dfrac{-qEx_B}{2kT}\right)\operatorname{csch}(\lambda_{nB}x_B)} \tag{3.42}$$

(ii) *Reverse Active* ($\phi_E < 0$, $\phi_C > 0$). In this region, the base-collector junction is forward biased, which results in electrons being injected from the collector (which now acts like an emitter) into the base. The carriers which survive the reverse transit across the base are now collected by the reverse biased base-emitter junction. Since the base doping profile is normally graded to give an electric field which aids the transport of carriers injected into the base from the emitter, the base transport of carriers injected by the collector is retarded.

For $\phi_E \ll -kT/q$ and $\phi_C \gg kT/q$, we have from (3.36a) and (3.36b)

$$J_E \approx -a_{12}\exp\left(\frac{q\phi_C}{kT}\right) \tag{3.43a}$$

$$J_C \approx -a_{22}\exp\left(\frac{q\phi_C}{kT}\right) \tag{3.43b}$$

In this case the reverse common-base current gain is

$$\alpha_R = \frac{a_{12}}{a_{22}} \tag{3.44}$$

and the corresponding common-emitter current gain is

$$\beta_R = \frac{a_{12}}{a_{22} - a_{12}} \tag{3.45}$$

(iii) *Saturation ($\phi_E > 0$, $\phi_C > 0$).* Here, both junctions are forward biased and hence both are injecting into the base. Even though the electric field in the space-charge region of each junction is reduced by the forward bias, the direction of each field is such that carriers arriving at the two depletion edges in the base are swept into the emitter and collector regions. Both junctions collect as well as emit, and the net behavior can be described by a superposition of the forward-active and reverse-active modes.

For $\phi_E \gg kT/q$ and $\phi_C \gg kT/q$,

$$J_E \approx a_{11}\exp\left(\frac{q\phi_E}{kT}\right) - a_{12}\exp\left(\frac{q\phi_C}{kT}\right) \tag{3.46a}$$

$$J_C \approx a_{21}\exp\left(\frac{q\phi_E}{kT}\right) - a_{22}\exp\left(\frac{q\phi_C}{kT}\right) \tag{3.46b}$$

and

$$J_B \approx (a_{11} - a_{21})\exp\left(\frac{q\phi_E}{kT}\right) + (a_{22} - a_{12})\exp\left(\frac{q\phi_C}{kT}\right) \tag{3.46c}$$

J_E and J_C may both be positive or negative depending upon which junction injects more heavily. The base current is always positive since it is supplying carriers for recombination in the base and for injection into the emitter and collector regions.

(iv) *Cutoff ($\phi_E < 0$, $\phi_C < 0$).* In this region, both junctions are reverse biased and the only currents which flow are those which comprise the small reverse saturation currents of the two junctions. For $\phi_E \ll -kT/q$ and $\phi_C \ll -kT/q$,

$$J_E \approx a_{12} - a_{11} \quad \text{and} \quad J_C \approx a_{22} - a_{21} \tag{3.47}$$

The minority carrier distributions in the neutral emitter, base, and collector regions for each of the four regions of operation are illustrated in Figure 3.9. Notice that in saturation, not only are additional carriers being injected into the base, but also large numbers of excess carriers are injected into the collector. This excess charge in the base and collector regions dominates the switching response of transistors which operate in saturation.

It is instructive to examine the distribution of minority carriers in the base more closely, in particular, to see the effect of the base doping profile on the distributions in the forward active and reverse active regions. If we assume the base doping profile to be exponential, then (3.18) gives the distribution of excess minority carriers in the base under low-level injection conditions. If we further assume that recombination is negligible, then (3.18) can be expressed in a simpler form. Noting that

$$\lambda_{nB}x_B \approx \frac{\ln(K)}{2}$$

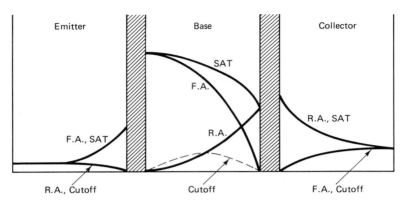

Figure 3.9 Minority carrier distributions for the four regions of operation.

where $K = N_{AB}(0)/N_{AB}(x_B)$, we obtain

$$\left.\frac{\bar{n}_{pB}(x)}{\bar{n}_{pB}(0)}\right|_{\phi_C=0} = \frac{K - \exp\left(\dfrac{x}{x_B}\ln(K)\right)}{K - 1} \tag{3.48a}$$

$$\left.\frac{\bar{n}_{pB}(x)}{\bar{n}_{pB}(x_B)}\right|_{\phi_E=0} = \frac{\exp\left(\dfrac{x}{x_B}\ln(K)\right) - 1}{K - 1} \tag{3.48b}$$

Alternately, (3.48a) and (3.48b) may be written as

$$\left.\frac{\bar{n}_{pB}(x)}{\bar{n}_{pB}(0)}\right|_{\phi_C=0} = \frac{K - K^{x/x_B}}{K - 1} \tag{3.49a}$$

$$\left.\frac{\bar{n}_{pB}(x)}{\bar{n}_{pB}(x_B)}\right|_{\phi_E=0} = \frac{K^{x/x_B} - 1}{K - 1} \tag{3.49b}$$

The normalized carrier profiles, as represented by (3.49a) and (3.49b), are shown plotted in Figures 3.10a and 3.10b, respectively, for various values of the base doping ratio, K. A value of $K = 1$ corresponds to a uniformly doped base region. Notice that for $K > 1$, the forward-injected profile is enhanced, while the reversed-injected profile is retarded. The physical reason for this effect is that electrons injected from the emitter under forward active bias see an aiding electric field in the base region which "pulls" them along toward the collector junction, while electrons injected from collector under reverse active bias see a retarding field which tends to "push" them back toward the collector junction.

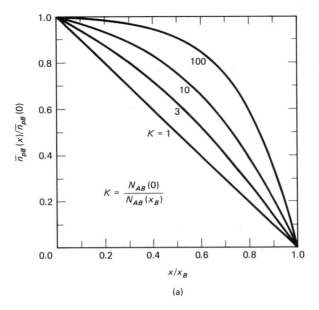

(a)

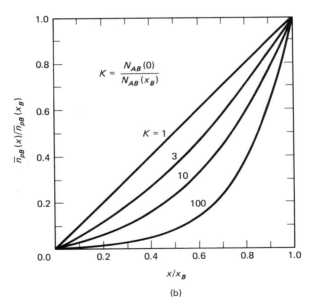

(b)

Figure 3.10(a)   Normalized carrier profile in an exponentially-doped base under forward active bias. (b) Normalized carrier profile for reverse-active bias.

3.1.6 Internal Parametrics

The parameters α_F, β_F, α_R, and β_R are useful because they relate directly to the terminal characteristics of the transistor. There are additional parameters which relate to physical mechanisms internal to the device.

3.1.6.1 Emitter efficiency.

In a transistor biased in the forward active region, the total emitter current is given by the sum of the electron and hole currents crossing the emitter-base junction. However, only the carriers injected into the base from the emitter contribute to the collector current; the back injection of carriers into the emitter from the base does not contribute to the useful transistor function. The emitter efficiency, γ, relates the injected minority carrier current in the base to the total emitter current. Using (3.35a),

$$\gamma = \frac{-J_{nB}(0)}{J_E} = \frac{1}{1 - \dfrac{J_{pE}(0')}{J_{nB}(0)}} \tag{3.50}$$

Taking $\bar{n}_{pB}(x_B) = 0$ in the forward active region, we have from (3.25)

$$J_{nB}(0) = qD_{nB}\bar{n}_{pB}(0)\left[\frac{qE}{2kT} - \lambda_{nB}\coth(\lambda_{nB}x_B)\right] \tag{3.51}$$

which when combined with (3.32), (3.24a), and (3.29) gives

$$\gamma = \frac{1}{1 + \dfrac{D_{pE}N_{AB}(0)\coth\left(x_E/L_{pE}\right)}{D_{nB}L_{pE}N_{DE}\left[\lambda_{nB}\coth(\lambda_{nB}x_B) - \dfrac{qE}{2kT}\right]}} \tag{3.52}$$

An alternate form for emitter efficiency in terms of the base doping ratio K is

$$\gamma = \frac{1}{1 + \dfrac{D_{pE}x_B N_{AB}(0)\coth\left(x_E/L_{pE}\right)}{D_{nB}L_{pE}N_{DE}\left[\Gamma_{nB}\coth(\Gamma_{nB}) + \ln(K)/2\right]}} \tag{3.53}$$

where

$$\Gamma_{nB} = \sqrt{[\ln(K)/2]^2 + [x_B/L_{nB}]^2}$$

In either case, it is seen that emitter efficiency is improved by the presence of the built-in field in the base. If the base region is uniformly doped, then $K = 1$, $\Gamma_{nB} = x_B/L_{nB}$, $N_{AB}(0) = N_{AB}$, and (3.53) reduces to the simpler form

$$\gamma_o = \frac{1}{1 + \dfrac{D_{pE}L_{nB}N_{AB}\coth\left(x_E/L_{pE}\right)}{D_{nB}L_{pE}N_{DE}\coth\left(x_B/L_{nB}\right)}} \tag{3.54}$$

3.1.6.2 Base transport factor.   In traversing the neutral base region some of the minority carriers injected by the emitter are lost to recombination. The base transport factor, α_T, is a measure of the resultant loss in current and is defined as

$$\alpha_T = \frac{J_{nB}(x_B)}{J_{nB}(0)} \tag{3.55}$$

Again taking $\bar{n}_{pB}(x_B) = 0$, we have

$$\alpha_T = \frac{\lambda_{nB}\text{csch}(\lambda_{nB}x_B)\exp\left(\dfrac{-qEx_B}{2kT}\right)}{\lambda_{nB}\coth(\lambda_{nB}x_B) - \dfrac{qE}{2kT}} \tag{3.56}$$

In terms of the doping ratio,

$$\alpha_T = \frac{\Gamma_{nB}\sqrt{K}}{\Gamma_{nB}\cosh(\Gamma_{nB}) + \frac{1}{2}\ln(K)\sinh(\Gamma_{nB})} \tag{3.57}$$

The effect of base grading on the base transport factor is illustrated in Figure 3.11. Notice that α_T is significantly improved by a graded doping profile. This is because the aiding field speeds the transport of carriers across the base, giving them less time to suffer recombination.

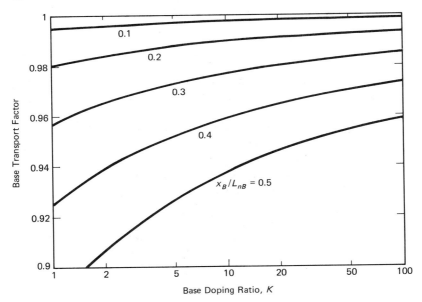

Figure 3.11   Variation in base transport factor with base dopant grading ratio (K). The dependence on minority carrier diffusion length is also shown.

3.1.6.3 Base transit time.   The base transit time, τ_t, is defined as the time it takes a carrier to traverse the neutral base region from $x = 0$ to $x = x_B$. While the transit time does not enter directly in the calculation of the dc characteristics of the transistor, it does directly influence the high-frequency performance and is thus one of the important parameters which determine the switching speed of digital bipolar integrated circuits.

If $v(x)$ represents the average velocity of carriers (electrons in this case) at a position x in the base, then the base transit time may be calculated from

$$\tau_t = \int_0^{x_B} \frac{1}{v(x)}\,dx \qquad (3.58)$$

This velocity is related to the excess minority carrier concentration in the base through the current

$$J_{nB}(x) = -q\bar{n}_{pB}(x)v(x) \qquad (3.59)$$

which upon substitution in (3.58) gives

$$\tau_t = \int_0^{x_B} \frac{q\bar{n}_{pB}(x)\,dx}{-J_{nB}(x)} \qquad (3.60)$$

If recombination in the neutral base region is small, then $J_{nB}(x)$ is nearly constant and can be taken outside the integral (3.60) without causing a significant loss in accuracy. Doing this,

$$\tau_t \approx \frac{1}{-J_{nB}} \int_0^{x_B} q\bar{n}_{pB}(x)\,dx = \frac{\overline{Q}_B}{|J_{nB}|} \qquad (3.61)$$

The transit time is thus seen to depend upon the total excess minority carrier charge stored in the base, $\overline{Q}_B$. Equation (3.61) is referred to as a charge-control equation.

In applying (3.61), we distinguish between a forward transit time, τ_{tF}, which describes the transit time for a transistor operated in the forward active region and a reverse transit time, τ_{tR}, which describes operation in the reverse action region. Using (3.49a) and (3.49b) to approximate the excess minority carrier densities in the base, we calculate

$$\overline{Q}_{BF} = q\bar{n}_{pB}(0)x_B \frac{K \ln(K) - (K - 1)}{(K - 1)\ln(K)} \qquad (3.62a)$$

and

$$\overline{Q}_{BR} = q\bar{n}_{pB}(x_B)x_B \frac{(K - 1) - \ln(K)}{(K - 1)\ln(K)} \qquad (3.62b)$$

The relations (3.49a) and (3.49b) are used in (3.14) to calculate forward and reverse currents. Defining

$$J_{CF} = |J_{nB}(\text{forward})| \quad \text{and} \quad J_{CR} = |J_{nB}(\text{reverse})|$$

we obtain

$$J_{CF} = \frac{qD_{nB}\bar{n}_{PB}(0)K\ln(K)}{x_B(K-1)} \tag{3.63a}$$

and

$$J_{CR} = \frac{qD_{nB}\bar{n}_{pB}(x_B)\ln(K)}{x_B(K-1)} \tag{3.63b}$$

The forward and reverse transit times are thus determined to be

$$\tau_{tF} = \frac{x_B^2}{D_{nB}}\frac{\ln(K)-1+1/K}{[\ln(K)]^2} \tag{3.64a}$$

and

$$\tau_{tR} = \frac{x_B^2}{D_{nB}}\frac{K-1-\ln(K)}{[\ln(K)]^2} \tag{3.64b}$$

The transit time in either case varies as the square of the neutral base width, x_B. For this reason, designers of BJTs used in high-speed digital ICs strive to make the base width as narrow as practicable within the constraints imposed by punch-through voltage limitations, maximum allowable base resistance, and process control.

In general, the base transit time can be expressed as

$$\tau_t = \frac{x_B^2}{\eta D_{nB}} \tag{3.65}$$

where η is a parameter that depends upon the base doping profile and the injection level of minority carriers in the base. For the case at hand where we are assuming an exponential doping profile (3.4) and low-level injection,

$$\eta(\text{forward}) = \frac{[\ln(K)]^2}{\ln(K)-1+1/K} \tag{3.66a}$$

$$\eta(\text{reverse}) = \frac{[\ln(K)]^2}{K-1-\ln(K)} \tag{3.66b}$$

The effect of the built-in field on the forward and reverse transit time is illustrated in Figure 3.12. For $K = 1$ (corresponding to a uniformly doped base), $\eta = 2$. For a typical device, suitable grading of the base can thus improve the forward base transit time by a factor of $\sim$ 2–3 over a comparable device of uniform doping. The effects of high-level injection on transit time will be discussed in Section 3.2.

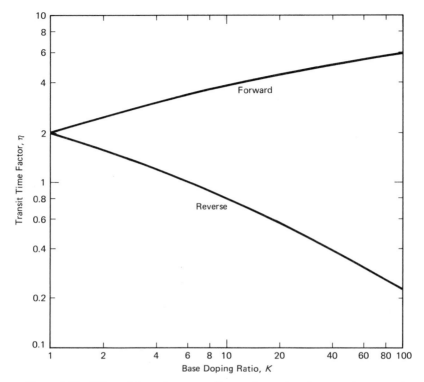

Figure 3.12 Effect of base dopant grading on forward and reverse base transit times.

3.1.7 Arbitrary Base Doping

Further insight into the physics of transistor action can be gained by considering the general case of a BJT with an arbitrary base doping profile. As we previously pointed out, closed form analytic solutions are, in general, not possible in such cases. However, if we neglect recombination in the neutral base region, a simple, but elegant, solution of the minority current transport equation can be obtained. While this is clearly an approximation, the resulting error can be expected to be minimal for modern BJT structures with narrow base widths.

For the electron current in the base we have

$$J_{nB} = qD_{nB}\left[\frac{dn_{pB}}{dx} + \frac{n_{pB}(x)}{p_{pB}(x)}\frac{dp_{pB}}{dx}\right] \qquad (3.67)$$

This equation differs from (3.14) in two respects: the first is that we are considering total carrier concentrations instead of excess concentrations, and secondly, the electric field term is written as

$$E = \frac{kT}{q} \frac{1}{P_{pB}(x)} \frac{dp_{pB}}{dx} \tag{3.68}$$

instead of (3.13). In this form, (3.67) remains valid for high-level injection conditions as well. Upon factoring $p_{pB}(x)$ from the right-hand-side of (3.67) and noting that the resulting factor contains an exact differential, we get

$$J_{nB} = \frac{qD_{nB}}{P_{pB}(x)} \left[P_{pB}(x) \frac{dn_{pB}}{dx} + n_{pB}(x) \frac{dp_{pB}}{dx} \right]$$

$$= \frac{qD_{nB}}{P_{pB}(x)} \frac{d(p_{pB}n_{pB})}{dx} \tag{3.69}$$

After further factoring, (3.69) may be readily integrated to yield

$$P_{pB}(x)n_{pB}(x) = \int^x \frac{P_{pB}J_{nB}}{qD_{nB}} d\zeta + \text{const} \tag{3.70}$$

The constant of integration may be found from the boundary condition at either $x = 0$ or $x = x_B$. Using the latter, (3.70) becomes

$$P_{pB}(x)n_{pB}(x) = P_{pB}(x_B)n_{pB}(x_B) - \int_x^{x_B} \frac{P_{pB}J_{nB}}{qD_{nB}} d\zeta \tag{3.71}$$

If recombination in the base is negligible, J_{nB} is constant and can be taken outside the integral (3.71). Setting $x = 0$, we obtain

$$J_{nB} = \frac{P_{pB}(x_B)n_{pB}(x_B) - P_{pB}(0)n_{pB}(0)}{\int_0^{x_B} \frac{P_{pB}}{qD_{nB}} dx} \tag{3.72}$$

The *law-of-the-junction* may be used to express the pn products in (3.72) in terms of the junction potentials:

$$P_{pB}(0)n_{pB}(0) = n_i^2 \exp\left(\frac{q\phi_E}{kT} \right) \tag{3.73a}$$

$$P_{pB}(x_B)n_{pB}(x_B) = n_i^2 \exp\left(\frac{q\phi_C}{kT} \right) \tag{3.73b}$$

Using these boundary conditions, (3.72) becomes

$$J_{nB} = \frac{qn_i^2 \left[\exp\left(\frac{q\phi_C}{kT} \right) - \exp\left(\frac{q\phi_E}{kT} \right) \right]}{\int_0^{x_B} \frac{P_{pB}}{D_{nB}} dx} \tag{3.74}$$

Thus we see that the minority-carrier transport current in the base depends upon the integrated distribution of *majority* carriers in the base. This form is referred to as the Moll-Ross relation [5], and describes the fundamental transistor action in all four regions of operation.

In the forward active region, $J_C \approx -J_{nB}$, $\phi_C \ll -kT/q$, and

$$J_C = J_S \exp\left(\frac{q\phi_E}{kT}\right) \tag{3.75}$$

where

$$J_S = \frac{qn_i^2}{\int_0^{x_B} \dfrac{p_{pB}}{D_{nB}} dx} \tag{3.76}$$

Under low-level injection conditions, $p_{pB}(x) \approx N_{AB}(x)$ and thus

$$J_S \approx \frac{qn_i^2}{\int_0^{x_B} \dfrac{N_{AB}}{D_{nB}} dx} = \frac{qn_i^2}{GU_B} \tag{3.77}$$

In (3.77), GU_B is referred to as the base *Gummel number* and is a measure of the integrated base doping concentration. Also for low-level injection we may take $n_{pB}(x_B) \approx 0$, which, using (3.71) gives

$$n_{pB}(x) = \frac{J_C}{qN_{AB}(x)} \int_x^{x_B} \frac{N_{AB}}{D_{nB}} dx \tag{3.78}$$

for the distribution of minority carriers injected into the base from the emitter. A similar relation can be written for the reverse injection of electrons from the collector.

As a simple example, consider the base to be uniformly doped. Then from (3.78)

$$n_{pB}(x) = \frac{J_C x_B}{qD_{nB}}\left(1 - \frac{x}{x_B}\right) \tag{3.79}$$

The first term on the right-hand side of (3.79) is simply $n_{pB}(0)$. So,

$$n_{pB}(x) = n_{pB}(0)\left(1 - \frac{x}{x_B}\right) \tag{3.80}$$

as expected.

3.1.8 Arbitrary Emitter Doping

As was done for the base, a similar analysis may be carried out for the minority current equation in the emitter:

$$J_{pE} = qD_{pE}\left[\frac{q}{kT}p_{nE}(x)E - \frac{dp_{nE}}{dx}\right] \tag{3.81}$$

Unlike the base, however, there is an additional component of electric field arising from the ohmic voltage drop across the neutral region in the emitter. This voltage drop arises from the x-directed emitter current and the finite ohmic resistance of the emitter. Consequently, the field, E, in (3.81) is not simply the field that arises from a non-uniform doping profile; it contains an additional term that depends upon the emitter current. In many cases, however, both the doping concentration and its gradient are large so that the built-in field due to the grading is much larger than the field due to the IR drop. Assuming this to be the case, we can take

$$E \approx - \frac{kT}{q} \frac{1}{N_{DE}(x)} \frac{dN_{DE}}{dx} \tag{3.82}$$

for the emitter. As written, (3.82) assumes low-level injection. But for heavily-doped emitters, high-level injection into the emitter (from the base) does not normally occur.*

Substituting (3.82) into (3.81) and integrating yields

$$p_{nE}(x')N_{DE}(x') = p_{nE}(x_E)N_{DE}(x_E) + \int_{x'}^{x_E} \frac{N_{DE}J_{pE}}{qD_{nE}} d\zeta \tag{3.83}$$

The corresponding boundary conditions (see Figure 3.8) are

$$p_{nE}(0')N_{DE}(0') = n_i^2 \exp\left(\frac{q\phi_E}{kT} \right) \tag{3.84a}$$

$$p_{nE}(x_E)N_{DE}(x_E) = n_i^2 \tag{3.84b}$$

In the latter (3.84b) we assume thermal equilibrium at the emitter contact. If recombination in the emitter is negligible then J_{pE} can be taken outside the integral in (3.83) giving

$$J_{pE} = \frac{-qn_i^2\left[\exp\left(\dfrac{q\phi_E}{kT} \right) - 1\right]}{GU_E} \tag{3.85}$$

where

$$GU_E = \int_{0'}^{x_E} \frac{N_{DE}}{D_{pE}} dx$$

and is the emitter *Gummel number*. Again we note the dependence of the minority current upon the integrated majority carrier profile.

The use of Gummel numbers provides a convenient means of estimating current gain. From (3.75) and (3.85) the emitter efficiency is

$$\gamma = \left(1 + \frac{GU_B}{GU_E} \right)^{-1} \tag{3.86}$$

---

*We should also point out that even in hetero-junction BJT structures with moderately-doped (or low-doped) emitters, the valence-band discontinuity between the emitter and base regions prevents high-level injection into the emitter.

In applying (3.85), we have assumed $\phi_E \gg kT/q$ so that the factor -1 in (3.85) can be neglected. Since we are assuming recombination in the base (and emitter) to be negligible, $\alpha_T = 1$ and therefore $\alpha_F = \gamma$. Thus

$$\beta_F(\text{max}) = \frac{GU_E}{GU_B} \tag{3.87}$$

and represents the maximum current gain obtainable for a given doping profile. Devices with significant recombination and/or which are operated under conditions of high-level injection will exhibit a current gain less than that predicted by (3.87). Nevertheless, (3.87) is useful in the design of BJT structures.

3.2 SECOND-ORDER CONSIDERATIONS

Our discussion thus far has centered on those physical mechanisms which describe the basic operation of the one-dimensional BJT structure. In many cases, in order to obtain tractable solutions, certain effects were neglected and operational limitations imposed (e.g., low-level injection). In this section we consider these so-called *second-order effects*. In doing so, it should be pointed out that as device structures are scaled down further in size, many of these effects become increasingly important to the extent that they are perhaps more properly termed *first-order*.

3.2.1 High-Level Injection

High-level injection is said to occur when the concentration of injected minority carriers becomes comparable to or greater than the background doping level. Such a condition is most likely to occur in the base region of a device operated at large values of forward base-emitter bias. As a consequence, several effects occur which are normally negligible when the transistor is operated at low injection levels:

1. Collector current increases less rapidly with respect to base-emitter bias, i.e., less than that predicted by (3.75). Current gain (β) is thereby reduced at high current levels.
2. There is an additional component of electric field in the neutral base region which further aids the transport of minority carriers injected from the emitter. This results in an increased carrier velocity in the base.
3. At high current densities there is a modulation of space charge in the base-collector depletion region. This results in a widening of the neutral base width, x_B, and a consequent increase in base transit time.

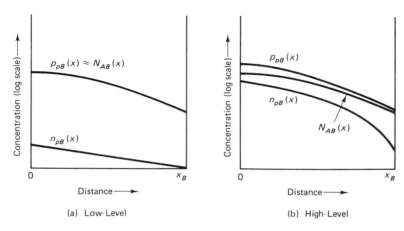

Figure 3.13 Carrier profiles in the base region of an NPN transistor. (a) Under low-level injection the majority carrier concentration equals the background doping concentration. (b) Under high-level injection the majority concentration is enhanced to preserve charge neutrality.

To properly account for the effects of high-level injection in the base region, it is necessary to consider both the minority and majority carrier distributions. Under high-level conditions, the majority carrier (hole) concentration is no longer equal to the concentration of ionized dopant atoms, such as illustrated in Figure 3.13a. To maintain charge neutrality, additional holes must be supplied by the base to balance the injected electrons (Figure 3.13b). That is,

$$p_{pB}(x) = N_{AB}(x) + \bar{n}_{pB}(x) \approx N_{AB}(x) + n_{pB}(x) \tag{3.88}$$

Because of the increase in majority carrier concentration, the built-in field is no longer given by (3.13)—which is valid for low-level injection—but rather

$$E = \frac{kT}{q}\frac{1}{p_{pB}(x)}\frac{dp_{pB}}{dx} = \frac{kT}{q}\frac{1}{N_{AB}(x) + n_{pB}(x)}\left[\frac{dN_{AB}}{dx} + \frac{dn_{pB}}{dx}\right]$$

$$\tag{3.89}$$

Substituting (3.89) into the electron current equation (3.14) gives

$$\frac{J_{nB}}{qD_{nB}} = \frac{N_{AB}(x) + 2n_{pB}(x)}{N_{AB}(x) + n_{pB}(x)}\frac{dn_{pB}}{dx} + \frac{n_{pB}(x)}{N_{AB}(x) + n_{pB}(x)}\frac{dN_{AB}}{dx} \tag{3.90}$$

We now consider two cases for the base doping profile, N_{AB}.

(i) **Uniform Doping, N_{AB} = Constant.**   If recombination in the neutral base region is negligible, then J_{nB} = constant = $-J_C$ and (3.90) can be integrated directly so that

$$\int \frac{N_{AB} + 2n_{pB}(x)}{N_{AB} + n_{pB}(x)}dn_{pB}(x) = \frac{-J_C}{qD_{nB}}\int dx \tag{3.91}$$

to give

$$2\left[n_{pB}(x) - n_{pB}(x_B)\right] - N_{AB}\ln\left[\frac{N_{AB} + n_{pB}(x)}{N_{AB} + n_{pB}(x_B)}\right] = \frac{J_C}{qD_{nB}}(x_B - x)$$

(3.92)

where we have expressed the constant of integration in terms of the boundary condition on n_{pB} at $x = x_B$. For a transistor operated in the forward active region, one would normally take $n_{pB}(x_B) = 0$. However, to support a given value of collector current density, J_C, there must be at least an electron density of $n = J_C/qv_{sat}$, where v_{sat} is the scattering-limited carrier velocity in the base-collector space-charge region. Since this current is supported by electrons arriving at the depletion edge at $x = x_B$, their concentration cannot be zero there. Under low-level injection, J_C is sufficiently small that taking $n_{pB}(x_B)$ to be zero introduces little error. Under high-level injection, however, $n_{pB}(x_B)$ is not negligibly small. To calculate the current we evaluate (3.92) at $x = 0$ so that

$$J_C = \frac{2qD_{nB}n_{pB}(0)}{x_B\left(1 + \dfrac{2D_{nB}}{v_{sat}x_B}\right)}\left\{1 - \frac{1}{2}\frac{N_{AB}}{n_{pB}(0)}\ln\left[\frac{N_{AB} + n_{pB}(0)}{N_{AB} + \dfrac{J_C}{qv_{sat}}}\right]\right\}$$

(3.93)

The boundary condition at $x = 0$ is evaluated using (3.73a) and (3.88), giving

$$n_{pB}(0) = \frac{N_{AB}}{2}\left\{\left[1 + \frac{4n_i^2}{N_{AB}^2}\exp\left(\frac{q\phi_E}{kT}\right)\right]^{1/2} - 1\right\}$$

(3.94)

To illustrate the effects of injection level on collector current, consider the two extremes of very low injection and very high injection:

(a) *Low-level limit.* Here $n_{pB}(0) \ll N_{AB}$ and $J_C \ll qv_{sat}N_{AB}$. The logarithmic term on the right-hand-side of (3.93) becomes approximately

$$\ln\left[1 + \frac{n_{pB}(0)}{N_{AB}}\right] \approx \frac{n_{pB}(0)}{N_{AB}}$$

so that

$$J_C \approx \frac{qD_n n_{pB}(0)}{x_B\left(1 + \dfrac{2D_{nB}}{v_{sat}x_B}\right)}$$

(3.95)

Also,

$$\left[1 + \frac{4n_i^2}{N_{AB}^2}\exp\left(\frac{q\phi_E}{kT}\right)\right]^{1/2} \approx 1 + \frac{2n_i^2}{N_{AB}^2}\exp\left(\frac{q\phi_E}{kT}\right)$$

giving

$$n_{pB}(0) \approx \frac{n_i^2}{N_{AB}} \exp\left(\frac{q\phi_E}{kT} \right) \qquad (3.96)$$

as expected.

(b) *High-level limit.* Here $n_{pB}(0) \gg N_{AB}$ and $\dfrac{4n_i^2}{N_{AB}^2} \exp\left(\dfrac{q\phi_E}{kT} \right) \gg 1$. Therefore, the second term inside the curly brackets of (3.93) is $\ll 1$, so that

$$J_C \approx \frac{2qD_{nB}n_{pB}(0)}{x_B\left(1 + \dfrac{2D_{nB}}{v_{\text{sat}}x_B} \right)} \qquad (3.97)$$

where

$$n_{pB}(0) \approx n_i \exp\left(\frac{q\phi_E}{2kT} \right) \qquad (3.98)$$

Two consequences of high-level injection are immediately obvious from (3.97) and (3.98). Under low-level injection the electron current in the base region is entirely a diffusion current. At high levels, the additional majority carriers (holes) required to balance the injected minority carriers (electrons) create an electric field which adds a drift component of current to J_C. In the high-level limit the drift component equals the diffusion component—hence the factor of 2 in (3.97). The main effect is that $\ln[n_{pB}(0)]$, and hence $\ln(J_C)$, increases at only half the rate with respect to increases in ϕ_E as compared to the low-level limit, as illustrated in Figure 3.14.

There is an additional effect associated with the required increase in majority carrier concentration. Since these carriers are supplied by the base, this results in an increase in base current. Consequently, β decreases from its low-level value.

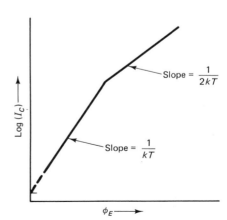

Figure 3.14 At high injection levels, the collector current increases less rapidly with increases in base-emitter bias.

(ii) *Exponential Doping*, $N_{AB}(x) = N_{AB}(0)\exp\left[-\dfrac{\ln(K)x}{x_B}\right]$. For this

case it is convenient to express (3.90) with the following normalizations:

$$\bar{x} = \frac{x}{x_B}$$

$$\bar{n} = \frac{n_{pB}(x)}{J_C x_B / q D_{nB}}$$

In our normalization for $\bar{n}$ we have again assumed negligible recombination in the base so that $J_C \approx -J_{nB}$. Further, it is profitable to define an injection factor, δ, such that

$$\delta = \frac{J_C x_B}{q D_{nB} N_{AB}(0)}$$

The physical interpretation of this factor is as follows. If, in a pure diffusion transistor, the injected electron concentration varies linearly from a value $\delta N_{AB}(0)$ at $x = 0$ to a value of zero at $x = x_B$, then the collector current would be equal to $q D_{nB} \delta N_{AB}(0)/x_B$. Thus, δ characterizes an injection level relative to $N_{AB}(0)$. Low-level injection would correspond to $\delta \ll 1$. With the above substitutions, (3.90) becomes

$$\{2\delta\bar{n}(\bar{x}) + \exp[-\ln(K)\bar{x}]\}\frac{d\bar{n}}{d\bar{x}} - \{\ln(K)\exp[-\ln(K)\bar{x}] - \delta\}\bar{n}(\bar{x})$$

$$= -\exp[-\ln(K)\bar{x}] \quad (3.99)$$

Equation (3.99) is solved numerically using the boundary condition $n_{pB}(x_B) = J_C/q v_{\text{sat}}$ (hence, $\bar{n}(1) = D_{nB}/v_{\text{sat}}x_B$). The results for $K = 100$ are shown in Figure 3.15. In this example, it was assumed that $D_{nB} = 12.5$ cm^2/s, $x_B = 0.25$ μm and $v_{\text{sat}} = 10^7$ cm/s, giving $\bar{n}(1) = 0.05$. From Figure 3.15 it is seen that high-level effects become significant when the injection level is about one-tenth the peak doping level. At the high-level limit ($\delta \to \infty$) the normalized carrier distribution approaches that of a uniformly doped base (at low level), but with half the value.

3.2.1.1 Effect on transit time. The neutral base transit time is also affected by high-level injection. That the transit time should depend upon the injection level is evident from (3.61). The stored base charge, Q_B, increases in proportion to the injection level. The collector current, J_C, however increases at a different rate owing to the high-level effect. Thus, the quantity Q_B/J_C (and hence τ_t) varies with the injection level. The dependence of transit time on injection level for the exponentially-doped base can be obtained by integrating the carrier distributions described by (3.99). Expressing (3.61) in

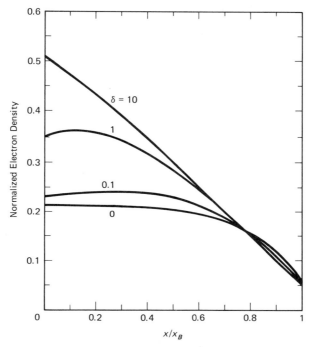

Figure 3.15 Normalized electron concentration in the base for various levels of injection.

terms of the normalized concentration,

$$\tau_t = \frac{x_B^2}{D_{nB}} \int_0^1 \bar{n} \, d\bar{x} \tag{3.100}$$

The result of this calculation for various values of K is shown in Figure 3.16. Notice that for the uniformly doped base, the transit time improves (decreases) with increased injection. This is due to the aiding field created by the injection. For graded-base dopings of $K > 10$, the transit time increases with increased injection. At high levels all profiles produce the same transit time limit

$$\tau_t \rightarrow \frac{x_B^2}{4D_{nB}} + \frac{x_B}{v_{\text{sat}}} \tag{3.101}$$

The reason for this behavior is that at large currents the resulting high concentration of injected minority carriers "swamps out" the built-in field of the dopant profile and creates its own field. At these levels the transit time is independent of the particular base doping profile.

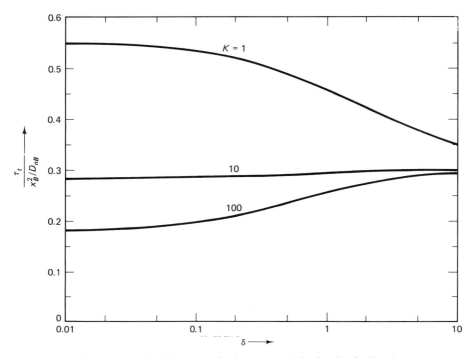

Figure 3.16 Normalized base transit time versus injection level. $K = 1$ corresponds to a uniformly doped base.

3.2.1.2 Effect on base width. The neutral base width, x_B, is also affected by high-level injection. At large current densities the number of mobile carriers passing through the base-collector depletion layer significantly alters the net space charge in that region. As a result, the position of the depletion edges changes to preserve charge balance across the junction. This depletion width modulation as a function of current is referred to as the *Kirk effect* [6]. This effect can substantially alter the performance of narrow base-width devices, such as those used in high-speed integrated circuits.

The Kirk effect is illustrated in Figure 3.17, which shows a portion of the net doping profile, $N(x) = N_{DC}(x) - N_{AB}(x)$, for the base-collector region. At low currents the concentration of mobile carriers in the B − C depletion layer is negligible with respect to the concentration of the fixed ionized dopant atoms and the depletion edges x_{Bo} and x_{Co} are determined by the normal balance of fixed space charge across the junction (see Figure 3.17a). At large currents, there is additional space charge given by

$$n(x) = \frac{J_C(x)}{qv(x)} \tag{3.102}$$

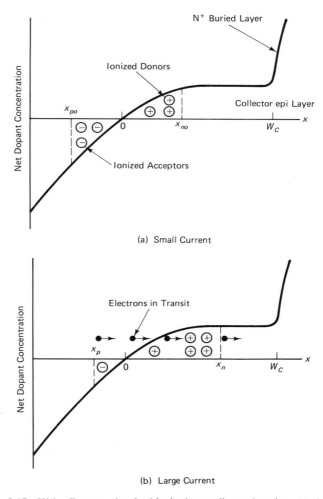

(a) Small Current

(b) Large Current

Figure 3.17 Kirk effect associated with the base-collector junction. (a) At small currents the depletion edges are determined only by the fixed dopant space charge. (b) At large currents mobile carriers modify the local space-charge density.

where $v(x)$ is the velocity of carries traversing the depletion layer. These electrons add to the negative space charge arising from the acceptors on the base side of the junction and subtract from the positive space charge arising from the donors on the collector side of the junction. The depletion edges shift as illustrated in Figure 3.17b.

Using (3.102), Poisson's equation for the $B - C$ space-charge layer becomes

$$\frac{dE}{dx} = \frac{q}{\varepsilon_o \varepsilon_r} \left[N(x) - \frac{J_{C(x)}}{qv(x)} \right] \tag{3.103}$$

with the boundary conditions

$$E(x_B) = E(x_C) = 0$$

To solve (3.103) we multiply both sides by $x\,dx$ and integrate across the depletion width:

$$\int_{x_p}^{x_n} x\,dE = \frac{q}{\varepsilon_o \varepsilon_r} \int_{x_p}^{x_n} x\left[N(x) - \frac{J_{C(x)}}{qv(x)}\right]dx \qquad (3.104)$$

The left-hand-side of (3.104) is integrated by parts to yield $\phi_{iC} - \phi_C$, where ϕ_{iC} is the built-in potential barrier of the B $-$ C junction. Thus

$$\int_{x_p}^{x_n} x\left[N(x) - \frac{J_{C(x)}}{qv(x)}\right]dx = \frac{\varepsilon_o \varepsilon_r}{q}(\phi_{iC} - \phi_C) \qquad (3.105)$$

In addition to Poisson's equation, we have the balance of space charge on both sides of the junction:

$$\int_{x_p}^{x_n}\left[N(x) - \frac{J_{C(x)}}{qv(x)}\right]dx = 0 \qquad (3.106)$$

With a known doping profile, (3.105) and (3.106) are solved simultaneously to give the depletion edges x_p and x_n, provided $J_C(x)$ and $v(x)$ are also known.

For all but the simplest profiles, application of (3.105) and (3.106) yields complicated expressions which must be evaluated numerically. For a uniformly-doped base-collector region we have

$$N(x) = -N_{AB}, x < 0 \qquad \text{and} \qquad N(x) = N_{DC}, x > 0$$

With reverse bias applied to the B $-$ C junction ($\phi_C < 0$), we may neglect recombination in the depletion layer and thus take J_C to be constant there. Additionally, the large electric field in the junction quickly accelerates carriers arriving from the base to their scattering-limited velocity, v_{sat}, and so as a further approximation, we will assume the velocity to be equal to v_{sat} throughout the entire depletion layer. With these approximations, the integrals indicated in (3.105) and (3.106) may be readily carried out and solved for x_p. The result is

$$|x_p| = \left[\frac{2\varepsilon_o \varepsilon_r(\phi_{iC} - \phi_C)}{q(N_{AB} + N_{DC})} \cdot \frac{N_{DC} - J_C/qv_{sat}}{N_{AB} + J_C/qv_{sat}}\right]^{1/2} \qquad (3.107)$$

For $J_C = 0$, we note that

$$|x_{po}| = \left[\frac{2\varepsilon_o \varepsilon_r(\phi_{iC} - \phi_C)N_{DC}}{q(N_{AB} + N_{DC})N_{AB}}\right]^{1/2} \qquad (3.108)$$

so that (3.107) may be expressed in terms of the zero (or low) current depletion width:

$$|x_p| = |x_{po}|\left[\frac{1 - J_C/J_1}{1 + J_C/J_1 R}\right]^{1/2}, J_C \lesseqgtr J_1 \qquad (3.109)$$

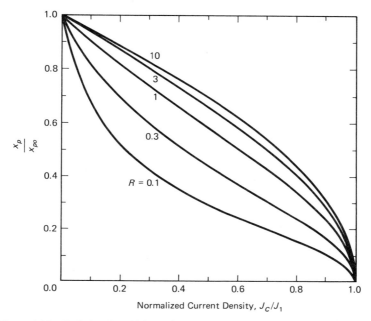

Figure 3.18 Variation in width of the depletion region on the base side of the base-collector junction with collector current density. Uniform doping is assumed and $R = N_{AB}/N_{DC}$.

where we have let

$$J_1 = qv_{sat}N_{DC} \quad \text{and} \quad R = N_{AB}/N_{DC}$$

The variation in width of the depletion edge with current is sketched in Figure 3.18. Concurrent with the decrease in $|x_p|$ with increased current is an increase in the neutral base width, x_B:

$$x_B = x_{Bo} + |x_{po}|\left\{1 - \left[\frac{1 - J_C/J_1}{1 + J_C/J_1 R}\right]^{1/2}\right\} \qquad (3.110)$$

The transistor parameters most affected by the Kirk effect are β and τ_i; they both worsen at high currents.

To consider the effect for current densities exceeding J_1, it is worthwhile to examine the electric field profile in the collector region. For simplicity, we assume an abrupt transition between the low-doped epitaxial collector region and the much higher-doped buried layer region. In Figure 3.19, we sketch the electric field for various current densities at a fixed base-collector bias, ϕ_C. Thus, the area under each field profile is constant and equal to $-(\phi_{iC} - \phi_C)$. At $J_C = J_1$, the net space charge in the epitaxial collector is reduced from a positive value to zero owing to the transport of electrons from the base. Since $dE/dx = 0$ at this current, E is constant as indicated in Figure 3.19. For

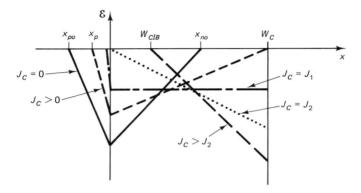

Figure 3.19 Electric field profiles in the base-collector junction region for various values of collector current density.

$J_C > J_1$ the space charge becomes negative because the injected electron density now exceeds the dopant density N_{DC}. The effect is to push the entire space-charge region, which was originally centered around the PN^- junction boundary at low currents, toward the N^-N^+ boundary.

At $J_C = J_2$ the electric field at the metallurgical junction $(x = 0)$ is reduced to zero and the current becomes space-charge limited. Solving Poisson's equation in the region $0 \leq x \leq W_C$ gives

$$E(x) = \frac{qx}{\varepsilon_o \varepsilon_r}\left(N_{DC} - \frac{J_2}{q v_{\text{sat}}}\right) \qquad (3.111)$$

Upon integrating (3.111),

$$\int_0^{W_C} E(x)\, dx = -(\phi_{iC} - \phi_C)$$

we obtain

$$J_2 = q v_{\text{sat}}\left[N_{DC} + \frac{2\varepsilon_o \varepsilon_r(\phi_{iC} - \phi_C)}{q W_C^2}\right] \qquad (3.112)$$

as the critical current density for the onset of space-charge limited current flow.

For $J_C > J_2$, there is a build-up of negative space charge in the region $W_{\text{CIB}} \leq x \leq W_C$. The space charge remains zero in the region $0 \leq x < W_{\text{CIB}}$, and thus the effective neutral base width, x_B, extends to W_{CIB}. W_{CIB} can be found by integrating the electric field profile in the region $W_{CIB} \leq x \leq W_C$. The result is

$$W_{CIB} = W_C \left[1 - \left(\frac{J_2 - J_1}{J_C - J_1} \right)^{1/2} \right] \qquad (3.113)$$

At high currents, such that $J_C \gg J_2$, the effective base width is pushed completely to the buried layer boundary W_C. This further reduces β and increases τ_t.

3.2.2 Low-Level Injection

At low current densities, recombination in the space-charge layer of the emitter-base junction can contribute a significant portion of the total base current. Since this junction is normally forward biased, there are large numbers of both holes and electrons traversing the junction region, which increases the probability for recombination. The situation is illustrated in Figure 3.20. As a result of recombination, $J_{nE}(x_n) > J_{nB}(x_p)$ and $J_{pB}(x_p) > J_{pE}(x_n)$. The recombination current, J_{RSC}, is supported by electrons from the emitter and holes from the base. Since the emitter is normally doped much heavier than the base, the primary effect is the increased base current.

To calculate the recombination current, we integrate the recombination rate in the space-charge layer, as

$$J_{RSC} = q \int_{x_n}^{x_p} r \, dx \qquad (3.114)$$

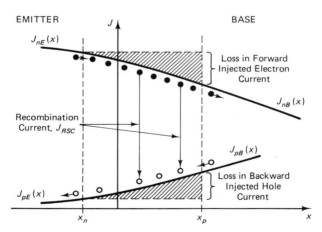

Figure 3.20 Recombination in the space-charge region of the emitter-base junction under forward bias.

Using (3.9), coupled with the relation $pn = n_i^2 \exp(q\phi_E/kT)$, and assuming that $n \gg n_i$, $p \gg n_i$ and $\tau_n = \tau_p = \tau$, we have

$$r = \frac{n_i^2 \exp(q\phi_E/kT)}{\left[n + \dfrac{n_i^2}{n}\exp(q\phi_E/kT)\right]\tau} \tag{3.115}$$

It may be easily shown that the recombination rate (3.115) is maximized for $n = n_i \exp(q\phi_E/2kT)$.
Thus,

$$r_{\max} = \frac{n_i \exp(q\phi_E/2kT)}{2\tau} \tag{3.116}$$

Using (3.116) in (3.114) then gives an upper limit estimate of J_{RSC}.

$$J_{\text{RSC}} \approx \frac{q n_i x_{DE}}{2\tau}\exp(q\phi_E/2kT) \tag{3.117}$$

where x_{DE} is the space-charge layer width, $x_p - x_n$.

3.2.2.1 Base Current.   Taking into account recombination in both the emitter-base space-charge and the neutral base regions, the total base current (forward active) is

$$J_B = J_{\text{RSC}} + J_{RB} + J_{pE}(x_n) \tag{3.118}$$

where

$$J_{RB} = (1 - \alpha_T)J_{nB}(x_p)$$

Thus,

$$J_B = \frac{q n_i x_{DE}}{2\tau}\exp(q\phi_E/2kT) + \left[(1 - \alpha_T) + \left(\frac{1 - \gamma}{\gamma}\right)\right]\frac{q n_i^2}{GU_B}\exp(q\phi_E/kT) \tag{3.119}$$

At low currents, base current is dominated by the $\exp(q\phi_E/2kT)$ term in (3.119) as illustrated in Figure 3.21.

The variation in common-emitter current gain, β, with collector current has the form depicted in Figure 3.22. The reduction in gain at low currents results from the increased base-current owing to recombination in the emitter-base space-charge region, such as described by (3.119). The fall-off in gain at high currents results from the decrease in collector current owing to

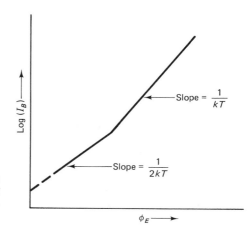

Figure 3.21 Asymptotic behavior of the base current, illustrating the effects of space-charge recombination at low currents.

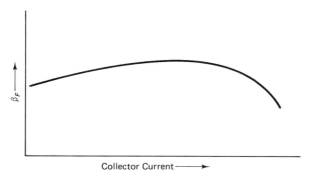

Figure 3.22 Typical variation in the forward common-emitter current gain with current.

high-level injection effects. In practice, one normally designs the transistor to operate over a range of currents in which β is relatively constant.

3.2.3 Heavy Doping Effects

When impurity doping levels exceed about $10^{17}\,\mathrm{cm}^{-3}$, additional effects take place which alter the basic behavior of the bipolar transistor. For example, it is observed experimentally that increasing the emitter concentration (N_{DE}) does not produce a corresponding proportional increase in emitter efficiency (γ), as (3.86) would suggest. In fact, for peak emitter doping levels in the $10^{20}\,\mathrm{cm}^{-3}$ range, as is common in modern homojunction BJT structures, the value for β calculated from (3.87) can be more than an order of magnitude higher than what is actually measured. This discrepancy can be explained in terms of an apparent reduction in the energy band gap brought about by the relatively large concentration of dopant atoms in the emitter.

3.2.3.1 Band gap narrowing.   At high doping concentrations, the distance between adjacent impurity atoms is reduced, which increases the interaction between them. This interaction causes the energy levels of the impurity atoms to broaden into a band in order to satisfy the Pauli exclusion principle. This large number of randomly distributed impurity atoms also disturbs the periodicity of the semiconductor lattice and results in the formation of band tails [7] rather than well-defined band edges. As a result, impurity levels and band tail levels may overlap and the effective band edge shifts as illustrated in Figure 3.23. Thus, in heavily doped material the energy band gap (E_G) is reduced from its value (E_{Go}) at low impurity concentrations.

The detailed dependence of the semiconductor band structure on impurity doping has been the subject of much study in recent years. As yet no complete unified theory has emerged which agrees with the variety of measured data. The problem is compounded in that the change in band structure must be inferred from electrical (and optical) measurements of device characteristics, many of which depend strongly on dopant concentration, even in the absence of band gap narrowing effects. An empirical model for the reduction in the band gap energy (E_G) as a function of doping, which agrees well with the data of several researchers, was proposed by Slotboom and

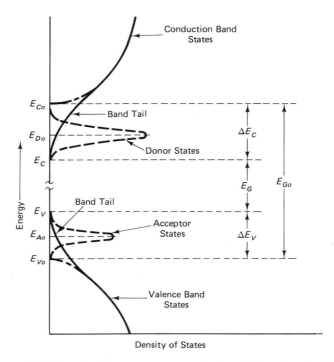

Figure 3.23   Density of states versus energy in a heavily-doped semiconductor.

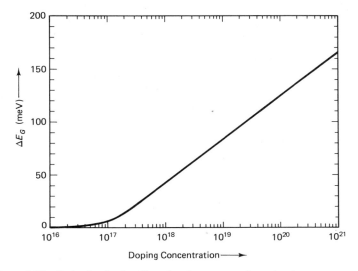

Figure 3.24   Reduction in the silicon band gap versus impurity dopant concentration as modeled by Slotboom and deGraaff [8].

deGraaff [8]. It states

$$\Delta E_G = 9 \left\{ \ln\left(\frac{N}{10^{17}} \right) + \sqrt{\left[\ln\left(\frac{N}{10^{17}} \right) \right]^2 + 0.5} \right\} \text{ meV} \qquad (3.120)$$

where $\Delta E_G = E_{Go} - E_G$ and N is the total impurity dopant concentration per cm³. The reduction in E_G with N, using (3.120), is illustrated in Figure 3.24.

3.2.3.2 Modified transport equations.   The current transport equations must be modified to take into account the position-dependent band structure. Writing the steady state current equations in terms of the quasi-Fermi potentials ϕ_n (electrons) and ϕ_p (holes) gives

$$J_n = -qn\mu_n \frac{d\phi_n}{dx} \qquad (3.121a)$$

$$J_p = -qp\mu_p \frac{d\phi_p}{dx} \qquad (3.121b)$$

Now,

$$n = N_C \exp\left(-\frac{E_C + q\phi_n}{kT} \right) \qquad (3.122a)$$

$$p = N_V \exp\left(\frac{E_V + q\phi_p}{kT} \right) \qquad (3.122b)$$

where N_C and N_V are the effective density of states for electrons and holes, respectively. In general both N_C and N_V are also position dependent in heavily doped material. However, if we assume Maxwell-Boltzmann statistics to be valid, then the effects of heavy doping may be imbedded in the position-dependent band edges E_C and E_V, and we may take N_C and N_V to have their unperturbed values. To do this, let

$$E_C = E_{C_o} - \Delta E_C \tag{3.123a}$$

$$E_V = E_{V_o} + \Delta E_V \tag{3.123b}$$

where E_{C_o} and E_{V_o} are the unperturbed conduction and valence band edges, respectively. The asymmetry factor

$$A = \frac{\Delta \chi}{\Delta E_G} \tag{3.124}$$

where χ is the electron affinity, has been used to describe the proportion of the total band gap reduction ascribed to ΔE_C [9]. Thus

$$\Delta E_C = A \, \Delta E_G \tag{3.125a}$$

$$\Delta E_V = (1 - A) \, \Delta E_G \tag{3.125b}$$

It should also be noted that the value of A (which varies from 0 to 1) depends upon the relative number of donor and acceptor impurities at a given position in the material. Using (3.122), (3.123), and (3.125) in (3.121) we obtain

$$J_n = qD_n \frac{dn}{dx} - q\mu_n n \frac{d}{dx} \left[\psi + \frac{A \, \Delta E_G}{q} \right] \tag{3.126a}$$

$$J_p = -qD_p \frac{dp}{dx} - q\mu_p p \frac{d}{dx} \left[\psi - \frac{(1 - A) \, \Delta E_G}{q} \right] \tag{3.126b}$$

where the electrostatic potential $\psi = -\frac{1}{q}E_{C_o} = -\frac{1}{q}E_{V_o}$. The effect of the position-dependent band gap is to introduce an additional term in the drift component of current. Physically, this appears as a modification of the local electric field.

3.2.3.3 Intrinsic carrier concentration.

In thermal equilibrium, (3.122a) and (3.122b) combine to give

$$n_o p_o = N_C N_V \exp \left[-\left(\frac{E_C - E_V}{kT} \right) \right] = n_i^2 \exp \left(\frac{\Delta E_G}{kT} \right) \tag{3.127}$$

This suggests the use of an *effective* intrinsic carrier concentration

$$n_{ie} = n_i \exp \left(\frac{\Delta E_G}{2kT} \right) \tag{3.128}$$

where n_i is the normal unperturbed value. In heavily doped material, n_{ie} can be substantially greater than n_i, as illustrated in Figure 3.25.

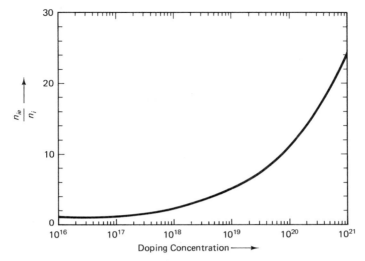

Figure 3.25 Effective intrinsic carrier concentration as a function of impurity dopant concentration.

3.2.3.4 Effect on device performance. The emitter efficiency is the parameter most affected by band gap narrowing. In the heavily-doped emitter, the interaction between the donor impurity band and the conduction band is the principal band gap narrowing mechanism. Consequently, we may take A to be unity in the emitter. Doing this and setting $J_n = 0$ in (3.126a), we calculate the built-in electric field in the emitter:

$$E = -\frac{d\psi}{dx} = \frac{1}{q}\frac{d(\Delta E_G)}{dx} - \frac{kT}{q}\frac{1}{n_{nE}}\frac{dn_{nE}}{dx} \qquad (3.129)$$

Alternately, we may express this field in terms of the effective intrinsic carrier concentration. Using (3.128)

$$E = \frac{kT}{q}\left[\frac{1}{n_{ie}^2}\frac{d(n_{ie}^2)}{dx} - \frac{1}{n_{nE}}\frac{dn_{nE}}{dx}\right] \qquad (3.130)$$

This field is then put into (3.81) and the minority hole current in the emitter is calculated.

$$J_{pE} = qD_{pE}\left[\frac{p_{nE}}{n_{ie}^2}\frac{d(n_{ie}^2)}{dx} - \frac{p_{nE}}{n_{nE}}\frac{dn_{nE}}{dx} - \frac{dp_{nE}}{dx}\right] \qquad (3.131)$$

which is equivalent to

$$J_{pE} = -\frac{qD_{pE}n_{ie}^2}{n_{nE}}\frac{d}{dx}\left[\frac{n_{nE}p_{nE}}{n_{ie}^2}\right] \qquad (3.132)$$

Since the hole injection into the emitter is normally low-level, we may take the electron concentration, n_{nE}, to be equal to the net donor concentration, N_{DE}. Integrating (3.132) then gives

$$\frac{N_{DE}(x)p_{nE}(x)}{n_{ie}^2(x)} - \frac{N_{DE}(x_E)p_{nE}(x_E)}{n_{ie}^2(x_E)} = \frac{1}{q}\int_x^{x_E} \frac{J_{pE}(\xi)N_{DE}(\xi)}{D_{pE}(\xi)n_{ie}^2(\xi)}d\xi$$

(3.133)

The boundary condition at the depletion edge ($x = 0'$) is

$$p_{nE}(0') = \frac{n_{ie}^2(0')}{N_{DE}(0')}\exp\left(\frac{q\phi_E}{kT}\right)$$

(3.134)

For an ideal ohmic contact at $x = x_E$, the other boundary condition is

$$p_{nE}(x_E) = p_{nEo}(x_E) = \frac{n_{ie}^2(x_E)}{N_{DE}(x_E)}$$

(3.135)

For a moderate bias ($\phi_E \gg kT/q$) this term (3.135) is negligible in comparison with (3.134). Thus,

$$\frac{1}{q}\int_0^{x_E} \frac{J_{pE}(x)N_{DE}(x)}{D_{pE}(x)n_{ie}^2(x)}dx \approx \exp\left(\frac{q\phi_E}{kT}\right)$$

(3.136)

If recombination in the emitter is negligible then J_{pE} may be taken outside the integral in (3.136). This gives

$$J_{pE} = \frac{qn_i^2\exp\left(\dfrac{q\phi_E}{kT}\right)}{GU_E'}$$

(3.137)

where the effective Gummel number for the emitter is

$$GU_E' = \int_{0'}^{x_E} \frac{N_{DE}(x)}{D_{pE}(x)} \frac{n_i^2}{n_{ie}^2(x)}dx$$

(3.138)

The effect of band gap narrowing on emitter Gummel number is illustrated in Figure 3.26. In this example it was assumed that the emitter is uniformly doped. As indicated in (3.138) the effect of band gap narrowing may be incorporated into an *effective* doping profile

$$N_{DE}(\text{effective}) = N_{DE}(\text{actual})\frac{n_i^2}{n_{ie}^2}$$

(3.139)

which at high doping levels is substantially reduced from the actual profile. The corresponding reduction in the emitter Gummel number results in an increase in the emitter hole current as shown by (3.137), and a decrease in the emitter efficiency as shown by (3.86).

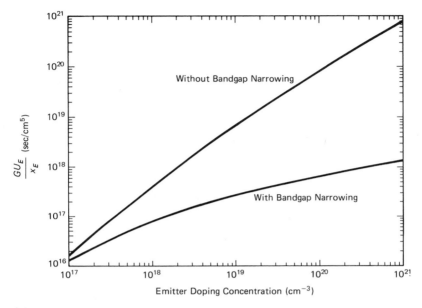

Figure 3.26   Emitter Gummel number (normalized with respect to neutral emitter width) as a function of doping concentration.

3.2.3.5 Auger recombination.   There is another effect associated with heavy doping of the emitter—increased recombination. At low-to-moderate doping concentrations, the recombination in silicon BJT structures is predominantly of the Shockley-Read-Hall (SRH) type. The SRH recombination lifetime for minority carriers is sufficiently long such that SRH recombination is negligible in shallow emitter structures (roughly 0.5 μm or less). In heavily-doped emitters, however, the increased minority carrier concentration results in an Auger recombination lifetime (which decreases as p_{nE}^2) which is significantly lower than the SRH lifetime. Consequently, recombination in the emitter may no longer be negligible. If recombination in the emitter is included then (3.138) takes the form

$$GU_E'' = \int_{0'}^{x_E} \frac{N_{DE}(x)}{D_{pE}(x)} \frac{n_i^2}{n_{ie}^2(x)} w(x) \ dx \qquad (3.140)$$

where $w(x)$ is a weighting function which describes the relative loss in emitter hole current owing to recombination. Specifically,

$$w(x) = \frac{J_{pE}(x)}{J_{pE}(0')} \qquad (3.141)$$

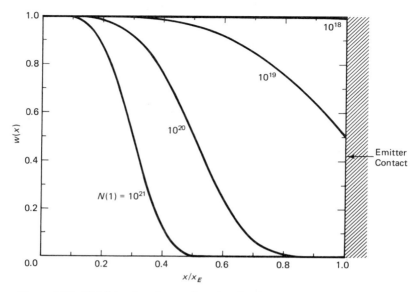

Figure 3.27 Weighting function used to describe the effects of recombination in heavily-doped emitters. N(1) represents various values of surface dopant concentration at the emitter contact. (After deGraaff, Slotboom, and Schmitz [10]).

Experimental and computer simulation studies [10] have shown $w(x)$ to be well approximated by the empirical relation

$$w(x) = \exp\left[-\left(\frac{x}{1.096 L_{p\,\text{eff}}}\right)^4\right] \qquad (3.142)$$

where $L_{p\,\text{eff}}$ is an effective diffusion length which is defined as the distance from the emitter depletion edge where J_{pE} has decreased to one half its value at $x = 0'$. $L_{p\,\text{eff}}$ is nearly independent of the shape or extent of the doping profile, but rather, is strongly dependent upon the surface doping concentration. Figure 3.27 illustrates the variation in $w(x)$ for various values of surface concentration. For concentrations less than about 10^{18} cm^{-3}, the recombination rate in shallow emitters is negligible. At about 10^{20} cm^{-3}, however, only one half of the emitter region is effective.

3.2.4 Collector Bias Effects

To first order, collector current is independent of collector bias for a BJT biased in the forward active region as shown by (3.36b). An increase in reverse bias at the base-collector junction, however, results in an increase in the B $-$ C depletion layer width and a corresponding decrease in the base width, x_B. The majority charge in the base is thereby reduced, resulting in a higher collector saturation current, as shown by (3.76). For a fixed base-emitter bias, the collector current is then seen to increase with the reverse collector bias, ϕ_C. This variation in collector current with collector bias is referred to as the *Early effect* [11].

Assuming low-level injection and a constant mobility in the base region, (3.77) may be expressed as

$$J_S = \frac{J_{So}}{1 - \dfrac{\Delta Q_B}{Q_{Bo}}} \tag{3.143}$$

where

$$Q_{Bo} = q \int_0^{x_{Bo}} N_{AB}(x)\, dx \tag{3.144}$$

and

$$J_{So} = \frac{q^2 n_i^2 D_{nB}}{Q_{Bo}} \tag{3.145}$$

As illustrated in Figure 3.28, ΔQ_B represents the change in base charge resulting from the shift in base width with changes in collector bias. Here, J_{So}, Q_{Bo}, and x_{Bo} refer to zero bias values. The balance of space charge in the depletion region requires $\Delta Q_B = \Delta Q_C$. Therefore,

$$\int_{x_B}^{x_{Bo}} N_{AB}(x)\, dx = \int_{x_{Co}}^{x_C} N_{DC}(x)\, dx \tag{3.146}$$

For most practical IC structures, the base is much more heavily doped than the collector. Consequently, most of the collector junction bias (ϕ_C) appears

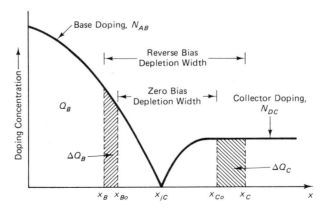

Figure 3.28 Base-width modulation with collector bias (Early effect). The shaded portions represent the change in base and collector space charge resulting from a reverse bias applied to the base-collector junction.

across the collector side of the junction. In addition, the doping is constant throughout most of the collector region (since the collector is formed in the uniformly doped epitaxial layer). Thus, the base-collector junction may, to first order, be approximated by a one-sided step junction. Hence,

$$x_C - x_{jC} \approx \left[\frac{2\varepsilon_o \varepsilon_r (\phi_{iC} - \phi_C)}{q N_{DC}} \right]^{1/2} \tag{3.147}$$

and thus

$$\Delta Q_B \approx q N_{DC} \left[(x_C - x_{jC}) - (x_{Co} - x_{jC}) \right]$$

so,

$$\Delta Q_B = \sqrt{2\varepsilon_o \varepsilon_r q N_{DC}} \left[\sqrt{\phi_{iC} - \phi_C} - \sqrt{\phi_{iC}} \right] \tag{3.148}$$

When $\Delta Q_B = Q_{Bo}$, the entire base region is depleted and results in a condition known as *punch-through*. This occurs at a collector bias equal to

$$V_{PT} = \frac{Q_{Bo}^2}{2\varepsilon_o \varepsilon_r q N_{DC}} \tag{3.149}$$

which was found from (3.148) by letting $-\phi_C$ equal the punch-through voltage, V_{PT}, and assuming that $V_{PT} \gg \phi_{iC}$. Substituting (3.148) and (3.149) into (3.143) gives

$$J_S = \frac{J_{So}}{1 + \sqrt{\dfrac{\phi_{iC}}{V_{PT}}} - \sqrt{\dfrac{\phi_{iC} - \phi_C}{V_{PT}}}} \tag{3.150}$$

Normally, $V_{PT} \gg \phi_{iC}$, so that

$$J_S \approx \frac{J_{So}}{1 - \sqrt{\dfrac{-\phi_C}{V_{PT}}}} \tag{3.151}$$

The effect of collector bias on collector current, as calculated using (3.75) and (3.151), is illustrated in Figure 3.29. For modeling purposes, a linear fit to the characteristics is often made. The extrapolated curves then intersect the negative collector voltage axis at a point which is defined as the *Early voltage*, V_A, shown in Figure 3.29. Using this parameter, the slope of the current-voltage characteristics is given by

$$\frac{dJ_C}{d(-\phi_C)} = \frac{J_C}{V_A - \phi_C} \tag{3.152}$$

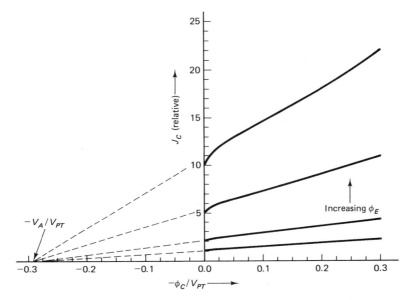

Figure 3.29   Variations in collector current with reverse collector bias as calculated from (3.150).

3.3 TWO-DIMENSIONAL CONSIDERATIONS

In this section we extend our analysis to include the predominant two-dimensional effects which occur in actual BJT device structures. Some of these effects arise purely from the two-dimensional nature of the BJT (Figure 3.1a), while others become significant owing to the small geometries employed in the fabrication of modern integrated circuit devices.

3.3.1 Current Crowding

In vertical bipolar structures (Figure 3.30), the base current is carried laterally in the neutral base region beneath the emitter. This current, coupled with the finite resistance of the base, results in a lateral voltage drop in the base. Consequently, there is a lateral variation in base-emitter junction potential, $\phi_E(y)$, which is highest at the edge of the emitter nearest the base contact and is lowest at the edge farthest from the contact. Since the emitter current varies exponentially with ϕ_E, this current also varies with lateral position, becoming crowded at the emitter periphery nearest the base contact. This current crowding increases the local current density in this region and can result in high-level injection effects occurring there. Consequently, the operating current range of the transistor is reduced.

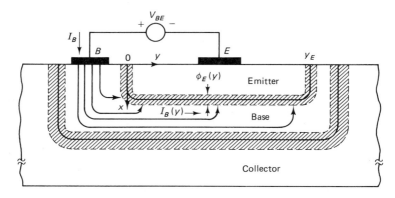

Figure 3.30   Emitter current crowding caused by lateral voltage drop in the base.

In analyzing the current-crowding effect, we make the following assumptions:

1. Any voltage drop in the emitter is negligible with respect to the lateral voltage drop in the base,
2. High-level injection effects are neglected, and
3. α_F is constant in the lateral direction (y).

With reference to Figure 3.31 we write

$$J_E(y) = J_S\left[\exp\left(\frac{q\phi_E(y)}{kT}\right) - 1\right] \approx J_S\exp\left(\frac{q\phi_E(y)}{kT}\right) \qquad (3.153)$$

Taking the base boundary at $y = 0$ to be an equipotential of value ϕ_E, we have

$$\phi_E(y) = \phi_E(0) - \int_0^y J_B(\xi)\rho_B\, d\xi \qquad (3.154)$$

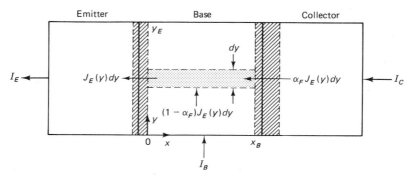

Figure 3.31   Model used to calculate the lateral (y direction) variation in transistor currents caused by the finite resistance of the base (after Hauser [12], ©1964, IEEE).

where ρ_B is the resistivity of the neutral base region. The lateral variation in base current is given by

$$J_B(y) = \frac{1 - \alpha_F}{x_B} \int_y^{y_E} J_E(\xi)\, d\xi + J_B(y_E) \tag{3.155}$$

Differentiating (3.155) and combining with (3.153) and (3.154) we obtain

$$\frac{dJ_B(y)}{dy} = -\left(\frac{1 - \alpha_F}{x_B}\right) J_S \exp\left[\frac{\phi_E(0) - \int_0^y J_B(\xi)\rho_B\, d\xi}{kT/q}\right] \tag{3.156}$$

which may be readily transformed into the following second-order differential equation:

$$\frac{d^2 J_B(y)}{dy^2} + \frac{q\rho_B J_B(y)}{kT}\frac{dJ_B(y)}{dy} = 0 \tag{3.157}$$

A general solution to (3.157) is [12]

$$J_B(y) = A \tan\left[A\frac{q\rho_B}{2kT}B\left(1 - \frac{y}{B}\right)\right] \tag{3.158}$$

where A and B are constants. For a single base contact $J_B(y_E) = 0$, so that $B = y_E$. Letting

$$Z = \frac{A q \rho_B y_E}{2kT}$$

we have

$$J_B(y) = \frac{2kT}{q\rho_B y_E} Z \tan\left[Z\left(1 - \frac{y}{y_E}\right)\right] \tag{3.159}$$

where Z is determined from the boundary condition at $y = 0$

$$Z \tan Z = \frac{q\rho_B y_E}{2kT} J_B(0) \tag{3.160}$$

In terms of the emitter current

$$I_B(0) = (1 - \alpha_F) I_E = J_B(0) x_B z_E$$

where z_E is the emitter length (in the directon normal to the x-y plane). Thus

$$Z \tan Z = \frac{(1 - \alpha_F) q R_{BB}}{2kT} I_E \tag{3.161}$$

where R_{BB} is the geometrical base resistance

$$R_{BB} = \frac{\rho_B y_E}{x_B z_E} \tag{3.162}$$

3.3.1.1 Potential variation. Substituting (3.159) into (3.154) and carrying out the indicated integration we obtain

$$\phi_E(y) = \phi_E(0) - \frac{2kT}{q}\ln\left\{\frac{\cos[Z(1 - y/y_E)]}{\cos Z}\right\} \qquad (3.163)$$

3.3.1.2 Emitter current variation. Substituting (3.163) into (3.153) gives

$$J_E(y) = J_E(0)\frac{\cos^2 Z}{\cos^2[Z(1 - y/y_E)]} \qquad (3.164)$$

where

$$J_E(0) = J_S\exp\left(\frac{q\phi_E(0)}{kT}\right)$$

The variation in emitter current with lateral position is illustrated in Figure 3.32. The current crowding ratio is

$$\frac{J_E(y_E)}{J_E(0)} = \cos^2 Z \qquad (3.165)$$

As an example, for the crowding factor to be less than 50%, $Z\tan Z$ must be

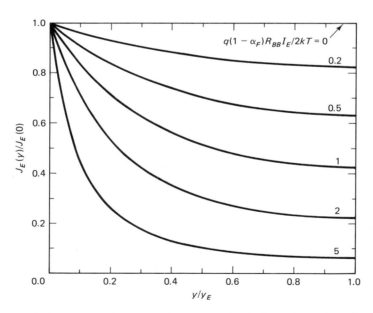

Figure 3.32 Lateral variation in emitter current density for various values of total emitter current.

less than about 0.8 (from Figure 3.32). Hence

$$I_E(\max) \approx \frac{1.6kT}{q(1 - \alpha_F)R_{BB}} \tag{3.166}$$

Typical IC transistors have base resistances ranging in value from a few hundred to a few thousand ohms. Taking $R_{BB} = 1$ K ohms and $\alpha_F = 0.98$ gives $I_E(\max) \approx 2$ mA. Therefore, base resistance must be kept as low as possible if current crowding effects are to be minimized.

3.3.1.3 Effective base resistance.

Because of the distributed nature of the base current (Figure 3.30) and the current crowding effect, the effective base resistance, R_B, is not equal to the geometrical resistance, R_{BB}. Hauser [12] calculates an effective base resistance based upon an equivalent power dissipation. The power dissipation in the base due to the base current is

$$p_B = \frac{1}{y_E} \int_0^{y_E} I_B^2(y) R_{BB} \, dy \tag{3.167}$$

An effective base resistance is calculated from

$$p_B = I_B^2(0) R_B \tag{3.168}$$

Therefore,

$$R_B = \frac{R_{BB}}{y_E} \int_0^{y_E} \frac{J_B^2(y)}{J_B^2(0)} \, dy \tag{3.169}$$

which, after substituting for J_B from (3.159) and integrating, gives

$$R_B = R_{BB} \left[\frac{\tan Z - Z}{Z \tan^2 Z} \right] \tag{3.170}$$

At low currents, $Z \to 0$ and $R_B \to R_{BB}/3$, as may be easily verified by expanding $\tan Z$ in a Taylor series. The variation in R_B with emitter current is illustrated in Figure 3.33. The decrease in effective base resistance with increased current is a direct consequence of the current crowding effect—at large currents only the emitter periphery region near the base contact is effective.

One can substantially reduce the effects of current crowding by fabricating the transistor with a double base contact, such as shown in Figure 3.34. In this case $R_B \to R_{BB}/12$ at low currents—the factor of 4 improvement results from the fact that each contact is supplying only half the total base current over half the emitter width. The double base contact scheme of Figure 3.34, is however, rarely used in integrated circuits because of the increased area required for such a transistor. Since most modern IC structures are limited by metalization pitch, the double base transistor requires nearly twice the chip area of a corresponding single base transistor.

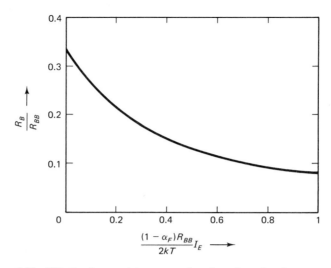

Figure 3.33 Effective base resistance as a function of total emitter current. The decrease in R_B with increased current is a direct consequence of current crowding.

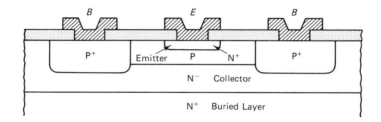

Figure 3.34 Double base contact structure to reduce effective base resistance.

3.3.2 Lateral Base Widening

In the one-dimensional model for base widening at high currents (Kirk effect), the base width is pushed into the epitaxial collector region when the collector current density exceeds J_2 (3.112). This analysis assumes that the carrier flux from emitter to collector is unidimensional for all current densities. Van der Ziel and Agouridis [13] argue that J_C cannot exceed J_2 because at this point the electric field at the metallurgical base-collector junction is reduced to zero and the current is thereby space-charge limited.* Therefore, any increase in collector current beyond this critical value must be accompanied by a lateral divergence in flux from the emitter, as illustrated in Figure 3.35. Consequently, the effective base width for additional carriers is increased

---

*In Section 3.3.3 we show that this limitation is not entirely valid.

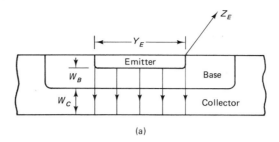

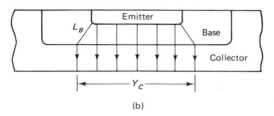

Figure 3.35   Lateral current spreading at high current densities. (a) $J_C < J_2$. (b) $J_C > J_2$ (after van der Ziel and Agouridis [13], ©1966, IEEE).

from W_B (Figure 3.35a) to L_B (Figure 3.35b). Accordingly

$$L_B = \sqrt{W_B^2 + \frac{(Y_C - Y_E)^2}{4}} \tag{3.171}$$

The critical current at which lateral divergence begins is

$$I_o = J_2 Y_E Z_E \tag{3.172}$$

For $I_C > I_o$, $J_C = J_2$, so $Y_C = I_C Y_E / I_o$.
Thus

$$L_B = \sqrt{W_B^2 + \frac{Y_E^2}{4}\left(\frac{I_C}{I_o} - 1\right)^2}, \; I_C \geqq I_o \tag{3.173}$$

3.3.2.1 Effect on base transit time.   When I_C exceeds I_o, any additional carriers injected from the emitter are assumed to follow the path length L_B with a corresponding transit time

$$\tau_t = \frac{L_B^2}{\eta D_{nB}} = \tau_{to}\left[1 + \left(\frac{Y_E}{2W_B}\right)^2\left(\frac{I_C}{I_o} - 1\right)^2\right] \tag{3.174}$$

where

$$\tau_{to} = \frac{W_B^2}{\eta D_{nB}}$$

The transit time thus increases with increased collector current, as is observed experimentally. This analysis neglects any base widening into the collector region (normal Kirk effect). In practice, both effects occur simultaneously and a two-dimensional simulation would be required to accurately model the process.

3.3.3 Sidewall Injection

As the width of the emitter (Y_E) is scaled down in size relative to the emitter junction depth (X_E), the sidewall regions of the emitter periphery contribute a significant portion of the total emitter current (Figure 3.36). Since emitter depths are typically a few tenths of a micrometer, the peripheral current arising from sidewall injection becomes important for emitter widths of about a micrometer or less—well within the range of geometries envisioned for ULSI device structures.

Accurate modeling of the peripheral injection requires at least a two-dimensional numerical simulation. Figure 3.37 illustrates the results of a simulation carried out by Slotboom [14]. Shown are the injected current flux lines and the lateral current density distributions for an NPN transistor operated at a collector current density in excess of the space-charge-limited value J_2. Shown also for comparison are the results obtained from the van der Ziel and Agouridis model [13]. Notice that, even at high current densities, most of the peripherally-injected current is confined to the lower portion of the sidewall.

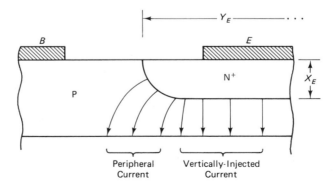

Figure 3.36 Additional emitter current arising from the emitter sidewall region.

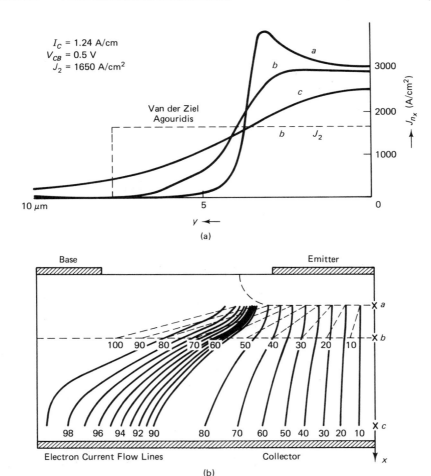

Figure 3.37 Results of a two-dimensional simulation illustrating the extent of peripheral current injection from the emitter sidewall. (a) Lateral variation in collector current density at the depth of the emitter junction (curve a), at the depth of the collector junction (curve b), and at the collector contact (curve c). (b) Flow lines indicating the percentage of the total current flowing between this line and the x axis (after Slotboom [14], ©1973, IEEE).

3.4 THREE-DIMENSIONAL CONSIDERATIONS

The principal three-dimensional effect in vertical bipolar transistors arises from the base area surrounding the emitter end walls (z direction in Figure 3.38a). In the two-dimensional models only the peripheral injection from the emitter sidewalls in the x-z plane are considered. Additionally, base current is

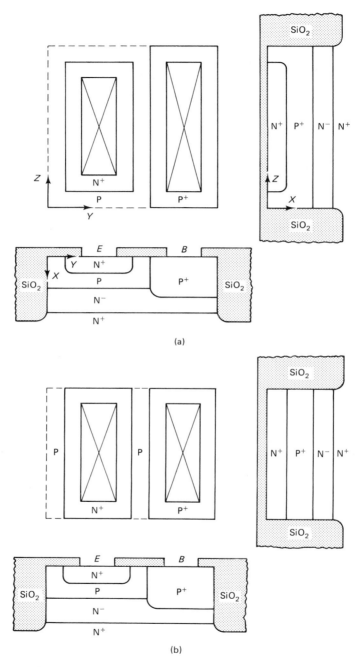

Figure 3.38 (a) Top and cross-sectional views showing a portion of a non-walled-emitter bipolar structure. (b) Walled-emitter structure.

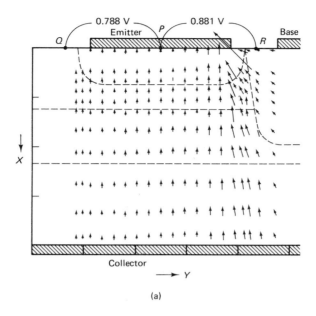

(a)

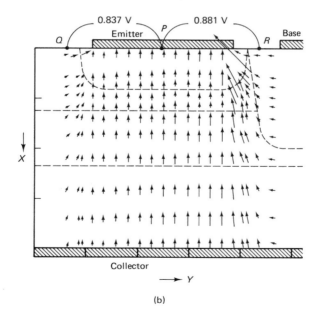

(b)

Figure 3.39 Comparison between (a) two-dimensional and (b) three-dimensional simulations of current density distribution under the emitter in a non-walled structure (after Yoshi *et al.* [15], ©1982, IEEE).

confined to flow laterally in the y direction beneath the emitter. As a consequence the two-dimensional model tends to underestimate the collector current and overestimate the effective base resistance. It should be remarked that for walled-emitter structures (Figure 3.38b) there is no end-wall injection so that for this structure a two-dimensional model is sufficient.

A comparison between two-dimensional and three-dimensional simulations for a *non-walled* emitter structure is shown in Figure 3.39a and Figure 3.39b, respectively [15]. Shown are current density distributions in the x-y plane beneath the emitter displayed as two-dimensional vectors. From these figures it is apparent that a two-dimensional simulation overestimates the lateral current crowding effect. As indicated in Figure 3.39a the base-emitter junction potential at the emitter edge farthest from the base contact is 0.788 volts versus 0.837 volts from the three-dimensional simulation (Figure 3.39b). Thus in this example the two-dimensional model would under-estimate the current density at the far emitter edge by an amount

$$\frac{J_C(\text{two-dimensional})}{J_C(\text{three-dimensional})}$$

$$= \exp\{q[\phi_E(\text{two-dimensional}) - \phi_E(\text{three-dimensional})]/kT\}$$

$$= 0.15 \tag{3.175}$$

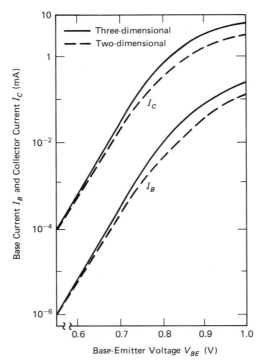

Figure 3.40 Comparison between two-dimensional and three-dimensional simulations of forward-active base and collector currents in a non-walled-emitter transistor (after Yoshi *et al.* [15], ©1982, IEEE).

Figure 3.40 shows the resulting terminal I-V characteristics for the two simulations [15]. At low current levels the two are comparable since lateral voltage drops in the base are small—the slight increase in current obtained by the three-dimensional simulation results from the current contribution from the emitter end walls. At large currents the characteristics differ widely due to the unrealistically high base resistance obtained from the two-dimensional model.

3.5 PARASITICS

In Figure 3.41 we show a portion of a bipolar integrated circuit structure, drawn approximately to scale, consisting of a single BJT and a load resistor connected to the collector. This serves to illustrate the point that the volume occupied by the active transistor is, in reality, small in proportion to the volume required for the complete device structure. Consequently, the non-active regions contribute significant parasitic effects, which if not minimized, can dominate circuit performance. In this section we identify the more

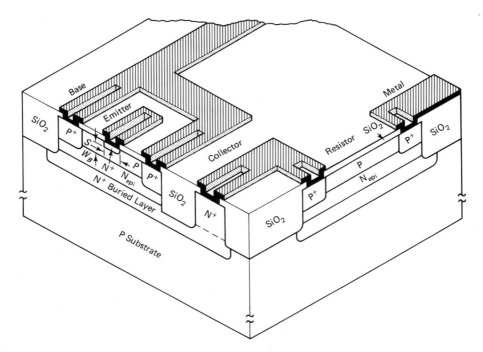

Figure 3.41   Three-dimensional view of a portion of a typical bipolar integrated circuit.

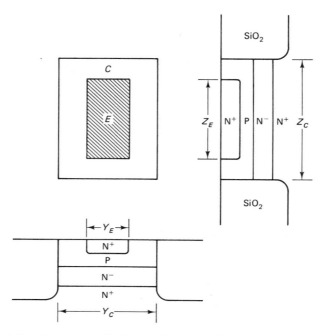

Figure 3.42 Geometry used in the calculation of collector saturation resistance.

important parasitic effects and indicate, at least qualitatively, their effect on digital circuit performance.

3.5.1 Collector Saturation Resistance

Most of the resistance associated with the collector region arises from the lightly doped epitaxial layer beneath the base region. The resistance of the heavily doped buried layer and the collector contact region is usually small in comparison. It is important that the collector saturation resistance (R_{sc}) be made as small as practicable because in certain circuit applications there is the possibility that the voltage dropped across this resistance can cause the base-collector junction to become forward-biased, thereby putting the transistor into saturation. This voltage drop also reduces the logic swing that is available to drive succeeding stages in the circuit.

We will calculate an approximate value for R_{sc} based on two limiting cases. For the structure depicted in Figure 3.42, an upper bound is calculated by considering only that portion of the epitaxial collector which lies directly beneath the emitter. In this case

$$R_{sc}^{u} = \frac{\rho_{\text{epi}} X_C}{Y_E Z_E} \tag{3.176}$$

where ρ_{epi} is the resistivity of the epitaxial layer and X_C its thickness (undepleted portion). To calculate a lower bound we approximate the effective collector region by a truncated pyramid of top dimensions Y_E, Z_E, and bottom dimensions Y_C, Z_C.
In this case

$$R_{sc}^1 = \frac{\rho_{epi} X_C}{\langle A \rangle} \qquad (3.177)$$

where $\langle A \rangle$ is the average cross-sectional area of the truncated pyramid and is given by

$$\langle A \rangle = \frac{Y_E Z_E + Y_C Z_C}{2} \qquad (3.178)$$

Taking the actual resistance to be the average of the upper and lower bound values gives

$$R_{sc} \approx \frac{R_{sc}^u}{2}\left[1 + \frac{2}{\left(1 + \dfrac{Y_C Z_C}{Y_E Z_E}\right)} \right] \qquad (3.179)$$

3.5.2 Emitter Metallization

The resistance of the metallization stripe used to contact the emitter can result in de-biasing effects. This is because the lateral voltage drop along the metal reduces the local emitter-base junction potential. As a result, the emitter current density decreases with distance away from the end of the emitter which is being fed (Figure 3.43). This is similar to the current-crowding effect associated with base resistance, but in this case it occurs in the z-direction.

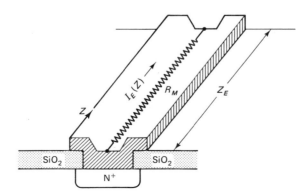

Figure 3.43   Emitter metallization resistance.

If the emitter is fed from the end at $z = 0$ then the emitter-base junction potential varies as

$$\phi_E(z) = \phi_E(0) - \int_0^z I_E(\zeta) R'_M \, d\zeta \qquad (3.180)$$

where R'_M is the resistance per unit length of the emitter metallization stripe. The variation in current density along the emitter due to de-biasing is then

$$J_E(z) = J_E(0)\exp[q\Delta\phi(z)/kT] \qquad (3.181)$$

where $J_E(0)$ is the current density in the emitter at $z = 0$ and $\Delta\phi(z) = \phi_E(z) - \phi_E(0)$. This reduction in emitter potential must be kept small if de-biasing effects are to be minimized. For $\Delta\phi(Z_E) \ll kT/q$ the emitter current is distributed nearly linearly along the metal stripe, so that to first order we may take

$$I_E(z) = I_E\left(1 - \frac{z}{Z_E}\right) \qquad (3.182)$$

where I_E is the total emitter current. Then from (3.180)

$$\Delta\phi(Z_E) = I_E R'_M \int_0^{Z_E}\left(1 - \frac{z}{Z_E}\right) dz = \frac{I_E R'_M Z_E}{2} \qquad (3.183)$$

But $R'_M Z_E = R_M$, the total resistance of the metallization stripe, so

$$\Delta\phi(Z_E) = I_E R_M/2 \qquad (3.184)$$

The ratio of the emitter current density at the two ends is then

$$\frac{J_E(Z_E)}{J_E(0)} = \exp(-qI_E R_M/2kT) \qquad (3.185)$$

As a practical limit, this ratio should be at least 0.8 if serious de-biasing is to be avoided. This limit corresponds to a maximum allowable metal resistance of roughly

$$R_M(\text{max}) \approx \frac{12}{I_E(\text{mA})} \text{ ohms} \qquad (3.186)$$

It should be remarked that this analysis does not include the contact resistance between the metal film and the underlying semiconductor (see Section 3.6.1). For metal contacting single crystal silicon this resistance is normally small compared to the resistance of the metallization stripe. For metal contacting polycrystalline silicon, however, the contact resistance can become significant as device dimensions are scaled down (since contact resistance scales inversely with contact area).

3.5.3 Substrate PNP

In addition to the passive parasitics (resistances and capacitances) associated with the extrinsic regions of bipolar IC structures, potentially active parasitics are also present. These occur in connection with the p type substrate

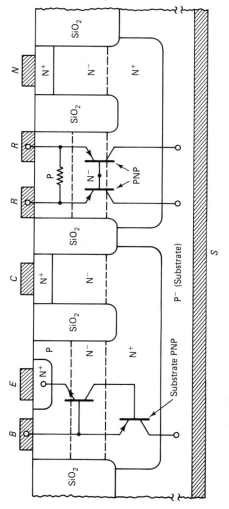

Figure 3.44 Origin of parasitic substrate PNP transistors in bipolar IC structures.

upon which are fabricated the desired transistor and resistor circuit elements. In Figure 3.44 we show a portion of an IC structure consisting of a vertical NPN transistor and a resistor. For both these elements there exist parasitic PNP transistor structures. For the NPN transistor, a PNP structure is formed between the substrate and the NPN's base; for the resistor, a PNP structure is formed between the substrate and the p region in which the resistor is formed.

The influence of these parasitic transistors on circuit performance depends upon their conduction state—a positive emitter-base potential turns them on, thereby shunting current away from the base of the NPN and away from the resistor. If the parasitic PNPs remain cutoff, their effect is minimal since only junction leakage and capacitive currents are present. To keep the base-collector junctions of the substrate PNP transistors from becoming forward-biased, the substrate (S) is connected to the most negative potential in the circuit and the isolation layer associated with resistor regions (N) is connected to the most positive potential in the circuit. This contact scheme insures that the parasitic PNP transistors associated with resistor elements remain cutoff, but not so for those associated with the active NPN transistors. Here the emitter-base junction of the substrate PNP can become forward-biased if the NPN is driven into saturation. Fortunately, the current gain of the substrate PNP is usually very low (since its base is comprised mainly of the large, heavily-doped, N^+ buried layer region), so that SCR-type latchup normally does not occur. Hence, for modeling purposes the substrate PNP elements are often represented by back-to-back junction diodes.

3.5.4 Equivalent Circuit Elements

In Figure 3.45 we illustrate the principal parasitic elements (excluding the substrate PNP) associated with a typical integrated circuit BJT. Table 3.2 identifies each component.

It should be pointed out that C_{BC}^s can either be a pn junction capacitance, as represented in Figure 3.45, or an oxide capacitance, in the case where an oxide spacer is used to isolate the collector contact region (such as illustrated in Figure 3.44). In either case, this capacitance is usually small in comparison with the capacitance associated with the bottom-wall portion of the collector-base junction (since the depth of this junction is much smaller than the lateral width of the P and P^+ regions).

The principal parasitic elements affecting circuit speed are R_B, R_B^+, C_{BC}^b, C_{jC}, C_{CS}, and to a lesser extent, C_{jE}. The total base resistance in combination with the various capacitive elements associated with the P^+/P base region produces an RC delay which slows the input response of the transistor. The capacitive elements connected with the base and collector regions also contribute delays resulting from Miller feedback effects. Of all the parasitic capacitances, these have the greatest effect on circuit speed, and given a choice of various fabrication technologies, those which minimize the overall base-to-col-

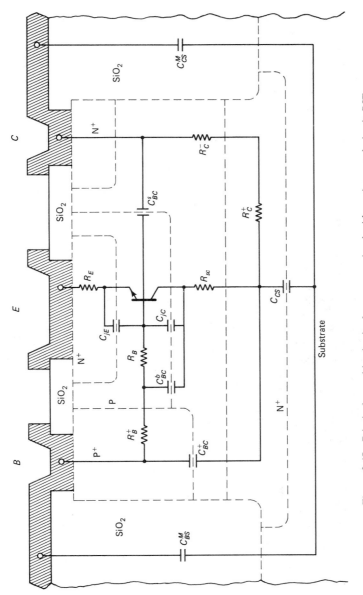

Figure 3.45 Principal parasitic circuit elements associated with an integrated circuit BJT. Not included is the active substrate PNP.

TABLE 3.2   Parasitic Elements for an Integrated Circuit BJT

Element	Description
R_B	Effective base resistance of the active transistor
R_B^+	Resistance of the extrinsic base region
R_C^+	Lateral resistance of the buried layer
$\dot{R}_C^-$	Vertical resistance of the collector epitaxial layer plus the resistance of the collector contact region
R_E	Emitter resistance
R_{sc}	Collector saturation resistance
C_{BC}^b	Bottom-wall junction capacitance of the extrinsic base-collector region
C_{BC}^+	Junction capacitance of the base contact and epitaxial collector region
C_{BC}^s	Sidewall capacitance of the extrinsic base-collector region
C_{BS}^M	Base metallization-substrate capacitance
C_{CS}	Buried layer-substrate capacitance
C_{CS}^M	Collector metallization-substrate capacitance
C_{ES}^M	Emitter metallization-substrate capacitance (not shown)
C_{jC}	Collector-base junction capacitance of the active transistor
C_{jE}	Emitter-base junction capacitance of the active transistor

lector feedback capacitance are favored. The capacitance formed by the N^+ buried-layout/P^- substrate junction (C_{CS}) can represent a significant portion of the total load capacitance seen by the collector. For use in circuit simulation, the simplified model shown in Figure 3.46 is usually adequate. Not included in this model are the resistive and capacitive parasitics associated with the interconnect metalization. These can be determined once the circuit layout is established.

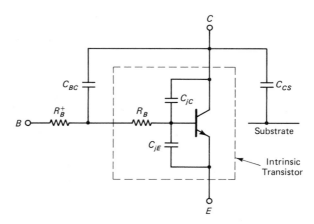

Figure 3.46 Simplified equivalent circuit which retains the major parasitic elements affecting circuit performance.

3.6 SCALING CONSIDERATIONS AND LIMITATIONS

In this section we examine the major scaling issues associated with bipolar integrated circuit transistors. Unlike FET devices, BJT devices do not follow simple scaling rules. This is due in large part to the more complicated nature of the bipolar structure and to the interaction of various physical effects. Nevertheless, the motivations for scaling remain the same:

1. increased circuit density,
2. higher speed, and
3. lower power.

For ULSI, the first of these is of prime importance. Unfortunately, simple geometrical shrinking does not necessarily yield improved speed and power performance. In reaching for higher speeds at low operating currents, the design of advanced bipolar structures must focus on the increasing dominance of second-order and parasitic effects on circuit performance as dimensions are reduced.

In addition, certain physical limitations, such as punch-through, tunneling, pipe defects, electromigration, and doping fluctuations must be considered.

3.6.1 Lateral Scaling

Lateral scaling is the shrinking of dimensions in the y-z plane (as shown in Figure 3.38), and is achieved directly as a result of improved lithography and/or fabrication techniques. In applying a *lateral shrink* to the design of a bipolar IC, the following points need to be considered:

3.6.1.1 Current density. Performance degradation resulting from high-level injection effects in small-geometry devices can be avoided if the collector current is scaled with emitter area to maintain a constant collector current density. However, unless all capacitances are similarly scaled, circuit speed may degrade owing to the slower charge and discharge rates. An example illustrating the effects of current density and emitter size on the frequency response of a small-geometry BJT is shown in Figure 3.47. Sketched is the variation in cutoff frequency (f_τ) with emitter current for various emitter widths (Y_E). The emitter length in all cases is 3 μm. At low currents, the frequency response is limited by device capacitance, and at high currents, transit time degradation resulting from high-level injection effects (Kirk effect) limits the response. Thus, for a given emitter size, there exists an optimum emitter current which maximizes frequency response. In the example shown, this occurs at a current density of roughly 120 μA/μm^2 (in practice, this optimum current density is usually in the range of about 100–200 μA/μm^2).

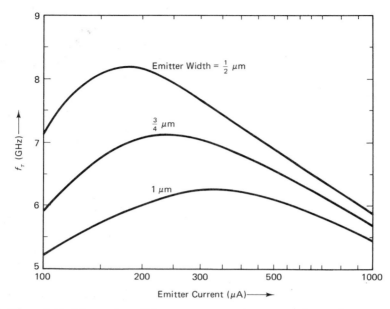

Figure 3.47 Measured cutoff frequency versus emitter current for small geometry bipolar transistors [16], ©1981, IEEE.

3.6.1.2 Sidewall injection. As discussed in Section 3.3.3, injection from the emitter sidewall regions can contribute a significant portion of the total device current when the lateral dimensions of the emitter are scaled down in size relative to the emitter junction depth. The electrical base width (the path taken by carriers injected from the sidewall) is larger than the metallurgical base width beneath the emitter bottom wall. Consequently, the effective base Gummel number for the sidewall region is increased, resulting in a decrease in current gain for the sidewall-injected carriers. The net current gain of the device is thereby reduced in proportion to the ratio of sidewall to bottom wall current. An example illustrating this effect is shown in Figure 3.48, which gives a plot of dc current gain for various emitter widths, at the same current density [16]. The emitter junction depth for these devices was 0.25 μm, which is typical of many IC bipolar structures. Thus, as emitter widths are scaled to sub-micrometer dimensions, significant reductions in β can be expected.

3.6.1.3 Base-contact enhancement. Figure 3.48 also illustrates a second effect associated with lateral scaling. Shown is a decrease in current gain as the spacing between the emitter and the heavily doped (P$^+$) base contact region is reduced. This reduction in gain results from the lateral diffusion of boron atoms from the heavily doped base contact enhancement (P$^+$) region into the lighter doped active base (P) region. As a result, the net

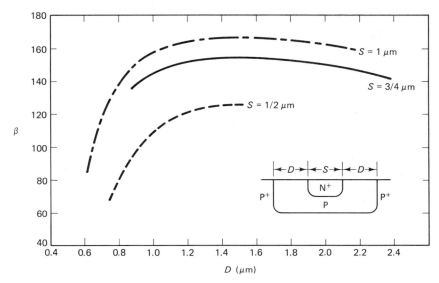

Figure 3.48 DC current gain versus separation between the heavily doped base contact region and the emitter.

doping in the base (especially near the emitter edges) is enhanced, which lowers the emitter efficiency (and hence β). This lateral encroachment of dopant atoms occurs naturally as a part of the normal diffusion process that takes place during the formation of the P^+ region. It also occurs during any high-temperature processing steps which follow.

3.6.1.4 Parasitics.   If the extrinsic (parasitic) areas of the device do not shrink in concert with the intrinsic (active) areas, then any gain in performance that might be achieved by reducing the active transistor area may be lost.

3.6.1.5 Electromigration.   Electromigration is the mass transport of atoms in a material in response to large electric fields and/or large current densities. In metallization lines carrying currents in excess of about 10^5 A/cm^2, metal atoms move toward the positive end of the conductor, with the resulting voids moving in the opposite direction. This process occurs primarily along grain boundaries in the metal film and is enhanced at elevated temperatures. Electromigration and the depletion of material along a section of a metal line results in a higher current density at that cross-sectional point of the line. This enhances the depletion at that point resulting in, ultimately, an opening on the line at that point. This is of concern in scaled bipolar integrated circuits because of increased current density in the narrower (but not necessarily thicker) metal lines. For example, a metal film 2 μm wide and 0.5 μm thick carrying a current of 1 mA would have a current density of 10^5 A/cm^2.

3.6.1.6 Contact resistance. As lateral dimensions of the device are reduced, the physical size of the metal-semiconductor contacts will also decrease, resulting in an increase in contact resistance. This resistance is particularly important with respect to the emitter contact, since any resistance associated with the emitter is magnified by a factor of $(\beta + 1)$ in relation to its degradation of the input response of the transistor. The situation is further compounded in that contact resistance does not scale linearly with contact area for contact window dimensions below about one micrometer. This is due to several effects: (1) incomplete oxide removal around the periphery of the contact window, (2) enhanced dissolution of silicon into the metal film in the periphery contact regions, and (3) incomplete metallization coverage in the contact window. As a result, the emitter contact resistance of a scaled bipolar transistor may be unacceptably large.

The situation is even worse for emitters employing polysilicon—currently, polysilicon films used to contact single-crystal emitters have specific contact resistances in excess of 10^{-7} ohm-cm^2 (10 ohm-μm^2).

3.6.2 Vertical Scaling

Vertical scaling is the shrinking of thickness dimensions (x direction, as depicted in Figure 3.38), and is achieved by reductions in junction depths and thicknesses of epitaxial layers and buried layers. Vertical scaling affects both the active transistor and the inactive parasitics. In reducing vertical dimensions, the following points need to be considered:

3.6.2.1 Emitter transparency. If the emitter junction is made shallow enough, minority carriers injected by the base can cross the neutral emitter region without appreciable recombination. The emitter thus appears *transparent* to these carriers and the resulting current (J_{pE}) becomes strongly dependent upon the surface recombination velocity (S_p) at the emitter surface. In this case, the boundary condition for the minority carriers at the emitter contact is, from (3.31),

$$\bar{p}_{nE}(x_E) = - \left. \frac{D_{pE}(x_E)}{S_p} \frac{d\bar{p}_{nE}}{dx} \right|_{x=x_E} \approx \frac{J_{pE}}{qS_p} \tag{3.187}$$

Re-evaluating (3.133), using (3.187) in place of (3.135), yields

$$J_{pE} = \frac{qn_i^2 \exp\left(\dfrac{q\phi_E}{kT}\right)}{GU_E' + \dfrac{N_{DE}(x_E)}{S_p} \dfrac{n_i^2}{n_{ie}^2(x_E)}} \tag{3.188}$$

where GU_E' is given by (3.138).

In general, the back-injected hole current in the emitter (J_{pE}) is reduced for non-ideal contacts ($S_p \neq \infty$). For extremely shallow emitters, the contribution of GU_E' to the denominator of (3.188) can become negligible with respect to the surface recombination term. In the limit

$$J_{pE} \rightarrow \frac{qS_p n_{ie}^2(x_E)}{N_{DE}(x_E)} \exp\left(\frac{q\phi_E}{kT}\right) \tag{3.189}$$

Thus, emitter efficiency (and hence current gain) becomes directly dependent upon the surface conditions at the emitter contact.

3.6.2.2 Base doping fluctuations.

As the base width is shrunk, the base doping concentration must be increased to maintain the punch-through voltage. As a result, the number of dopant atoms in a cube of volume W_B^3 in the base increases as the base width (W_B) is decreased. Since impurity atoms are placed randomly in the lattice, there will be a statistical fluctuation in the number of dopant atoms in any given elemental volume (cube) in the base. For a transistor of emitter area $A_E = Y_E Z_E$, there will be $N_B = A_E/W_B^2$ cubes in the active base; the cube containing the lowest dopant concentration then determines the punch-through voltage for the transistor. Consequently, in a circuit of N_T transistors, there will be a statistical distribution of punch-through voltages resulting from doping fluctuations.

Taking into account the probability that no cube contains fewer than $N_{AB} - \Delta N_{AB}$ atoms, the following expression for the peak doping fluctuation is obtained [17]:

$$\Delta N_{AB} = \left[2\ln(N_B N_T)\frac{N_{AB}}{W_B^3}\right]^{1/2} \tag{3.190}$$

As an example, consider a chip containing 10^6 transistors of active base area 1 μm $\times$ 2 μm. Then from (3.190),

$$\Delta N_{AB} = \left[2\ln\left(\frac{0.2}{W_B^2}\right)\frac{N_{AB}}{W_B^3}\right]^{1/2} \tag{3.191}$$

where W_B is in cm. The variation in peak doping fluctuation versus peak base doping for various values of base width, for this example, is shown in Figure 3.49.

To illustrate the design constraints imposed by doping fluctuations, consider a device in which the base doping profile may be approximated by an exponential function, as illustrated in Figure 3.50. Punch-through occurs when the collector depletion edge, x_B, in the base reaches the emitter depletion edge at $x = 0$. Solving Poisson's equation for the potential drop across the base-collector depletion region at punch-through yields

$$V_{PT} = \frac{qN_{DC}}{\varepsilon_o\varepsilon_r}\left[\frac{W_B x_C}{a}\left(\frac{N_{AB}}{N_{DC}} - 1\right) - \frac{x_C^2}{2}\right] - \phi_{iC} \tag{3.192}$$

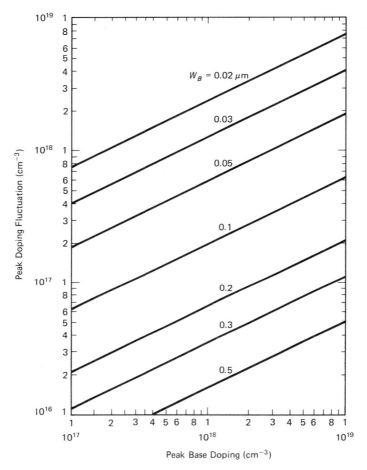

Figure 3.49 Variation in peak base doping fluctuation versus doping concentration and base width for a chip containing 10^6 transistors of active base area 1 μm $\times$ 2 μm.

where

$$\phi_{iC} = \frac{kT}{q} \ln\left[\frac{|N(0)|N(x_C)}{n_i^2}\right] \tag{3.193}$$

and

$$a = \ln\left(\frac{N_{AB}}{N_{DC}}\right) \tag{3.194}$$

The charge balance equation

$$\int_{x_B}^{x_C} N(x)\, dx = 0 \tag{3.195}$$

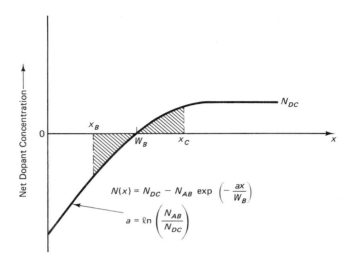

Figure 3.50   Base region doping profile used to calculate punch-through voltage.

is solved for x_C at punch-through to give

$$x_C = \frac{N_{AB}W_B}{N_{DC}a}\left[1 - \exp\left(-\frac{ax_C}{W_B}\right)\right] \tag{3.196}$$

The requirement on base doping to insure a desired punch-through voltage in the presence of doping fluctuations is found by incorporating (3.191) into (3.192). The results for our example are shown in Figure 3.51. For this example, we have further assumed that $N_{DC} = 5 \times 10^{16}$ cm^{-3}. As an illustration, consider a device with a base width of .05 μm and a desired punch-through voltage of 10 volts. Then from Figure 3.51, the peak base doping concentration must be at least 3×10^{18} cm^{-3}.

3.6.2.3 Diffusion pipes and spikes.   Process-induced defects, such as stacking faults and slip dislocations, can cause localized paths for emitter-collector shorting in narrow base-width transistors. Enhanced diffusion of dopant atoms from the emitter can occur along these defects, creating conducting channels from the emitter into the base. A *diffusion pipe* occurs if the defect channel extends through the base and into the collector—if the channel does not extend completely through the base, it is termed a *diffusion spike*. A transistor containing diffusion pipes exhibits FET-like characteristics with large output conductance. This behavior arises from the modulation of the depletion region surrounding the pipe channels by the applied junction potentials. Also, since diffusion pipes provide a majority carrier path from emitter to collector, the open-base emitter-to-collector leakage current, I_{CEO}, will be large and will not track I_{CBO}. A transistor containing diffusion spikes

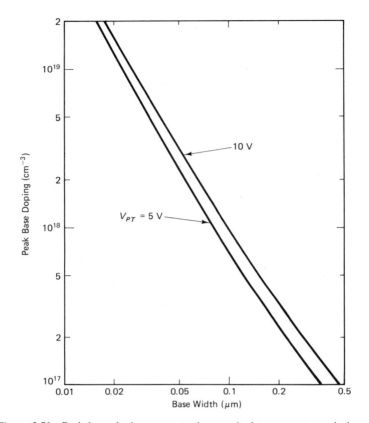

Figure 3.51 Peak base doping concentration required to prevent punch-through due to statistical doping fluctuations.

will exhibit reduced breakdown due to localized regions of high electric field and punch-through. These transistors also exhibit abnormally high leakage currents. In both cases, current gain (β) degradation is also often observed [18]. The probability that these defects create shorting channels increases as the base width is narrowed. Consequently, it becomes increasingly important to employ processes which minimize the creation and propagation of these defects.

3.7 TECHNOLOGIES FOR HIGH-PERFORMANCE DEVICES AND CIRCUITS

In this section we briefly discuss some of the major technologies currently in use and in development for the fabrication of high-performance bipolar transistors suitable for use in ULSI circuits and systems. As the number of logic gates per chip increases, the operating currents of individual devices must be reduced to keep chip power dissipation within manageable limits. If circuit speed (e.g., gate delay) is to be maintained, then the RC delays associated with the transistors and other circuit elements must remain constant. Capacitive elements (both parasitic and active) are charged and discharged through device and circuit resistances, some of which increase with reduced operating currents. For example, emitter resistance, $r_e = kT/qI_E$, and collector load resistance (non-saturating logic), $R_C = v_L/I_C$, both increase as the transistor operating current is lowered (assuming logic swing, v_L, remains the same). Consequently, capacitance values must be reduced as well.

3.7.1 Impacts of Technology

As discussed in Section 3.6, a simple lateral shrink of geometries does not necessarily result in the parasitic (extrinsic) and active (intrinsic) elements being reduced in equal proportions. Consequently, different fabrication technologies, even with the same *design rule* (e.g., feature size) constraints, will produce circuits which operate at different speeds. As an illustration, consider the three technologies depicted in Figure 3.52. Shown is a cross-section of a vertical npn transistor as produced by each technology. For comparison, a "standard" device fabricated by conventional planar technology is shown in the middle portion of the figure. Because of the limitations of metal pitch, this structure has an extrinsic (P^+) base region which is large in comparison to the intrinsic (P) base region. Consequently, the extrinsic base resistance (R_B^+) and the extrinsic base-collector capacitance (C_{BC}^+) are both large with respect to their intrinsic region counterparts.

An example of a simple lateral shrink is shown in the lower portion of Figure 3.52—in this case the same structure is fabricated using electron beam lithography to allow smaller lateral geometries. While the overall size of the device has been reduced, the ratio of extrinsic to intrinsic areas remain roughly the same.

The upper portion of Figure 3.52 (Polysilicon Self-Aligned—PSA) illustrates a technology which significantly reduces the extrinsic base region as compared to a conventional planar structure fabricated with the same lithography constraints. With PSA a layer of polysilicon is used to contact the base which allows the base metallization to be located over field oxide. This substantially reduces C_{BC}^+ and to a lesser extent R_B^+, depending upon the resistivity of the polysilicon film relative to the P^+ region in the conventional structure. Further, self-alignment of the emitter region to the polysilicon base contact eliminates the need for a large separation between the two because misalignment tolerance is eliminated. In the sections that follow we present some of the newer technologies currently being developed in use for the fabrication of high-performance integrated circuit bipolar transistors.

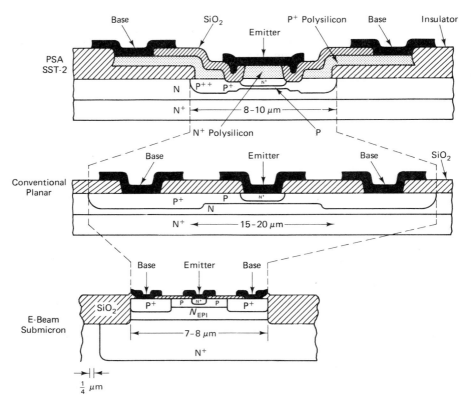

Figure 3.52 NPN transistor structure fabricated by three different technologies.

3.7.2 PSA

Two embodiments of the Polysilicon Self-Aligned (PSA) technology are illustrated in Figure 3.53. In both cases the emitter and active base regions are formed in a single (and therefore self-aligned) mask step, and contact to the base is made via a doped polysilicon layer which extends over the surface of the wafer.

Figure 3.53a illustrates the sequence of processing steps used to fabricate one version of the PSA structure, originally developed by IBM [19]. In (i) the wafer, which contains the N^+ buried layer, the N epitaxial layer and the SiO_2 isolation regions, receives a layer of deposited P^+ doped polysilicon, followed by a deposited SiO_2 layer, both roughly 0.3 μm thick. The patterned SiO_2/P^+ poly layers in (ii) are then Reactive Ion Etched (RIE), stopping part way through the P^+ poly layer. The remaining poly is then etched away using a preferential chemical etch which stops at the epitaxial (N) surface. This leaves an undercut P^+ poly region, as shown in (ii). In (iii) the wafer is oxidized, which forms the sidewall spacer (SiO_2) on the P^+ poly layer and also forms

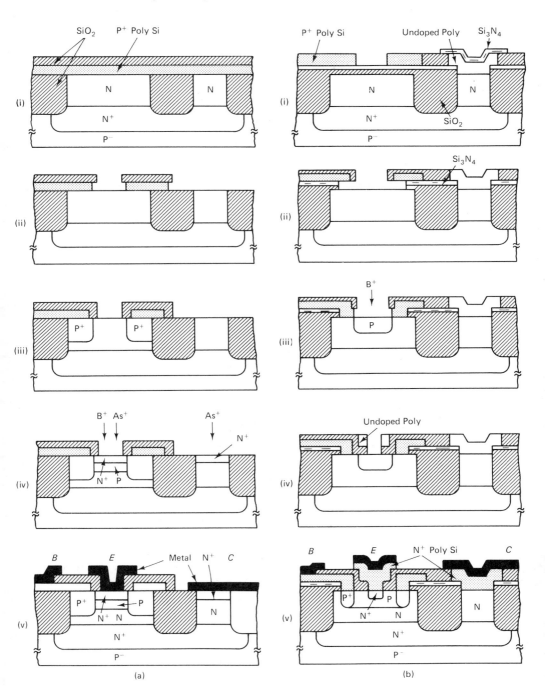

Figure 3.53   Two versions of Polysilicon Self-Aligned (PSA) technology.

the P^+ base contact enhancement regions by diffusion from the poly layer. The SiO_2 layer over the exposed N Si surface is removed by RIE. Ion implanted boron and arsenic form the base and emitter regions, respectively, in (iv). Finally, in (v) a contact opening to the P^+ poly layer over the field oxide region is made, followed by the metallization step. If desired, an N^+ polysilicon layer may be deposited and patterned over the emitter prior to metallization. This would increase the current gain of the transistor. This PSA process has been used to fabricate transistors with emitter widths (Y_E) of 1.25 μm using standard optical lithography, and Emitter Coupled Logic (ECL) circuits using these transistors have achieved gate delays of 114 ps [20].

Details of a self-aligned process developed by NTT [21] are shown in Figure 3.53b. As in the structure depicted in Figure 3.53a, a P^+ polysilicon layer is used to provide contact to the base region. In (ii) a second polysilicon deposition and etching step fills the space under the overhanging portion (ii) with P^+ poly, the edge of which is oxidized in (iv). An undoped polysilicon layer is then deposited and etched (RIE), which fills in the corners of the spacer layer (iv). These poly "corners" are then oxidized which creates a base-emitter spacer width of about 0.35 μm. This results in an emitter opening width of less than 0.5 μm for a lithographic design rule of 1 μm. The emitter region is formed by arsenic diffusion from an N^+ polysilicon layer (v). N^+ poly is also used to contact the collector. This process technology has been used to fabricate very-high-speed digital integrated circuits. An example of the impressive results obtainable with this technology is given in [22]. Here, a 1/8 frequency divider, operating at an input frequency in excess of 9 GHz, and driving a 50 ohm load was built. This is the highest reported speed for a practical digital circuit for any device technology. This high speed results primarily from the combined high f_τ (17 GHz), low R_B (67 ohms), and low C_{BC} (16 fF) values for the transistor. Gate delays of 30 ps have been obtained in ring oscillator circuits using these transistors [23].

3.7.3 SICOS

Further reductions in extrinsic base resistance and extrinsic base-collector capacitance can be achieved with a structure in which the doped polysilicon layer directly contacts the active (intrinsic) base region. Such a structure, termed SICOS (SIdewall base COntact Structure), is illustrated in Figure 3.54. In this structure the intrinsic emitter and base regions, as well as the isolation regions between adjacent devices, are defined by a single lithographic step. This results in a structure with minimal extrinsic (parasitic) areas and, therefore, allows circuits with large packing density to be built. The fabrication process makes use of the preferential etching of doped polysilicon versus non-doped polysilicon to delineate the sidewall poly layer (Figure 3.54e). An additional feature of this structure is that the area of the epitaxial collector region ($Y_C \times Z_C$) is nearly equal to that of the emitter ($Y_E \times Z_E$). As a result,

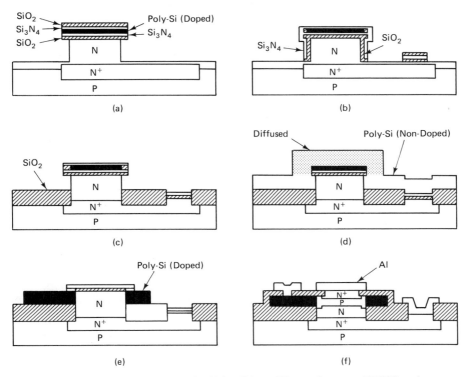

Figure 3.54 Fabrication steps for SIdewall base COntact Structure (SICOS) technology (after Nakamura, *et al.* [24], ©1982, IEEE).

the current gain of this device when operated in the reverse active (upward) mode, is much higher than in a conventional structure, making it suitable for Integrated Injection Logic (I^2L) circuits. I^2L gates have been built using this structure with measured switching speeds of nearly 1 ns/gate and power-delay products as low as 20 fJ/gate [24].

3.7.4 SICOSOI — The Future?

The collector-substrate capacitance (C_{CS}) may be reduced by imposing a layer of SiO_2 between the buried layer of the collector and the semiconductor substrate. The Silicon-On-Insulator (SOI) structure is formed either by recrystallization of a semiconductor film which is deposited on top of a thermally-grown SiO_2 layer, or by deep ion implantation of oxygen ions through the silicon epitaxial layer.

Figure 3.55 illustrates a proposed bipolar transistor structure which combines the sidewall contact/isolation features of the SICOS device with the substrate isolation feature of SOI. The resulting structure, which we term

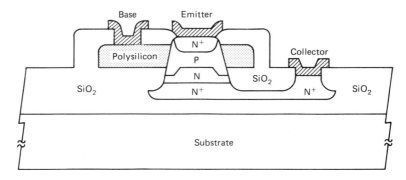

Figure 3.55 SICOSOI. Proposed transistor structure combining SICOS with Silicon-On-Insulator (SOI) isolation.

SICOSOI, results in a transistor which is completely surrounded by oxide, and should thereby exhibit the lowest capacitance per unit area of any bipolar device. Although this structure has not yet been built, "standard" bipolar devices have been built with SOI which exhibit I-V characteristics comparable to similar devices fabricated without SOI [25]. The combination of SICOS with SOI should be relatively straightforward.

REFERENCES

1. H. K. Gummel, *IEEE Trans. Electron Devices*, vol. ED-11, p. 455 (1964).

2. W. Shockley and W. T. Reed, *Phys. Rev.*, vol. 87, p. 835 (1952).

3. R. N. Hall, *Phys. Rev.*, vol. 87, p. 387 (1952).

4. J. J. Ebers and J. L. Moll, *Proc. IRE*, vol. 42, p. 1761 (1954).

5. J. L. Moll and I. M. Ross, *Proc. IEEE*, vol. 44, p. 72 (1956).

6. C. T. Kirk, *IRE Trans. Electron Devices*, vol. ED-9, p. 164 (1962).

7. E. O. Kane, *Phys. Rev.*, vol. 139, p. 79 (1963).

8. J. W. Slotboom and H. C. deGraaff, *Solid State Electronics*, vol. 19, p. 857 (1976).

9. A. H. Marshak, M. A. Shibib, J. G. Fossum and F. A. Lindholm, *IEEE Trans. Electron Devices*, vol. ED-28, p. 293 (1981).

10. H. C. deGraaff, J. W. Slotboom, and A. Schmitz, *Solid State Electronics*, vol. 20, p. 515 (1977).

11. J. M. Early, *Proc. IRE*, vol. 40, p. 1401 (1952).

12. J. R. Hauser, *IEEE Trans. Electron Devices*, vol. ED-11, p. 238 (1964).

13. A. van der Ziel and D. Agouridis, *Proc. IEEE*, vol. 54, p. 411 (1966).

14. J. W. Slotboom, *IEEE Trans. Electron Devices*, vol. ED-20, p. 669 (1973).

15. A. Yoshi, H. Kitazawa, M. Tomizawa, S. Horiguchi, and T. Sudo, *IEEE Trans. Electron Devices*, vol. ED-29, p. 184 (1982).

16. E. W. Greeneich, D. L. Tolliver, and A. J. Gonzales, *IEEE Trans. Electron Devices*, vol. ED-28, p. 1346 (1981).

17. R. W. Keyes, *Proc. IEEE*, vol. 63, p. 740 (1975).

18. A. C. M. Wang and S. Kakihana, *IEEE Trans. Electron Devices*, vol. ED-21, p. 667 (1974).

19. T. H. Ning, R. D. Isaac, P. M. Solomon, D. D. L. Tang, H. N. Yu, G. C. Feth, and S. K. Wiedman, *IEEE Trans. Electron Devices*, vol. ED-28, p. 1010 (1981).

20. D. D. Tang, P. M. Solomon, T. H. Ning, R. D. Isaac, and R. E. Burger, *IEEE J. Solid State Circuits*, vol. SC-17, p. 925 (1982).

21. T. Sakai, S. Konaka, Y. Kobayshi, M. Suzuki, and Y. Kawai, *Electron. Lett.*, vol. 19, p. 283 (1983).

22. M. Suzuki, K. Hagimoto, H. Ichino, and S. Konaka, *IEEE Electron Device Letters*, vol. EDL-6, p. 181 (1985).

23. S. Konaka, Y. Yamamoto, and T. Sakai, *Extended Abstracts of the 16th Conf. on Solid State Devices and Materials*, p. 209 (Kobe, Japan, 1984).

24. T. Nakamura, T. Miyazaki, S. Takahashi, T. Kure, T. Okabe, and M. Nagata, *IEEE J. Solid State Circuits*, vol. SC-17, p. 226 (1982).

25. E. W. Greeneich and R. H. Reuss, *IEEE Electron Device Letters*, vol. EDL-5, p. 91 (1984).

4

SMALL-GEOMETRY METAL-SEMICONDUCTOR DEVICES

By far, the majority of all semiconductor devices, even the MOSFETs discussed in Chapter 2, are interconnected in integrated circuits by metallic lines which produce metal-semiconductor contacts of one type or another. In fact, the earliest studies of semiconductors, carried out more than a century ago, were in connection with effects occurring at a metal-semiconductor interface. The application of such contacts in integrated circuits is widespread, varying from "ohmic contacts" to Schottky-diode logic arrays. These logic applications, particularly in gallium arsenide (GaAs) and related compounds, rely upon the fact that the devices themselves are very fast and can be made with very small dimensions, thus reducing the active device capacitance that must be switched. Of perhaps as much interest, however, is the fact that this metal-semiconductor contact has an active depletion region on the semi-conductor side of the contact; and that the width of this region is readily modulated by applied voltages to the contact. In recent years, the depletion-width modulation control of such Schottky barriers has found considerable application in field effect transistors.

The earliest ideas for control of charge, in a field effect transistor, related to the use of reverse biased p-n junctions to control the effective area of a conducting channel. These *junction* field effect transistors, or JFETs, are similar in nature to the MOSFET, but rely upon the capacitance of the reverse-biased gate junctions, rather than the capacitance of the MOS capacitor, to control the effective charge in the channel. In fact, these JFETs are channel area modulation devices rather than channel charge modulation devices. However, it rapidly became apparent that the depletion region under the metal-semiconductor Schottky barrier would serve as well as the p-n junction to modulate the conducting channel. For this reason, we shall treat JFETs and metal-Schottky gate FETs, or MESFETs, together as the theory is the same, only the fabrication technology and the built-in potentials differ between them.

We are already beginning to see integrated circuits based upon GaAs technology appear in the market place. Although these circuits are not at the level of integration found in the Si MOS field, they constitute modest LSI levels. Indeed, 32 bit microprocessors, based upon a variety of GaAs circuit and device families, are expected to appear in developmental form in 1988. What brings these devices into consideration for the ULSI topic area is the fact that the gate lengths found in these devices are already as small or smaller than those found in Si VLSI. GaAs devices began the integrated circuit approach with gate lengths at the 1.0 μm level and have been reduced below that. The relevant physics for submicron devices will appear at larger gate lengths in GaAs (by a factor of 5 or so) than for Si so that study of these devices allows us to estimate the important transport effects that will ultimately limit the downscaling of all ULSI devices.

4.1 JFETs AND MESFETs

A typical MESFET device is depicted in Figure 4.1. Here, the channel in which the current is carried lies between the gate depletion region and the semi-insulating substrate (or p-type substrate for the n-channel device shown). As in MOSFET devices, the MESFET can be either a depletion-mode or enhancement-mode device. In the depletion-mode device, the channel is normally open and allows the flow of current. The application of a negative

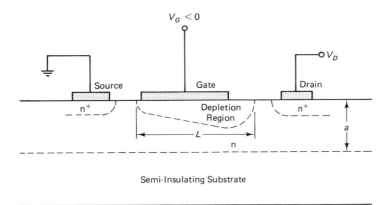

Figure 4.1 A typical MESFET in schematic view.

potential to the gate, which reverse biases this junction, widens the depletion region and closes down the channel, thus reducing the current. In the enhancement-mode device, the channel thickness is made very thin so that the built-in potential of the junction is sufficiently large to cause the depletion region to punch through to the substrate and "pinch off" the channel. In this latter case, a positive gate potential which forward biases the junction will open the channel and allow current to pass.

The MESFET, and its cousin the JFET, are primarily used in GaAs logic and microwave devices at the present time, although Si active devices can also be made with this technology. These devices are not favored in Si circuitry due to the low value of forward bias that can be applied to the enhancement mode devices (less than the built-in potential) if large gate currents are to be avoided. On the other hand, the lack of a viable oxide technology in GaAs has forced designers to turn to this type of device structure. Whatever the reason, GaAs MESFET technology is the preferred choice for microwave integrated circuits and is finding growing usage in very high speed logic circuitry. Indeed, the transistors with the smallest written gate length, < 20 nm, are GaAs MESFET devices.

In this chapter, we want to review the theory of the junction FET, its applications to logic circuitry, and the state of the art of this technology. We shall also look at the relatively new pseudo-MOS devices, in which a GaAlAs layer is used to provide an inversion type device called the selectively-doped heterojunction transistor (also called the two-dimensional electron gas FET, the high-electron mobility FET, or the modulation-doped FET).

4.2 THE GRADUAL CHANNEL APPROXIMATION

In the device depicted in Figure 4.1, a junction has been generated. The case shown here is for a Schottky barrier junction, but the approach and effects are the same for a p-n junction. The charge control aspects of the device are characterized by the width of the depletion region under this junction. When the depletion region punches through to the substrate, the channel will be cut-off. There are two characteristic voltages for such a device. The first of these is the *pinch-off* voltage, which is the necessary voltage applied to the gate electrode to cause the depletion region to just reach the substrate and pinch off the channel. The second characteristic voltage is the *saturation* voltage which is the voltage at which the current through the channel saturates. In this latter case, the saturation voltage is the drain voltage required to saturate the drain current. As in MOSFETs, this voltage will also cause the depletion region to reach through to the substrate, but current flow is not stopped due to the injection of charge into the depletion region. In JFETs and MESFETs, however, the pinch-off voltage and the saturation voltage are not equal to each other, as we shall see below.

In treating the description of the transistor, we must actually solve Poisson's equation. In previous chapters, we used the gradual channel approximation, which separates the longitudinal and transverse portions of this equation. Thus, we assume that the variation of potential along the channel can be separated from that normal to the channel and a quasi-one-dimensional treatment used. While this is not exceedingly accurate, it is adequate to study the physics of the device operation. All relevant physics can be incorporated in such a model to a degree necessary to understand the device performance.

As in the MOSFET, the actual bias across the gate junction is a function of position in the channel, due to the drain-source potential. In the simplest case, the voltage in the channel is given by

$$V_c(x) = V_D x / L_g \qquad (4.1)$$

where V_D is the drain potential and L_g is the gate length. Since this potential appears on the channel side of the junction, the actual bias across the gate junction is just

$$V_a(x) = V_G - \phi_m - V_c(x) \qquad (4.2)$$

where ϕ_m is the built-in potential of the junction. In the case of the Schottky barrier, ϕ_m is the Schottky barrier height, which typically is 0.8–0.9 V for Al on GaAs. (Here, ϕ_m differs from the true metal-semiconductor barrier by the displacement of the Fermi level from the conduction band edge in n-type material. For most cases of interest, this displacement is very small, but for completeness, the ϕ_m here is $\phi_B - (E_c - E_F)/q$, where E_c is the conduction band edge. The number usually quoted for real devices is the quantity ϕ_m. If the gate junction is a p-n junction, then ϕ_m is the built-in potential of the junction, and is given by

$$q\phi_{m,j} = E_G + kT \ln(N_A N_D / N_C N_V) \qquad (4.3)$$

where N_A and N_D are the doping on the p-side and n-side of the junction, respectively, E_G is the energy gap, and N_C and N_V are the effective densities-of-states for the conduction and valence bands, respectively. The junction-gate is most effective when the gate side of the p-n junction is very heavily doped with respect to the channel side.

4.2.1 The Simple Theory

We will begin with the classical treatment, in which high electric field effects in the channel are ignored, and it is assumed that the mobility in the channel is constant over the entire length of the device. Then, the width of the depletion region of the gate junction is just

$$w(x) = (2\varepsilon_S V_a / q N_D)^{1/2} \qquad (4.4)$$

for an n-channel device, which is the case we will treat here. N_D is then the doping on the channel side of the junction, which is the actual doping of the active layer of the device. The active layer itself is usually obtained either by implanting into the semi-insulating substrate (or p-type substrate) or by growing a thin, doped epitaxial layer on top of the substrate. As the drain voltage V_D is increased, the reverse bias across the junction is increased, and the width of the depletion region also increases. At some critical value of V_D, the depletion region just touches the semi-insulating substrate at the drain end of the channel. While the junction width is increasing, the cross-sectional area of the active channel is decreasing and hence the channel resistance is increasing. When the depletion region punches through to the substrate, this area is reduced to zero, and the resistance is very large. The channel current, which has been increasing with the voltage V_D, saturates. The current does not go to zero, since if it did, the voltage drop at the channel would not be present and the channel would once again open for current flow. Thus some stable point for which the channel is almost, but not quite, pinched off must be reached; the current flows through the portion of the channel that is open and is then *injected* into the gate-drain depletion region at the saturation point. The total device resistance is very high, and the current is nearly saturated and does not increase with further increases in V_D. By varying the gate voltage, the saturation voltage, and hence the saturation current, can be readily varied.

One can determine an expression which relates the drain current I_D to the drain voltage V_D and the controlling gate voltage V_G (both are referenced to the source end of the channel). When the voltage applied to the gate is sufficiently large, a pinch-off is achieved with $V_D = 0$. In this case $w = a$, the active channel thickness (the thickness of the epitaxial or implanted layer). Thus, we have

$$V_a = qN_D a^2/2\varepsilon_S = \phi_m - V_{G,p} \tag{4.5}$$

We define this value of gate voltage ($V_{G,p}$) as the *pinch-off voltage*

$$V_p = \phi_m - qN_D a^2/2\varepsilon_S \tag{4.6}$$

If a drain voltage is applied, the channel is reverse biased with respect to the gate ($V_G < 0$), so that channel pinch-off occurs earlier and at the drain end of the channel first. The value of drain voltage for which this occurs is just

$$V_{Dsat} = V_G - \phi_m + qN_D a^2/2\varepsilon_S = V_G - V_p \tag{4.7}$$

which is a positive quantity if the device is a normally-on (depletion mode) device, but can be a negative quantity in an enhancement-mode device.

Consider an increment of resistance dR along the channel in the x-direction. This increment of resistance at point x contributes a voltage drop of

$$dV = I_D \, dR \tag{4.8}$$

since we recall that the actual current in this model is constant all along the channel. The resistance itself is just

$$dR = (\rho/A)\,dx = dx/[\sigma Z(a - w)] \tag{4.9}$$

so that

$$[a - w(x)]\,dV = I_D\,dx/\sigma Z \tag{4.10}$$

where Z is the lateral extent of the gate, or the gate width as it is normally called. In the constant mobility case, σ is constant along the channel, and we can now integrate (4.10) from the source to the drain sides of the gate. This gives

$$(I_D L_g/\sigma Z) = a\int_{V_S}^{V_D}\left\{1 - [(2\varepsilon_S/qN_D a^2)(V - V_G + \phi_m)]^{1/2}\right\}dV \tag{4.11}$$

where we have used (4.4) for the width of the depletion region. Carrying out this integration we have

$$I_D = G_o\Big\{V_D - V_S - (2/3)(2\varepsilon_S/qN_D a^2)^{1/2}\big[(V_D - V_G')^{3/2}$$

$$- (V_S - V_G')^{3/2}\big]\Big\} \tag{4.12}$$

where $V_G' = V_G - \phi_m$ and $G_o = \sigma Z a/L_g = N_d e\mu Z a/L_g$. We must be concerned with the potential drop across the parasitic source resistance. In actual fact, we write $V_S = V_{S0} + V_S'$, where V_S' is this latter potential drop. In general, $V_S' \ll V_G'$, since it arises primarily from the parasitic source resistance. Therefore, we will ignore it in the square-bracketed term. In addition, we reference all other voltages to the source (e.g., $V_{DS} = V_D - V_{S0}$), and set $V_S' = R_S I_D$ in the linear term. This then gives us

$$I_D = G_o'\Big\{V_{DS} - (2/3)(2\varepsilon_S/qN_D a^2)^{1/2}\big[(V_{DS} - V_{GS}')^{3/2} - (-V_{GS}')^{3/2}\big]\Big\} \tag{4.13}$$

where

$$G_o' = G_o/(1 + G_o R_S) \tag{4.14}$$

In the linear region, where $V_{DS} \ll -V_{GS}'$, $(V_{DS} \ll V_p)$ we can expand the first term in the square brackets and gain the simple form

$$I_D \simeq G_o'V_{DS}\big[1 - (2\varepsilon_S/qN_D a^2)^{1/2}(-V_{GS}')^{1/2}\big] \tag{4.15}$$

In this regime, the device acts simply as a resistance modulation device with a linear response to applied gate voltages.

At large drain biases, the current reaches a maximum and saturates. Using (4.7) for the saturation voltage gives

$$I_{D\,\text{sat}} = G_o'\Big\{(qN_D a^2/6\varepsilon_S) + V_{GS}'\big[1 - (2/3)(-2\varepsilon_S V_{GS}'/qN_D a^2)^{1/2}\big]\Big\} \tag{4.16}$$

Most MESFET devices are fabricated with $-V_p = 2\text{--}3$ V, so that logic devices will swing over both the linear and saturation regions. As with many logic implementations, however, the drive current needed to charge the load capacitances is determined primarily from the saturation values of the current, so that (4.16) is probably the form that is of most interest in device circuits.

4.2.2 High Electric Field Considerations

Although we inherently included the presence of the source parasitic resistance in the intrinsic treatment of the previous section, we did not take account of the fact that the velocity-electric field characteristic shows the presence of saturation. In GaAs devices, we expect that the presence of negative differential conductivity should affect the performance due to the strongly nonlinear shape of the velocity-field characteristic. In fact, this does not occur to the extent expected, because of the strong interactions between the intrinsic (active) region and the external circuits which serve to mask any internal variations of the local conductivity [1]. What does occur is a strong, but simple, saturation of the velocity that is reflected in the characteristic drain current versus drain potential curves of the device. The fact that the negative resistance regions are not seen is tied to the perception that these regions are not stable. Rather, the redistribution of potential and charge that normally occurs will shield the device from any static occurrences of negative conductivity. This is probably no more than the application of Shockley's positive conductance theorem to the case of a three terminal device [2].

In the present section, we want now to treat the actual device performance in the presence of the nonlinear velocity-field characteristic. To do this, we divide the channel into sections, each of which utilizes a piece-wise linear portion of the velocity-field curve. We will treat a more correct and general form later, but this regional approximation allows us to concentrate on the physical properties that really govern the operation of the device. In the first region, illustrated in Figure 4.2, we assume that the field is below that necessary to achieve velocity saturation, and that the mobility is constant. In this region, we can solve for the channel current in terms of the source potential and the boundary potential at the end of this region, using the normal theory discussed in the previous section. In the second region, the velocity is assumed to be saturated at its effective saturation value, but that the channel itself is not pinched off. In this region, the current itself is saturated, but the charge density can deviate from its equilibrium value. Finally, the third region corresponds to the pinched-off channel just as in the previous section. We will not deal explicitly with this latter region, but remark that the current in this region is set by the necessity of current continuity with regard to the level of current injected from region two. In dealing with the first two regions, we will follow closely the approach of Pucel et al. [3], although we will deal with a one-sided device as in Figure 4.1.

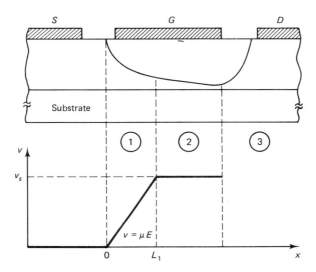

Figure 4.2 Various operating regions in the velocity saturated MESFET.

In the piece-wise linear model, we must divide the active channel into two primary regions. In the first of these, we assume that $0 < x < L_1$, where L_1 is the boundary between the ohmic and velocity-saturated regions. Here, we note that typical values of the low-field mobility and effective saturation velocity in GaAs are 4×10^3 cm^2/V-s and 1.4×10^7 cm/s, respectively. These lead to a critical field of 3.5×10^3 V/cm for the onset of saturation. These values are typical of material used in devices with gate lengths of 1 μm or less, in which fairly high doping levels are used. In the region $L_1 < x < L_g$, we assume that the device is characterized by the saturated velocity. For this approach to be valid, the device must not have reached pinch-off at the drain end, or else must have the active length L_g adjusted for this effect.

As previously done, we take the source end of the channel as the reference point for all of the potentials in this discussion. Rather than the drain potential, however, we now just integrate (4.11) to L_1 and V_1, the potential corresponding to E_s (the critical field for saturation) and L_1. Thus, (4.13) becomes

$$I_D = G_o'' W f_1(p, s) \tag{4.17}$$

where

$$G_o'' = \sigma Z a / L_1 (1 + \sigma Z a R_S / L_1) \tag{4.18}$$

replaces G_o' and

$$f_1(p, s) = p^2 - s^2 - (2/3)(p^3 - s^3) \tag{4.19}$$

In (4.16–4.18), we have introduced the reduced quantities

$$W = N_D q a^2 / 2\varepsilon_S \tag{4.20}$$

$$p^2 = (-V_{GS} + \phi_m + V_1)/W \tag{4.21}$$

and

$$s^2 = (-V_{GS} + \phi_m)/W \tag{4.22}$$

The actual value of L_1 is determined by matching a boundary condition on the potential at the interface between regions 1 and 2.

In region two, the carriers are assumed to travel at their saturated velocity, given by

$$v_s = \mu E_s \tag{4.23}$$

Thus, in this region, the current is completely determined by the degree to which the channel is open, and

$$I_D = \sigma Z a E_s (1 - p) = I_{DSS}(1 - p) \tag{4.24}$$

where we have introduced the open-channel current I_{DSS}. This latter quantity is the maximum possible drain current that can exist, and occurs when there is no depletion region under the gate. Contrary to the normally used form, which occurs when $V_G = 0$, this quantity is essentially unmeasurable (the required flat-band condition is essentially unobtainable) and is only relatable to device parameters once the doping density and built-in potential are known. Here, it is a natural normalizing constant, as can be seen from this equation.

We can now determine the parameter L_1 from equations (4.17) and (4.24) by equating the current as determined from these two different regions. This gives

$$L_1 = L_g[f_1(s, p)/K(1 - p)] \tag{4.25}$$

where

$$K = E_s L_g / W \tag{4.26}$$

is a dimensionless parameter which Pucel et al. [3] have termed the saturation index. In most applications, K relates the saturation voltage to the pinch-off voltage in the absence of a built-in potential. This number is typically of the order of 0.1 or less, since W can be a few volts and $E_s L_g = 0.35$ V for a 1 μm gate and the above value of E_s. We can see from this that $E_s L_g$ is the voltage drop along the channel that would exist if there were no space charge build-up in the channel and the longitudinal field were uniform and equal to E_s. The size of K in comparison with the drain potential (normalized to W) expresses in a quantitative manner the importance of velocity saturation in the channel. The smaller that K becomes, the more important the role of velocity saturation becomes in the operation of the particular device.

Once we have determined the reduced potentials p and s, the length of the unsaturated velocity region 1 is known. It still remains for us to calculate the potential distribution to the drain end of the channel, region 2, and possibly region 3. Here, we will only deal with the case of region 2, assuming that we only take those values of drain potential up to the point where pinch-off occurs at the drain end of the channel. From (4.24), it is apparent that the current flowing to the drain is independent of the actual drain potential. However, as the potential in the channel increases toward the drain, we expect that the channel is closed down due to the depletion width widening. In order to counteract this, it is imperative that current begin to be carried by diffusion as well as drift and that the density in the channel increase so that the net channel current remains constant. By using (4.24) along the channel, we find that at any point $L_1 < x < L_g$, where the reduced potential is given by $w(x)$, the local carrier density is related to the background doping by evaluating the current at L_1 and recognizing that the velocity is constant. This gives

$$n(x)[1 - w(x)] = N_D(1 - p) \qquad (4.27)$$

In (4.27), the reduced potential that is introduced may be defined as

$$w(x) = [-V_{GS} + \phi_m + V(x)]/W \qquad (4.28)$$

What (4.27) tells us is that as pinch-off is approached, there is a tremendous build-up of charge in the very narrow channel. This charge actually prevents the total closing of the channel, although our present approach, which is not self-consistent and quantization effects are not considered, to the depletion layer does not allow us to calculate the residual channel opening. To actually calculate self-consistently the quantization effects requires an approach similar to that of the MOSFET inversion layer, where the actual channel thickness normal to the oxide interface is determined by a self-consistent calculation involving the wave-functions (and wavelength) of the electrons. The properties of the quantized electrons are then more quasi-two-dimensional. This characteristic has been observed at low temperatures [4]. However, this is beyond our present treatment and will not be pursued further here. We do note though that the level of charge build-up near the pinch-off point will be reduced due to the existence of diffusion contributions to the current. Such charge build-ups are found though in fully two-dimensional numerical solutions to Poisson's equation for MESFETs. In Figure 4.3, we show such density profiles calculated by such a numerical simulation, and it can be seen that the density increase near the pinch-off point is not dramatic because of the logarithmic scale. Such build-up does not occur in the usual gradual-channel approximation, but is a direct consequence of the presence of velocity saturation in the channel.

Because the channel width and the carrier concentration track together for (4.24) to remain valid, the details of the charge along the channel are

Source   Gate   Drain

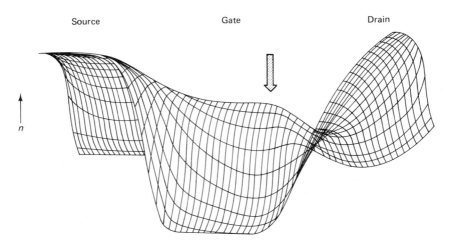

Figure 4.3 Charge density profile in a MESFET. The slight peak near the pinch-off point (arrow) is attributed to velocity saturation.

actually unimportant in ascertaining the potential in region 2. Thus, for this purpose, we can use the results introduced by Pucel *et al.* [3], and the source-drain potential drop is given by

$$V_{DS} = W\left[p^2 - s^2 + (2ak/\pi L_g)\sinh(\pi L_2/2a) \right] \qquad (4.29)$$

where $L_2 = L_g - L_1$, and L_g is adjusted for shortening due to the onset of region 3. Equation (4.29), in conjunction with (4.25), forms a pair of equations which allow us to solve for the current I_D after eliminating the parameter L_1. In practice, the currents are usually assumed and the resulting potential drops are calculated. In Figure 4.4, the values of L_1 are shown for a variety of gate and drain potentials for a 1.0 and a 0.5 μm gate length device. For these calculations, it was assumed that $L_g/a = 7$ for the 1.0 μm device and $L_g/a = 3.5$ for the 0.5 μm device.

We now turn to an alternative approach to including both velocity saturation and channel pinch-off in considering the saturation of the drain current has been put forward by Lehovec and Zuleeg [5]. In principle, this approach is much more accurate, in that the details of the velocity-field characteristic are incorporated and there is no artificial linearization and regional discretization of the device. Here, we assume that the velocity varies as

$$v = \mu E/(1 + \mu E/v_s) \qquad (4.30)$$

This is then used in the gradual channel approximation of above, and the drain current is found to be

$$I_d = I_p\left[3(u^2 - s^2) - 2(u^3 - s^3)\right]/\left[1 + z(u^2 - s^2)\right] \qquad (4.31)$$

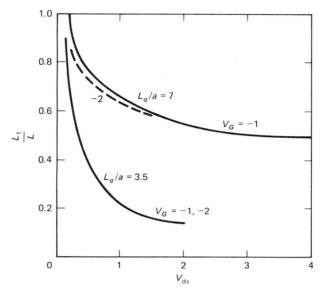

Figure 4.4   The saturation distance L_1 for two different short-channel MESFETs. The curve for $L_g/a = 7$ is for a 1.0 μm gate length device, while that for $L_g/a = 3.5$ is for a 0.5 μm gate length device.

where

$$u^2 = (V_{DS} - V'_{GS})/V_p \tag{4.32}$$

$$z = \mu V_p/Lv_s, \quad s^2 = V_{GS}/V_p \tag{4.33}$$

and

$$I_p = V_p G'_o/3 \tag{4.34}$$

The function I_d has a maximum for $u = u_m$, and this is given by the solutions of the equation

$$u_m^3 - 3u_m(s^2 - 1/z) + 2s^3 - 3/z = 0 \tag{4.35}$$

This determines the value at which the drain current reaches saturation, and this saturation may be due to velocity saturation or it may be due to channel pinch-off. The results of the model are comparable to that presented earlier, but this latter result does not provide as much insight into the operation of the device itself. In particular, it does not at present lead us to the conclusion that a large, non-equilibrium density must exist in the velocity saturated region of the device in order to maintain current continuity. There is one important consequence of (4.35), however. If the value of s^3, from (4.35), is inserted into the equation for I_d, we discover that

$$I_d = I_o(1 - u_m) \tag{4.36}$$

where $I_o = 3I_p/z$ is a function of the saturation velocity v_s, and not of the mobility of the material. Regardless of the actual mechanism for which current saturation is achieved, the drain current saturation value reflects an apparent velocity saturation in its dependence upon the gate voltage. In fact, plotting the drain current as a function of the square root of gate voltage, i.e., plotting the drain current as a function of u_m, gives a relatively straight line from which the *effective* saturation velocity within the device can be determined. The form of (4.36) brings us back to the form obtained in the regional approximation and draws us once again to the conclusion that non-equilibrium charge must exist in the saturated, or pinched-off, portion of the device.

4.2.3 Transconductance

Whether we are interested in logic applications or microwave applications, the major part of the gain mechanism is embodied in the active channel transconductance g_m. The output, or drain, conductance r_d^{-1} is also important for microwave applications, but is less so for logic applications. In this section we want to focus on the former, as the drain conductance is generally small for properly designed devices. The transconductance is evaluated by a perturbative procedure in which small changes in the channel current, due to small changes in the gate potential with the drain potential held constant, are evaluated. Thus, we may define the transconductance by

$$g_m = (\partial I_D/\partial V_G)_{\delta V_D = 0} = (\sigma a E_s Z/2sW)\, dp/ds \qquad (4.37)$$

The gate potential is characterized here by the reduced potential s. It causes not only a direct change in I_D, but also causes a change in L_1, which in turn causes an additional change in I_D. We can evaluate these individual effects by first differentiating (4.27) and (4.29), using the relationship on L_2, and then solving for dp/ds. This yields

$$g_m = (I_{DSS}/W)f_g(p, s) \qquad (4.38)$$

where

$$f_g(p, s) = \frac{(1 - s)\cosh(\pi L_2/2a) - (1 - p)}{\left[2p(1 - p) + k(L_1/L_g)\right]\cosh(\pi L_2/2a) - 2p(1 - p)} \qquad (4.39)$$

In Figure 4.5, we plot a general curve for g_m as a function of the gate length for a device with a pinch-off voltage $V_p = 2$ V. In this case, the transconductance is evaluated for the applied DC gate voltage set equal to zero, and the device parameters are such that the current at this bias is 0.8 A/mm. (The width normalization is usually used, i.e., the current is normalized to a fictitious device whose gate width is 1 mm. While 1 mm is quite large when we talk about submicron devices, it is the common width for GaAs circuits, as it arises from the microwave power usage of these devices.)

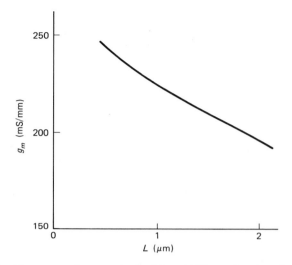

Figure 4.5 The transconductance obtained from (4.31) as a function of gate length for a device with $V_p = -2$ V.

4.3 LOGIC CIRCUITRY

The largest amount of development work in GaAs integrated circuits has been directed toward depletion mode devices, primarily because of the limitations imposed by the small voltage swings in enhancement mode devices. Consequently, the normal circuits that are common for MOSFET devices (in silicon) are inappropriate to the GaAs devices. Consider for example the direct-coupled inverter circuit in Figure 4.6. Generally, transistor T_1 plays the role of the pull-down device and is an enhancement mode device. Positive voltages applied to the gate will turn the device "on" and lower the output voltage. The active load is commonly a depletion device in Si circuits, or a saturated resistor (gateless transistor) in GaAs circuits, or simply a high resistance region delineated in the material itself. On the other hand, if we are constrained to use depletion mode devices for the pull-down device, we are required to

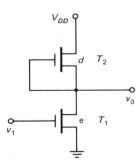

Figure 4.6 Direct-coupled FET logic (DCFL).

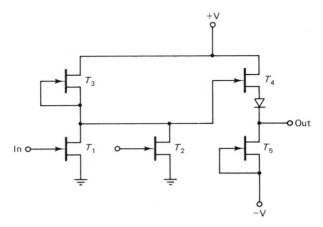

Figure 4.7 Buffered FET logic (BFL).

introduce another bias source to hold the gate sufficiently negative in the absence of an input logic signal. While direct-coupled FET logic (DCFL) has been utilized, it is not the primary logic circuit for GaAs circuits. However, it does illustrate the general problem of requiring multiple power supplies in this technology.

The use of all depletion-mode transistors in the logic circuitry has led GaAs designers to develop different implementations of the logic. In particular, the two most used circuits are buffered FET logic (BFL) and Schottky-diode FET logic (SDFL). These two circuits are shown in Figures 4.7 and 4.8, respectively. In the BFL circuit, the three transistors T_1, T_2, and T_3 form a normal two-input inverter that performs the NOR function. This inverter then

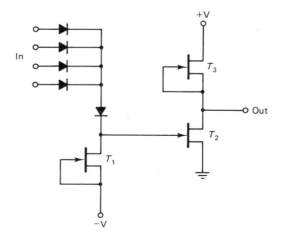

Figure 4.8 Schottky-diode FET logic (SDFL).

drives a buffering network that provides the drive current for the fan-out circuit as well as shifting the voltage level to that desired for subsequent logic circuits. The Schottky diodes provide a constant level of voltage offset. We can still see the requirement for two power supplies.

In the SDFL circuit, most logic functions are performed by the Schottky diode circuits. The diodes themselves are very small switching diodes. The FETs can then be low power versions of high-performance depletion-mode MESFETs which are used for logic inversion and gain functions. The pull-down transistor T_1 provides the current drive for the gate of T_2, which is the actual inverter transistor. Transistor T_3 is then the active load. Again, we have two power supplies which provide for compatible input and output logic levels within the circuit itself. The logic function is carried out by the single transistor T_1 and the very small switching diodes. These diodes also provide some or all of the level shifting required between gate and drain in the depletion-mode logic. In addition to the savings in area because of the small size of these diodes (compared to the FET in BFL), additional area can be saved by the SDFL circuit because the diodes are only two-terminal devices, so that there are fewer wire crossings within the circuit cell. Since most of the power dissipation in these circuits lies in the FETs, the current-voltage curves of these devices are crucial to the overall performance.

4.4 SCALING THE MESFET

In this section, we want to begin discussing the manner in which the individual devices are scaled to smaller sizes in order to incorporate increased packing density. Although the scaling theory has been widely used in the past as a guide to MOSFET miniaturization, it has not been widely applied to the metal-semiconductor devices. In achieving the desired scaling, we are governed by the desire to generalize any scaling theory and to identify the design criteria that are crucial in maintaining the shape of the electric field and potential distributions constant while still allowing the local fields to increase if desired. Here, we will scale the physical dimensions and the potentials by different factors. This yields a considerably increased flexibility while still maintaining adequate control of the various two-dimensional effects.

We note in passing at this point that MESFETs (and JFETs) do not suffer from most of the small device effects inherent in MOSFETs. There are multiple reasons for this. First, the gate metallization usually extends well beyond the source and drain regions (in the width direction), so that there is very little narrow-gate effect in the device. Secondly, pinch-off is readily seen to already be a reaction of the interaction between the drain and gate depletion regions, so that this process is already built into the model, and we are not required to incorporate corrections due to short-channel effects. There are some effects, such as non-saturation of the output characteristics, which we will treat below. However, these devices tend to be much more amenable to scaling in the sub-micron region than their insulated-gate counterparts. It is perhaps for this reason that GaAs circuits, based upon these devices, could begin with effective gate lengths at 1.0 μm and below, while the Si MOSFET circuits are only now reaching, and passing, this frontier.

For any particular device geometry, the field configuration in the channel arises from a local solution to Poisson's equation

$$\nabla^2 V = -q(p - n + N_D - N_A)/\varepsilon_S \qquad (4.40)$$

and the current continuity equation

$$\nabla \cdot J = -\partial\rho/\partial t \qquad (4.41)$$

Our prime concern is with (4.40), since it is this equation which will actually set the conditions for the scaling of the potential and the shape of the electric field. We consider the variable transformation [6]:

$$V' = V/K \qquad (4.42a)$$

$$(x', y', z') = (x, y, z)/\lambda \qquad (4.42b)$$

and finally the last term

$$(n', p', N_D', N_A') = (n, p, N_D, N_A)\lambda^2/K \qquad (4.42c)$$

The set of equations (4.42) assure that Poisson's equation remains unchanged by the scaling, which infers that the shape of the potential solutions to this equation retain their pre-scaled form, if the boundary conditions are also scaled.

The earlier forms of constant field scaling assumed that $\lambda = K$, although several other forms have appeared in the literature (see the discussion in Chapter 2), including constant-voltage scaling and quasi-constant-voltage scaling (not quite constant field or constant voltage). In Table 4.1, we list the scaling factors associated with the more important physical quantities.

One approach is to assume that the depletion layer thickness is scaled down linearly with all other dimensions, although this is not required with the above approach, since the Debye length $(\varepsilon_S kT/q^2 N_D)^{1/2}$ scales as $K^{1/2}/\lambda$.

TABLE 4.1 Scaling Factors in MESFETs

Parameter	Scaling Factor
Linear Dimensions	$1/\lambda$
Voltages	$1/K$
Carrier Density	λ^2/K
Electric Field	λ/K
Depletion Depth	$1/\lambda$
Current	λ/K^2
Current (with v_s)	λ/K
Power	λ/K^3 or λ/K^2

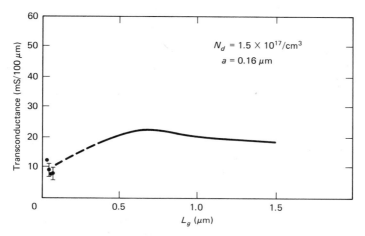

Figure 4.9 Variation of the transconductance in a very short channel MESFET with gate length for a constant epitaxial layer thickness and a constant doping in the layer. The data points at ultra-short gate lengths are for experimental MESFETs fabricated with e-beam lithography in the authors' laboratory.

Only for constant voltage scaling ($K = 1$) is the depletion region actually scaled linearly with the other dimensions. This freedom of choice of active layer thickness independent of the actual lateral dimensions of the device gives extra control in the device design process. The actual scaling rules imposed by the design constraints will dictate the relationship to be imposed between λ and K. Failure to scale the depletion layer, and the epitaxial layer, thickness with the gate length will result in actual degradation of the performance. In Figure 4.9, we show the trends of the transconductance in very small MESFETs, in which the epitaxial layer thickness is maintained at 160 nm and the doping at $1.5 \times 10^{17}\,\text{cm}^{-3}$, which are values typically used for 0.5–1.0 μm gate length devices. The solid curve is a full two-dimensional simulation including transient overshoot effects. It may be seen from this figure, that such effects are not evident for gate lengths as short as 40 nm, and that the scaling rules must be followed if device improvements are to be obtained by reducing the gate length of the individual devices. Also shown are some data on a higher doped, and thinner, epitaxial layer, which is required by the scaling rules, used to fabricate short-channel devices. The rise in g_m as L_g is reduced in the region $L_g > 0.75\ \mu$m is the effect shown in Fig. 4.5. The drop at shorter L_g is due to $L_g < a$, and the failure of the "parallel plate" approach to modeling.

4.4.1 Short-Channel Effects

In the above equations for the drain current in the saturation region, one is led to believe that the current is actually constant with further increases in the drain-source potential. However, this generally does not occur, and further slight increases in current will follow with increases in the drain potential. In general, the slight potential barrier between the active channel and the semi-insulating substrate serves as a relatively effective channel stop. In addition, there is usually a slightly lower mobility, due either to interface traps or to additional scattering centers, at the interface. With these conditions, the channel is usually well constrained, and the device shows a high output resistance in saturation. Still, there are substrate currents that arise in the device and this leads to non-saturation of the output current.

The exact cause of the substrate currents is not yet well pinned down. There is usually a trapped high-electric field domain at the interface, near the drain end of the gate metallization. This domain pushes some carriers into the substrate so that there is a channel spreading into the substrate region. There may well also be a contribution from weak ionization processes in the high fields of the domains. The widening of the channel, and the additional carriers if ionization is present, directly affect the pinch-off condition. The non-saturation is worse in power FETs and is expected to become a factor in sub-micron dimensioned devices as well.

It has been conjectured that velocity overshoot, or as it is often termed "ballistic transport," will occur for gate lengths below 0.25–0.5 μm (the onset length depends upon the source of the claim). From the data shown previously in Figure 4.9, we may see that there is little evidence of this effect at room temperature for devices as short as 50 nm gate length, although there may be an onset of the effect in devices shorter than this. This is not unreasonable, in that the mean-free path for optical phonon scattering is only 40–60 nm at the high fields found in the channel of the MESFET. Moreover, regions where the velocity is higher than average will also show carrier densities lower than average in order to satisfy Kirchoff's current law. The spatially inhomogeneous field in the channel will also mask the presence of overshoot if it were to occur in longer gate length devices. Thus, we really do not expect to see such effects until the entire high-field region is contained in a distance less than the mean-free path mentioned above. This is in keeping with the results of Figure 4.9.

4.4.2 Device-Device Interactions

Gallium arsenide integrated circuits are particularly susceptible to a process known as back-gating, or side-gating. This process is believed to be due to the generation of leakage currents in the semi-insulating substrate, which in turn affect the substrate potential seen by any particular device. The effects are observed regardless of whether the active devices are fabricated by implantation into the substrate or by mesa isolation of an epitaxial layer. The general observation is that a positively biased contact in the vicinity of the active device will tend to open the channel more than expected from the gate and drain potentials. Conversely, a negatively biased contact in the vicinity of the device will serve to cut down the channel opening, thus tending to turn the device off. In either case, the presence of these side-gating effects can work to upset the operation of the particular gate. Clearly, the effect will be most pronounced when the potential difference between the side-gate contact and the source of the active gate is largest. The side-contact can actually be the drain of another transistor. In particular, in the SDFL circuit of Figure 4.8, there are several ohmic contacts to the substrate that can side-gate the inverter transistor T_2. These are the ohmic contacts of the level-shifting diodes and the source and drain contacts of the pull-down transistor T_1 [7]. Since the source of the latter device is at a bias potential, it will provide a constant level of interaction, independent of logic state, and is not particularly of concern. Since T_1 is a current source, the drain will not be particularly effective as it will also provide a constant effect.

On the other hand, the source of the pull-up or active-load transistor T_3 can take values anywhere between ground and $+V$. The load current can be reduced by any ohmic contact within the circuit. One may safely assume that the dominant contact will be the grounded source of transistor T_2 because of the natural proximity of these devices. If these contacts are only 10 μm apart, backgating effects can be expected to affect the output characteristics of T_3 when the source potential is anywhere above about 2 V [7]. Any output source follower, such as in the BFL circuit, will have similar effects. Finally, side gating will also lower the "on" forward conductance of the level shifting and logic diodes in the SDFL circuit by reduction of the effective channel (negative backgate potential).

Fortunately, careful layout of the integrated circuits can minimize the effects of side-gating. Moreover, because there is a threshold voltage for the effect in the range 2–5 V, we can expect that the effects *may* be reduced in small-geometry devices, where lower values of the bias potentials will be used. On the other hand, the inter-device dimensions are also reduced in the small-geometry circuits, so that the effect may not be reduced at all. There is some feeling that the physical source of side-gating is space-charge injection and trap filling of the deep levels in the semi-insulating substrate, and that this effect is characterized by a critical *electric field*, rather than a voltage threshold. If this turns out to be the case, then reduced geometries will not be a solution, and one must turn to clever circuit layouts, and perhaps trenches, as is done for Si CMOS. At this time, we feel that side-gating is perhaps only the first manifestation of a process that could become as critical as latch-up in CMOS.

4.5 THE HIGH ELECTRON MOBILITY TRANSISTOR

The approach to GaAs field effect transistors changed in 1978, when Dingle *et al.* [8] demonstrated that very high mobilities could be obtained in modulation-doped structures grown by molecular beam epitaxy. Synthetic semiconductor superlattices are of both fundamental and technological interest. However, most early work focused upon multilayer heterojunctions. In a GaAlAs/GaAs heterojunction, the GaAlAs has a considerably larger band-gap than the GaAs. As a consequence, dopant atoms placed in the former material will become ionized with the free electrons falling into the narrower band-gap material. As a result, the electrons are spatially separated from the compensating ionized impurities, so that there is a drop in the strength of the Coulombic scattering of the carriers. Resultant Hall mobilities are thus larger than either bulk mobilities or those of uniformly doped heterojunctions. Indeed, mobilities of more than 10^6 cm^2/V have been obtained in GaAs "inversion" layers at 4.2°K and almost 10^4 cm^2/V at room temperature.

The higher mobility achievable in the modulation doped structures was immediately recognized as being beneficial for transistors, whether these were to be used for logic or for high-frequency applications. However, it remained for the Japanese and the French to first demonstrate actual FETs incorporating the modulation doping approach. Since this time, room-temperature logic devices, with single gate delays of 12.2 psec [9], have been produced from this technology and VLSI/ULSI integrations of these so-called selectively doped heterojunction transistor (SDHT) devices are in progress.

4.5.1 Modulation Doping

When modulation doping is utilized to provide the carriers for the active FET channel, these carriers accumulate at the GaAs/GaAlAs interface, forming a two-dimensional electron (or hole) gas. As discussed above, this carrier gas exhibits a very high mobility, especially at low temperatures. Two factors contribute to this higher mobility, both arising from the selective doping of the GaAlAs layer rather than the GaAs layers in which the carriers reside. The first is the natural separation between the donor atoms in the GaAlAs and the electrons in the GaAs. The second is the inclusion of a "spacer layer" in the structure to enhance this separation. This latter layer arises by its incorporation in the growth process and is made possible by the selective doping ability of molecular beam epitaxy (and by organometallic CVD as well).

The typical structure grown for the SDHTs begins with a bulk GaAs wafer, upon which is grown a GaAs undoped buffer layer, which also serves as the active layer. Then, an undoped GaAlAs layer is grown. (There is no intentional doping so that the carrier concentration is at the background level, usually $< 10^{14}$ cm^{-3}.) This layer is the spacer layer and is usually in the range of 3–5 nm in thickness (see Figure 4.10a). Finally, the doped GaAlAs layer is grown. The doping of this layer will determine the actual charge that resides in the inversion channel on the GaAs side of the GaAs/GaAlAs interface. The doped layer is often uniformly doped, but some people now place only a sheet of charge adjacent to the spacer layer, and leave the remaining GaAlAs

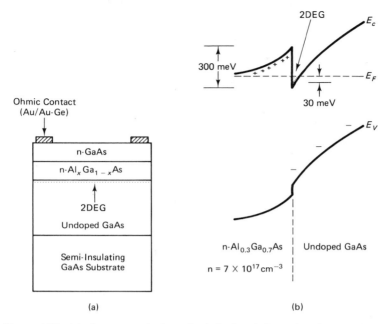

Figure 4.10 (a) Structure of the selectively-doped heterojunction transistor. (b) Conduction band energy levels for the modulation-doped heterojunction.

undoped. Finally, a thin GaAs capping layer is grown to ease the fabrication of ohmic contacts.

Normally, the electrons in a semiconductor remain close to their donor atoms. In the SDHT, however, the band discontinuity between the GaAlAs and the GaAs creates a different possibility. This is shown in Figure 4.10b. The discontinuity in the conduction band edge (we work only with n-channel devices in this discussion), and the required constancy of the Fermi level lead to the band bending shown at the interface. The conduction band in the GaAlAs is pushed upward, ionizing the donor atoms near the interface. On the other hand, the conduction band edge in the GaAs is pushed downward, leading to an accumulation of electrons in the potential well formed at the interface. In many respects, this potential well is similar to that in a Si MOSFET, except that the GaAlAs is not a wide-band gap insulator like SiO_2 and the band discontinuity is an order of magnitude smaller in the SDHT structure. However, in most cases the extent of the electron wave function is larger than in the equivalent Si case, so that the same two-dimensional electron gas forms.

In Figure 4.10b, the surface potential barrier has been made sufficiently small that the surface depletion does not punch through to the region of consideration (at the heterojunction interface) and can be ignored. In this way,

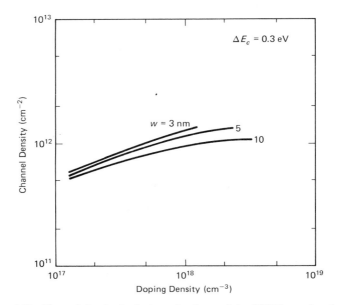

Figure 4.11 Channel density in the inversion layer of the SDHT as a function of the doping level in the GaAlAs, for $x = 0.3$.

we can use the known doping levels to calibrate the channel charge density itself. This is shown in Figure 4.11, where the channel density is plotted as a function of doping in the GaAlAs layer for several values of the spacer layer. This calculation is made by writing a simple energy balance equation for the various levels in the band diagram of Figure 4.10. Beginning at the Fermi level in the GaAlAs doped layer, we recognize that this level must be at the donor level E_d, since both electrons and ionized donors are at this level. In a normal bulk semiconductor, the Fermi level would lie between the donor level and the conduction band for this condition, but here the electrons do not remain in the GaAlAs conduction band but shift to the inversion layer. For this reason, equilibrium conditions require that the Fermi level lies nearly at E_d. If the GaAlAs is doped only with a localized sheet of charge, which is fully ionized, this is no longer a constraint on the system and the Fermi level will be determined by other impurity atoms in the GaAlAs. At present, we assume the case of uniform doping of the modulation doped layer.

We then rise to the conduction band edge by an amount E_d. The potential drop across the depletion layer of ionized donors is given by

$$qV_d = e^2(N_D - N_A)d^2/2\varepsilon_S = q^2n_s^2/2\varepsilon_S(N_D - N_A) \tag{4.43}$$

where $N_D - N_A$ is the net donor concentration, ε is the dielectric constant of the GaAlAs, d is the width of the depletion layer, and $n_s = N_{\text{depl}} + n_{\text{inv}} = d(N_D - N_A)$ is the total charge in the GaAs layer. In the spacer layer, the potential varies linearly since there is no free charge in this region. The field in the layer is determined by the modulation doping induced free carrier concentration in the inversion layer. The electrons from the donors in the GaAlAs go to create the two-dimensional carrier gas and to neutralize any doping atoms in the GaAs itself. Thus, the charge at each side of the spacer layer is given by n_s, and the field is

$$E_{s1} = qn_s/\varepsilon_S \qquad (4.44)$$

which leads to a potential drop of

$$V_{s1} = qn_s w/\varepsilon_S \qquad (4.45)$$

which depends linearly upon the spacer layer thickness w. The nonlinear dependence apparent in Figure 4.11 arises from the reduction in the charge transferred to the inversion layer as the sum of the spacer and depletion layers increases.

At the interface, the conduction band is offset by the amount ΔE_c. In the early work on the multi-layer superlattices, it was estimated that this discontinuity was some 85% of the band-gap discontinuity. There currently is some disagreement on the value of this number, but is now thought to be in the range of 60–65% of the band-gap discontinuity. In the channel itself, we must still rise from the bottom of the conduction band to the Fermi level. This amount is determined by the lowest quantum level in the well and the amount of charge in the channel.

The lowest subband level has usually been calculated by utilizing the equivalent MOSFET arguments. In this case, the substrate is typically weakly p-type and a triangular potential well may be assumed. The wave functions are then Airy functions, and the lowest subband is given by [10]:

$$E_o = \left(\hbar^2/2m\right)^{1/3}(9\pi qE_s/8)^{2/3} \qquad (4.46)$$

where $E_s = q(N_{depl} + N_{inv}/2)/\varepsilon_S$ is the average field in the inversion layer.

Finally, we must estimate the position of the Fermi level in these structures. The statistics of the carriers is governed by the two-dimensional nature of the transport. In this case, the number of carriers in the subband is given by

$$N_{inv} = N_c \ln\left\{1 + \exp\left[(E_F - E_o)/kT\right]\right\} \qquad (4.47)$$

where $N_c = mk_BT/\pi\hbar^2$ is the effective density of states in two dimensions. Now, the set of equations (4.43)–(4.47) forms a set that can be solved by iteration to obtain the inversion layer density once the doping levels are set. This is shown in Figure 4.11 above.

For sheet doping, it is necessary to know the depletion layer thickness for the above calculations. This is shown in Figure 4.12. If the sheet thickness is less than d, then the sheet is fully ionized with all of the electrons residing in

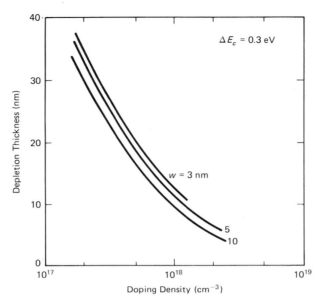

Figure 4.12 Depletion layer thickness of the doping region corresponding to Figure 4.10.

the inversion layer. This number is of course smaller than that obtained by the uniform doping case but is easier to determine.

4.5.2 Gate Charge Control

In order to make the above structure into a MESFET, we need only to place a metal Schottky-barrier gate onto the free surface. This barrier introduces additional band bending into the GaAlAs, and the depletion region under the gate pushes carriers out of the modulation doped layer and out of the channel itself if the barrier is sufficiently strong. In this manner, the charge in the inversion channel can be modulated by the potential applied to the metal gate.

In Figure 4.13, the band diagram of the heterojunction structure and the Schottky barrier is shown. It is clear that for this device to work as a transistor, it is necessary that the two depletion regions, one from the gate and one from the modulation doping interaction, interact with each other. For this to occur, we must have either a sufficiently high reverse bias on the metal gate or the thickness of the GaAlAs layer must be sufficiently thin. Of course, a properly designed device will trade off the thickness with the bias levels in order to achieve operation at appropriate circuit voltage levels.

In the regime where the inversion charge is controlled by the gate, the GaAlAs layer is totally depleted of charge. In this region, the potential is

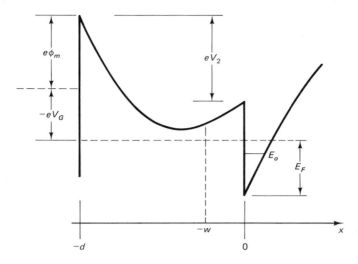

Figure 4.13   Energy diagrams for the full SDHT gated structure.

determined by Poisson's equation, with the charge given by

$$N_2 = N_D - N_A = N_{2o}, \; x < -w \tag{4.48}$$

and $N_2 = 0$ in the spacer layer, in the notation of Figure 4.10. We have taken the origin at the heterojunction interface, where we shall also take $V_2(0) = 0$. Now, a double integration of Poisson's equation gives

$$V_2(x) = -E_s x - (q/\varepsilon_S)\int_0^x dx' \int_0^{x'} N_2(x'') \, dx'' \tag{4.49}$$

and

$$v_2 = -V_2(-d_2) = qN_{2o}(d_2^2 - w^2)/2\varepsilon_S - E_s d_2 \tag{4.50}$$

The first term on the right-hand-side of (4.50) is defined as V_{d2}, the voltage required to completely deplete the GaAlAs layer. In referencing the voltage as zero at the interface, we are of course referencing it to the conduction band edge on the GaAlAs side of the interface. By examination of Figure 4.13, we can relate this voltage to the built-in potentials as

$$v_2 = \phi_m - V_G + E_F - \Delta E_c \tag{4.51}$$

and (4.50) can be rewritten as

$$E_s = (V_{d2} - \phi_m - E_F + \Delta E_c + V_G)/d_2 \tag{4.52}$$

It is now fairly well established that there is very little charge at the heterojunction interface. We can therefore use Gauss' law to find

$$qn_s = \varepsilon_S(V_{d2} - \phi_m - E_F + \Delta E_c + V_G)/d_2 \tag{4.53}$$

In general, the Fermi level is relatively small when compared to the other potentials in the system. This is not always true, but will certainly be true near channel pinch-off where there is little charge in the channel. We can then ignore this source of nonlinearity in the characteristics and evaluate the approximate form of (4.53) as

$$qn_s = \varepsilon_S (V_G - V_T)/d_2 \qquad (4.54)$$

where

$$V_T = \phi_m - \Delta E_c - V_{d2} \qquad (4.55)$$

is the threshold voltage, below which there is no charge in the channel. Ignoring the exact position of the Fermi energy in (4.55) means that we do not need to know the exact levels of the subbands in the potential well. However, near threshold this is a good approximation. The threshold voltage here is more analogous to the pinch-off voltage of a MESFET, but we have used the MOS terminology for convenience.

There is a second critical voltage in the SDHT. For a sufficiently large value of (hopefully forward) bias, the depletion region no longer punches completely through the GaAlAs layer. The gate can then no longer control the inversion charge, since the heterojunction region is in equilibrium with the modulation doping. For proper operation of the device, this critical voltage must be designed to be out of the operating region. The critical voltage can be found by equating the equilibrium value of the Fermi level (which we denote as E_{F_o}) found in the previous section with the local potential above. This yields

$$V_{GC} = \phi_m - E_d - \left[\left(qN_{2o}d_2^2/2\varepsilon_S \right)^{1/2} \right.$$

$$\left. - \left(\Delta E_c - E_d - E_{Fo} + qN_{2o}w^2/2\varepsilon_S \right)^{1/2} \right]^2 \qquad (4.56)$$

This equation represents a major limitation on the control of the inversion charge by the gate. Clearly, the equilibrium voltage is maximized when the term in the brackets is zero. Generally this can be achieved only by a narrow, or sheet, doped region. However, such a region decreases the total capacitance of the gate and so reduces the transconductance of the device itself. For voltages above V_{GC}, the gate no longer influences the amount of charge in the conduction channel, and there is significant charge residing in the GaAlAs. This latter charge can also contribute to the conduction and lowers the transconductance of the device. For typical devices, such as those with a uniform doping in the neighborhood of 10^{18} cm^{-3} and spacer layers of 3–5 nm, V_{GC} is of the order of -2 V, which means that this effect becomes significant over a major portion of the operating curve.

4.5.3 The Current-Voltage Relation

In treating the I-V characteristics of the SDHT, we must incorporate the actual potential in the channel due to the drain-source voltage, just as in the earlier treatments of the MESFET and the MOSFET. We shall call this potential the channel voltage $V_c(x)$. Then, (4.54) becomes

$$qn_s = \varepsilon_S [V_{GS} - V_T - V_c(x)]/d_2 \tag{4.57}$$

In normal fashion, we can now write the channel current as

$$I = qn_s v(x) Z \tag{4.58}$$

where Z is the gate width, and $v(x)$ is the velocity in the channel. To proceed further, we must divide the channel into three regions: (1) a linear region where the electric field satisfies $E < E_s$, and E_s is the saturation field (the field at which the velocity saturates), (2) a saturated velocity region where the velocity is given by its saturated value v_s, and (3) a pinched-off region. It is of course possible that some of these regions will overlap, but it is only in the first two regions that we can actually solve for the detailed current-voltage relationship.

In region 1, the velocity rises in the channel as the electric field is increased in response to the decrease of the charge along the channel. The latter decreases due to the rise in potential along the channel and the consequent decrease in (4.57). The resulting increase in field and potential go together to assure that a constant current exists along the channel. In this region, the constant mobility accounts for the increasing velocity with decreasing density. We can now write the current by combining (4.57) and (4.58) to give

$$I = \mu Z C_o (V_G - V_T - V_c) \, dV_c/dx + Z D C_o \, dV_c/dx \tag{4.59}$$

where $dV_c/dx = E$, the electric field along the channel, $C_o = \varepsilon_S/d_2$. The second term on the right-hand side represents the diffusion contribution to the current with the density given by (4.57). We now integrate this over the distance from the source to a point $x = s$, at which point $E = E_s$, the field at which the velocity becomes saturated. When we introduce the Einstein relation $D/\mu = kT/q = V_t$, (4.59) becomes

$$I = (\mu Z C_o/s)(V_G - V_T + V_t - V_s - V_1/2)V_1 \tag{4.60}$$

where V_s is the potential drop across the source resistance and V_1 is the potential at $x = s$ with respect to the source position in the channel. If we now take $V_s = R_s I$, we may rewrite (4.60) as

$$I = GV_1(V_G - V_T + V_t - V_1/2) \tag{4.61a}$$

with

$$G = \mu Z C_o/s(1 + V_1 R_s C_o Z/s) \tag{4.61b}$$

In treating the above equations, we have included explicitly the diffusion current, although this is not normally done. However, it may be an important part of the total current, and is significant in regions 2 and 3.

In region 2, the velocity is saturated, so it cannot continue to increase as the carrier density decreases along the channel with continuing increases in V_D (the drain potential). Consequently, the current must be kept constant by two effects. First, a larger proportion of the total current is carried by diffusion, and secondly an increase in the carrier density (over the equilibrium value determined by the potentials) occurs. This latter effect clearly shows up in full two-dimensional models of all devices in which velocity saturation occurs. However, the effect is numerically small when considering the effect on the channel potential. We can therefore actually use only the former effect to determine the current. The current is now given by

$$I = Zn_s qv_s - ZqD' \, dn_s/dx$$
$$= ZC_o v_s (V_G - V_T - V_c) + WD'C_o \, dV_c/dx \tag{4.62}$$

where D' is the diffusion parameter in the saturated region. We cannot just assume that D' is a constant saturated value, as is the velocity, since this does not relate properly to the mobility. A constant D' would actually imply a carrier temperature increasing linearly with the electric field. In fact, most hot electron studies show that the temperature increases quadratically with the field. This would give a linearly increasing D', except that most studies also show that D' actually decreases with increasing field in the saturation regime. To account for this, we shall take D' in the form

$$D' = v_s (\mu/v_s)^{1/2} (kT/q)(dV_c/dx)^{-1/2}$$
$$= v_s \beta (dV_c/dx)^{-1/2} \tag{4.63}$$

which is the geometric mean between the constant value and the velocity saturated assumption. Thus, (4.55) becomes

$$I = ZC_o v_s (V_G - V_T - V_c) + ZC_o v_s \beta (dV_c/dx)^{1/2} \tag{4.64}$$

and for pinch-off occurring at $x = p$ $(V_c = V_G - V_T)$,

$$I = ZC_o v_s [V_G - V_T - V_1 + \beta^2/(p - s)] \tag{4.65}$$

is found for the current. By equating this with the previous form for the current, we find that s and p are related by

$$p = s[1 + 2(V_t/V_1)H] \tag{4.66}$$

where

$$H = 3(1 + \alpha)/[3 + 2\alpha - (\alpha/3V_t)(V_G - V_T)] \tag{4.67}$$

is a correction factor for the source resistance R_s, and $\alpha = v_s R_s C_o Z/2$. In actual usage, the pinch-off point is found from the voltage along the channel to achieve this effect. This determines p, and (4.66) can be used to find s, which in turn determines the current. In most cases, however, $V_1 = E_s s/2$ (the velocity increases linearly), and we can simplify the results. Although the linear portion (region 1) determines the total current in the device, the resultant equation for the current depends only upon the gate potential and saturated velocity value as

$$I = ZC_o v_s (V_G - V_T + V_t)/(2 + v_s R_s C_o Z) \qquad (4.68)$$

In region 3, the current is carried entirely by diffusion of carriers injected into the space-charge region from the pinched-off channel. The current is determined by the previous two regions, and the space-charge region serves merely as a resistive layer to drop the remaining drain potential.

For a 1.0 μm gate length device, with a channel mobility of 8000 cm^2/V and an effective saturation velocity of 1.5×10^7 cm/sec, we find that $V_1 = 0.094$ V. This is the maximum value that this parameter can take for this structure, as shorter values of s will arise as the drain current is increased in response to increases in the drain potential. Thus, this potential is comparable to the thermal voltage which appears in (4.67), or is smaller over much of the bias range. As a result, the current level is primarily determined by the gate voltage and the saturation velocity, even though it is region 1 that is metering the current into the channel. The high mobility serves only to make the metering more efficient and to reduce the effective source resistance.

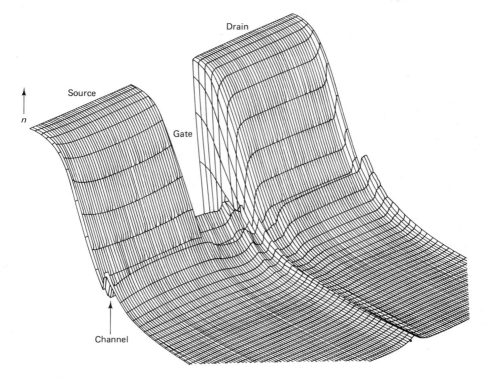

Figure 4.14   Two-dimensional profile of charge density along the SDHT channel.

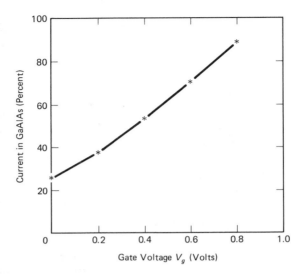

Figure 4.15 Fraction of drain current carried in the GaAlAs for the enhancement-mode SDHT. Here, we have taken the substrate bias as 0.8 V, and the calculation is for $x = 0.3$.

Full two-dimensional numerical solutions to Poisson's equation are not very plentiful at this time for the SDHT. One has been carried out however, in a case that assumes the drift-diffusion approximation for the transport, as we have done here. The primary results are in keeping with the conclusions of the above section. In Figure 4.14, we show a plot of the charge density along the channel. It is apparent from this picture, that there is an increase in charge in region 2 (the saturated velocity region) over the equilibrium level expected from the above discussion. Moreover, it is also apparent that there is significant charge in the GaAlAs itself. In Figure 4.15, we plot the fraction of current carried in the GaAlAs layer. The device simulated was a normally-off device, but it is clear that even here the potential in the modulation doped layer is such that the gate loses effective control over the channel charge over a significant portion of the dynamic range of the device.

4.6 THE CURRENT STATE OF THE ART

Finally, we want to discuss just where the status of these devices is today. It is clear that one measure with which to compare devices is the speed-power product, which is the product of the power dissipation per gate and the delay time per gate. We will discuss this more fully in the next chapter, but want to present a few details here on these devices. Another measure is the product of the power dissipation per gate and the square of the delay time per gate, which is the action or energy-time product for the logic family. The best current SDHT data at room temperature is that taken by Rockwell International [9], which is for a 1.0 μm channel length device. They achieved a minimum delay time of 12.2 psec at a power level of 1.1 mW/gate. This gives a speed-power product of 13.4 fJ and an energy-time product of 0.164×10^{-24} J. For comparison, the best GaAs MESFET data is for a device with an active channel length of 0.3 μm, fabricated by self-aligned gate technology by NTT (Nippon Telephone and Telegraph) in Japan [11]. For this technology, they achieved a minimum delay time of 16 psec at a power dissipation of 0.75 mW/gate or 12 fJ speed-power product. On the other hand, they could achieve a lower speed-power product of 1.2 fJ, but at the expense of a slower delay time of 163 psec due to the lower power dissipation of 7.4 μW/gate. In either case, this technology has a constant action product of 0.192×10^{-24} J which is only slightly higher than the SDHT technology (but at a much shorter, and therefore technologically more difficult, gate length). For comparison, low power Si CMOS has achieved 50 psec delay times at 1.8 mW/gate for a speed-power product of 90 fJ and an action of 4.5×10^{-24} J, more than an order of magnitude higher than the GaAs technology. As a consequence of this low-power, high-speed technology, integration of the GaAs devices into memory systems is proceeding rapidly. In early 1987, 16K static RAM circuits containing over 10^6 active MESFET devices were built. The SDHT circuitry is lagging this development only slightly.

REFERENCES

1. M. P. Shaw, H. L. Grubin, and P. R. Solomon, *The Gunn-Hilsum Effect* (Academic Press, New York, 1979).

2. W. Shockley, *Bell. Sys. Tech. J.*, vol. 33, p. 799 (1954).

3. R. A. Pucel, H. A. Haus, and H. Statz, in *Adv. Electronics and Electron Phys.*, vol. 38, p. 195 (Academic Press, New York, 1975).

4. M. Pepper, *Phil. Mag. B*, vol. 38, p. 515 (1978).

5. K. Lehovec and R. Zuleeg, *Solid State Electronics*, vol. 13, p. 1415 (1970).

6. G. Baccarani, M. R. Wordeman, and R. H. Dennard, *IEEE Trans. Electron Devices*, vol. ED-31, p. 452 (1984).

7. M. S. Birrittella, W. C. Seelbach, and H. Goronkin, *IEEE Trans. Electron Devices*, vol. ED-29, p. 1135 (1982).

8. R. Dingle, H. L. Stoermer, A. C. Gossard, and W. Wiegmann, *Appl. Phys. Letters*, vol. 33, p. 665 (1978).

9. C. P. Lee, D. Hon, S. J. Lee, D. L. Miller, and R. J. Anderson, in *Proc. 1984 GaAs Integrated Circuits Conference*, p. 162.

10. F. Stern and W. E. Howard, *Phys. Rev.*, vol. 163, p. 816 (1967).

11. K. Yamasaki, N. Kato, Y. Matsuoka, and K. Ohwada, in *Proc. 1982 Intern. Electron Device Mtg.*, p. 166.

5

CIRCUITS AND INTERCONNECTIONS

As has been evident during the previous chapters of this book, the drive to ever smaller devices and more complex levels of circuit integration on a single chip is not expected to end in the near future. This push to ultra-large-scale integration is a result of the market pressures for more extensive computation on a single functional chip. So far, however, we have limited ourselves to the types of devices themselves. At this point, we want now to begin to talk about the manner in which these devices are interconnected on the chip, as well as how the chips are interconnected.

The continued miniaturization of individual semiconductor devices leads to reduced dimensions of the devices and closer packing. As a consequence, the transit time between devices is also reduced which allows a generally higher operating frequency for the circuit. On the other hand, it is not clear (at least in the minds of many) whether the interconnections between the devices can continue to be scaled along with the devices. Consequently, the interconnections between the devices and between individual chips rapidly are becoming a problem. Moreover, these interconnections can themselves set some limits on the ultimate level of integration that can be achieved with a given technology. We explored this briefly in the Introduction (Chapter 1), when we talked about the energy stored in the interconnects. This led to different lower limits on logic delay times, depending upon whether the chip was device-limited or interconnect-limited in its performance. Such factors led to the conclusion that the most prominent interconnect-limited chip was a gate array. Other commonly discussed limits arise from the pin-out requirements, commonly discussed as "Rent's Rule." While this so-called rule is often quoted, it is usually misrepresented, as many do not recognize that VLSI (and ULSI) *satisfy a different form of the rule* than that usually found and applied to arrays of special logic circuits. A casual observation of the slow growth of pin requirements in microprocessors and memory chips clearly points out that the long predicted pin-out catastrophe is not likely to occur in properly designed ULSI circuits (e.g., as long as we do not succumb to a misplaced love for gate arrays).

In this chapter, we want to discuss these issues in some depth. We will begin with a discussion of the impedance of interconnect lines and devices, as these impedance levels will set certain limits on the energy-time product which seem to be relatively independent of the particulars of technology. We then turn to Rent's rule, partitioning, and average interconnect lengths in the circuits. Following this, a discussion of the special requirements for high-speed switching is presented along with the special requirements for driving off-chip lines. Then multi-level interconnects are treated. Finally, a discussion is presented of the relatively new area of optical interconnections.

5.1 INTERCONNECTIONS

It is still necessary within large integrated systems to communicate the results of a computation, no matter how large or small, with other parts of the system. Generally, this is done through the use of the interconnect signal lines, and the path can be circuitous around the chip, or even extend to other chips via off-chip pins and lines. As a consequence, it is necessary that devices be able to drive these interconnections. There are several approaches to this problem. The simplest case is to consider that a drive device must charge and discharge the entire line for each bit. In reality, this is a very stringent requirement, since the lines may in fact be rather long. In a machine such as the Cray, the long lines feeding the memory are several clock cycles long and are in fact treated somewhat as a pipeline, so that the drivers must produce good pulses, but do not have to charge the entire capacitance of the interconnect lines. On the other hand, within integrated circuits the common practice is for the lines to be RC lines rather than RL lines and to be rather short, so that the entire length is charged by the driver. In this case, the capacitance of the line is a major limitation.

Suppose that we can assume that the line to be driven has a capacitance C per unit length of line. If the line has length l, and is required to transmit a pulse voltage level V for a duration t seconds, then the power introduced into the line each pulse is

$$P = ClV^2/t \qquad (5.1)$$

From this equation, we can look at some of the basic compromises that must be made among the speed, the power, and the delay of the logic incorporated into the circuitry. We can lower the power in the interconnections by lowering the voltage or by slowing down the logic. Conversely, increasing the power allows for faster switching. In fact, these conclusions are in general true for high-density integrated circuits regardless of whether we look at device limitations or interconnect limitations.

Consider for example a ULSI circuit extrapolated from today's VLSI. One of the densest of the latter circuits is a microprocessor containing approximately 0.5 M devices on a single chip of roughly 0.4 cm², for a density of 1.25 M/cm². Let us assume that this chip dissipates approximately 5 W/cm², so that the power per device is approximately 4 μW. The chip runs at approximately 20 MHz, which corresponds to a delay time of 3 ns. This gives a speed-power product of about 12 fJ. Although this is a somewhat unrealistically low number, as it assumes that every gate switches each clock cycle (which is seldom the case), it clearly indicates the trade-offs mentioned above. If we want to increase the speed of this chip, we will be limited by the ability to remove heat and must therefore choose a technology with a lower speed-power product. If we want to increase the number of devices on the same size chip, while maintaining the speed, we must also change to a technology with a lower speed-power product if we want to be able to remove the heat.

There is however a lower limit to the power that can be utilized in driving the interconnection lines [1]. This is set by the actual lower limit on the system signal voltage $k_B T/e$. Indeed, the power that can be introduced to a line with impedance of Z_o is given by $(k_B T/e)^2/Z_o$. If we take the impedance value as that of free space, 377 ohms, then this level is 1.8×10^{-6} W at 300 K. In practice, it is relatively easy to lower the impedance level of the line or device, but is difficult to raise the impedance level above that of free space. Another way of looking at this power level is to normalize it to the thermal energy. Then, we find that this lower limit is $2.65 \times 10^3 \ k_B T/$psec. This is well above the thermodynamic limits and allows for a sizable signal level to be maintained.

Let us now turn to the concept of the limitation of RC lines. In a general LC transmission line, the normalized time constant of the line is approximately given by the frequency of the resonant line, or $T_d = \omega/c_1^2$ (in sec/cm²), where c_1 is the velocity of propagation. Now, the resistance per unit length of a transmission line is given by the thickness of the metallization h' and width of the line w as [1]

$$R = \rho/h'w \tag{5.2}$$

The capacitance is given in terms of the thickness of the insulation h and the width as

$$C = \varepsilon w/h \tag{5.3}$$

Thus, the delay of the RC line is given by

$$T_d = \varepsilon\rho/hh' \tag{5.4}$$

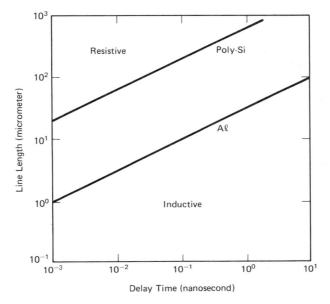

Figure 5.1 Separation of the speed-power plane for resistive versus inductive transmission lines for on-chip interconnections.

and the line is resistive when

$$\varepsilon\rho/hh' > \omega/c_1^2 \tag{5.5}$$

We recall, however, that this equation is valid only for a unit length of interconnection. Now, the line length is a multiple of the circuit pitch, while the parameters h, h' are usually limited to a value comparable, but less than, the width of the lines. Thus, we may write [1]:

$$\ell > Mh, \; \ell > Mh'$$

where M is an integer, usually in the range of 10–20 for modern ULSI. We can then combine this with (5.5) to give

$$\ell^2/\tau > M^2\varepsilon\rho c_1^2/G \tag{5.6}$$

where $\omega = G/\tau$, and G has a value of about 5–10 with τ being the delay time of the circuit. This result can be combined with (5.1) to yield a boundary curve in the power-delay plane that delineates resistive lines from inductive (transmission) lines. This is shown in Figure 5.1 for polysilicon lines over SiO_2 and 5 V logic swings.

The equation for power (5.1) is sufficiently general that we want now to try to achieve it from the device point-of-view. From the above discussions, it is clear that we can write the total capacitance of the device plus the transmission line as ($C_T = C\ell$)

$$C_T = \varepsilon A_c/h \tag{5.7}$$

where A_C is the area of the capacitor that is considered. In general, the area is scaled in terms of the insulator thickness by some relatively technology independent factor so that we can write $A_c = G_1 h^2$, where G_1 is a numerical factor. Thus, for a typical technology, we might expect that G_1 is about 100 or so. The area of the circuit is considerably greater than the area of the device, due to the presence of the interconnections. Thus, we can imagine that there is a second numerical factor G_2 such that [1]:

$$A_c < a^2 < G_2 A_c \qquad (5.8)$$

where a^2 is the circuit area. We can then write the capacitance in terms of the device area as

$$C_T^2 > \varepsilon^2 a^2 G_1 / G_2 \qquad (5.9)$$

where we have included both discussions of size and h. We can now replace the capacitance in (5.1) with this expression. From basic electromagnetic theory, we can write the impedance of the interconnect lines in terms of the velocity as

$$Z = 1/\varepsilon c_1 \qquad (5.10)$$

Now, we can replace ε from (5.7), and use $c_1 = A_c/\tau h = G_1^{0.5} a/\tau$, so that we get

$$Z = (G_1/G_2)^{0.5} m\tau / \varepsilon l \qquad (5.11)$$

where we have used $ma = l$ for the path length of the interconnection.

We can now use the above results to estimate the power limitation that can arise in the integrated circuit due to the interconnection of the devices. If P is the power dissipation per circuit on the chip, and Q_m is the maximum rate at which power can be dissipated to the substrate, then these are related through the area of the circuit as

$$a^2 > P/Q_m \qquad (5.12)$$

The line length is $ma = l$, so that

$$l^2 > m^2 P / Q_m \qquad (5.13)$$

Now, (5.1), (5.9) and (5.10) can be combined to give

$$P > V^2 (G_1/G_2)^{0.5} a / Z\tau c_1 \qquad (5.14)$$

but with (5.12), we have

$$P\tau^2 > (V^2/Zc_1)^2 G_1/G_2 Q_m \qquad (5.15)$$

This result is applicable for relatively short lines and relatively high impedance levels, such as found in highly-integrated circuits. Keyes [1] suggests that this limit is in fact a circuit limit, and is not particularly dependent upon the details of the devices used. Thus, (5.14) should be relatively independent of the technology adopted. In addition, he points out that current VLSI is pressing the limits given by (5.15), which suggests that circuit problems will be far more prevalent in future ULSI. We can estimate the limits. Let us assume that $V = 2$ V, $Z = 50$ ohm, $c_1 = 0.3c_o$, $G_1/G_2 = 1$, and $Q_m = 10$ W/cm^2. Then, we find that the limit on $P\tau^2$ is 6.4×10^{-24} J-sec, which is comparable to the Si CMOS reported at the end of Chapter 4, but is still almost a factor of 60 greater than that achieved for the short-channel GaAs circuits mentioned there. To put this into perspective, we can consider the 10 fJ (speed-power product) logic mentioned above. This logic would then be usable with a minimum delay time of about 0.64 ns (10 psec for the short-channel GaAs logic), which within the various approximations and estimates is the order of magnitude of the actual propagation delay found with the circuitry. At least for this example, the above-mentioned assertion of Keyes is found to hold only for a particular range of logic types.

As a consequence of these discussions, we can summarize the principal limitations of the interconnections in well-designed ULSI circuits as those normally found in considerations of heat removal from the chip. Limitations on the speed-power product in more complex levels of integration are driven by the enlarged power dissipation requirements, rather than the speed requirements. Once the power dissipation is reduced to acceptable levels, the required speed-power product will indicate the achievable speed levels, but these may be further limited by interconnection delays. This is true in ULSI circuits which have rather short average interconnection lengths (discussed in the next section), but in gate arrays the problem is more severe. Gate arrays will be seen to have longer average interconnection lengths below, and this accentuates the interconnection limitations on the achievable speeds in the circuit. As we saw in Chapter 1, chips which are dominated by the long interconnections generally are limited to being much slower than their properly designed ULSI counterparts. Sometimes, this speed difference can be several orders of magnitude. Let us now turn to Rent's rule and interconnection lengths and pins.

5.2 PINS AND WIRES—THE INTERCONNECTIONS

It is generally felt that large-scale integration of semiconductor devices will eventually entail a significantly large number of interconnection pin-outs at the periphery (or distributed throughout) the chip. This fact has led to a number of studies which invariably give the results in terms of a relationship that has become known as "Rent's rule." Empirically, this relationship gives the number of pins, for a given size module, in terms of a power law dependence upon the number of gates (or the effective number of functional blocks) in the module. The validity of this relationship is based upon a number of studies of possible interconnections of present gate arrays, or of experiments actually carried out on master slice type chips. These latter chips are arrays of devices, whose final architectural interconnection is determined by the final mask structure. Consequently, these chips have become known as gate arrays.

The considerations that lead to ideas such as Rent's rule arise from topographical details of the implementation of a given architecture in an integrated system. In the earliest form, the problem is one of partitioning the system graph into appropriate modules, each of which would probably be a separate chip in early configurations. The partitioning problem is one of assigning the required logic blocks in such a manner that the total number of pins and interconnection wires could be simultaneously minimized. In this context, a logic block is some arbitrary (and usually not specified) primitive function. These blocks are then interconnected by the system graph, called a block graph or net. In early machines, the modules would be composed of at most a few blocks. The choice of assigning blocks and nodes into modules is the partitioning problem.

5.2.1 Rent's Rule

Since each possible assignment of blocks into modules specifies the necessary module-module interconnections, the total number of pins and interconnections is then dependent upon the details of the partition selected. In fact, however, the beauty of Rent's rule is that there is a perhaps general rule that buries the details and concentrates upon the more universal aspects. Experimentally, then, Rent's rule has been formulated as

$$P = KB^p \qquad\qquad (5.16)$$

where P is the number of pins, B is the number of blocks, K is the number of pins per block, and p is a general exponent. Values of the parameters K and p have been found for early IBM machines, for RCA machines, and for others. One particularly useful study was carried out by Landman and Russo [2]. They considered graphs of 670–12,700 logic circuits and blocks ranging from a single NOR gate to 30 circuits. Rent's rule was also found to be obeyed, and the parameters varied over the range 3–5 for K and 0.6–0.7 for p.

While the requirement on pins and interconnections is significant for predicting growth in future machines, Rent's rule also is significant in that the exponent p is very important in predicting what the average interconnection length *within the chip* will be. Chips with an exponent $p > 0.5$ generally are found to have long interconnection lengths as a rule, while chips with an exponent $p < 0.5$ have an interconnection length (in terms of circuit pitches) that is independent of the overall number of gates. We return to this below.

Other studies by Chiba [3] give a similar result to that above. However, he has also shown that we can replace the number of blocks in (5.16) by the number of gates, as

$$P = CG^r \qquad\qquad (5.17)$$

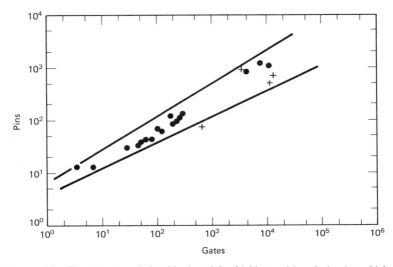

Figure 5.2 The pin-gate relationship found for highly partitioned circuits, which has led to early forms of "Rent's Rule." The dots and the +s denote various data from the referenced early papers.

where G is the number of gates in the module. In Figure 5.2, we show the results of these latter two groups of authors. In general, their data can be fit with $r = 0.5$ to 0.6 ($= p$ it appears) and $C = 4$ to 6 (slightly larger than K). It is particularly evident in the work of Landman and Russo that some chips began to show a different relationship, when the number of gates on a single chip became large. More recent studies by Gilbert [4] indicate that 10^5 gates could be configured in a manner to yield a much smaller exponent in (5.17).

Indeed, it has generally been the experience in VLSI that the number of pins is much smaller than expected in Rent's rule, at least in terms of the exponents found in gate arrays. In Figure 5.3, we show this trend by plotting the reported number of pins for microprocessor chips and for functional chips (other than gate arrays) of both GaAs and Si. In addition to microprocessors, these chips include memories, multipliers, and multiplexers. From this figure, the best fit to the pin requirements of highly integrated circuits is found to be

$$P = 7G^{0.21} \qquad (5.18)$$

which differs appreciably from the earlier forms. These circuits are called *functionally partitioned* circuits. The far fewer number of pins required for such highly integrated circuitry suggests that future pin-intensive circuits, such as super-computers, will more than likely be found to evolve toward single-chip integration. Indeed, we found in Chapter 1 that interconnection-intensive circuits, such as gate arrays, eventually reached a point where the speed was independent of the technology. Only for the short interconnection circuits could very fast logic be obtained. The functional integration that was dis-

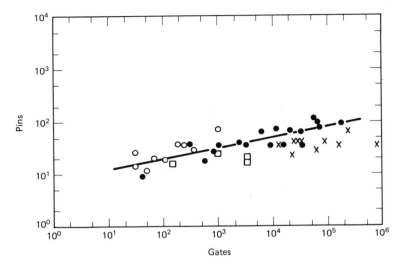

Figure 5.3 The pin-gate relationship found in functionally partitioned circuits used in modern ULSI. The open symbols are for various GaAs chips, while the closed symbols are Si chips (the particular function is not important here, but none is a gate array).

cussed there can be expected to be pursued not only for economic reasons, but also for interconnection optimization.

5.2.2 Interconnection Lengths

Estimating the average interconnection length on an integrated circuit chip has been a very active area of investigation. It turns out that modern ULSI circuitry is very regular in its layout, and usually approximates a very square array. Such structures have been studied by Donath [5], and his results give good insight into the role that the number of gates and Rent's rule play in this area. Consequently, we shall follow his development quite closely. These results indicate that, for a square array, the average interconnection length is given by

$$\langle R \rangle = G^m \tag{5.19}$$

where $m = p - 0.5$, if $p > 0.5$. On the other hand, *if $p < 0.5$, it is found that $\langle R \rangle$ is independent of the number of gates in the circuit.* This is a significant result, because we found above that highly integrated functions on a single VLSI chip generally have $p = 0.2$. It is apparent therefore that ULSI can continue to be developed with ever larger numbers of gates, with the pinout requirements determined by the function of the chip and not by the increasing number of gates.

In developing a relationship between the average interconnection length $\langle R \rangle$, we use the empirical form of Rent's rule given above. The pre-factor K (or $C = 7$) is in fact relatively independent of the hierarchical level of the circuitry. This is evident by the independence of the empirical form on the details of the module assignments that went into the various data points in the figures. Consequently, we can adopt a hierarchy that is suitable for the calculations of $\langle R \rangle$ without concern about variations among implementations. The hierarchy we adopt consists of a number of levels. At the lowest level, we assume that the node contains just 4 elements, each of which is subsequently connected to its nearest neighbor. Each adjacent level consists of interconnecting 4 adjacent nodes to create the equivalent node for the next level. Thus, there are 4^L gates in the circuit, where L is the number of levels required to accommodate these gates. From this placement, we can easily find n_k, the average number of connections at the kth level and can deduce the average lengths r_k at this level. Then, we may simply relate these to the total average length as

$$\langle R \rangle = \left(\sum_{k < L} n_k r_k \right) \Big/ \sum_{k < L} n_k \qquad (5.20)$$

Generally, n_k decreases with increasing level as we move through the hierarchy, and this will work to lower the value for $\langle R \rangle$.

The connection to the pins and gates is made via Rent's rule. If we have K gates in a particular sub-complex of a level, we can say that the average number of pins T is given by

$$T = AK^p \qquad (5.21)$$

where p has the same meaning as before. Here, we are using the form given in (5.17), with slightly modified coefficients and terms, since it directly relates to gates rather than blocks. Through this relation we can now begin to develop relationships for n_k and r_k. If there is a total of C gates, which we want to divide into groups of K in size, we can use (5.21) to give the total number of pins as

$$T_{\text{total}} = (AK^p)C/K = ACK^{p-1} \qquad (5.22)$$

Now, in general the number of interconnects in a given complex is somewhat smaller than the actual number of pins. We introduce this, by defining the number of interconnects as

$$n_k = \alpha T_{\text{total}} = \alpha ACK^{p-1} \qquad (5.23)$$

To determine the value for n_k, we need only use (5.23) for the number of connections at the kth level and subtract the number that go to the next higher level, or

$$N(k) = N(4^k) - N(4^{k+1}) \qquad (5.24)$$

Here, the first term gives us the number of connections between groups of size 4^k, but this also includes all of the connections between groups of size 4^{k+1}. Thus, we subtract these with the second term. We can now use (5.22) in each of these terms, and

$$n_k = \alpha A C [1 - 4^{p-1}] 4^{k(p-1)} \tag{5.25}$$

In the beginning of this effort, we pointed out that there were just 4^L gates in the circuit. But, this is just the parameter C which appears in the above equation. Therefore, the number of levels required to achieve the circuit is given by

$$L = \log(C)/\log(4) \tag{5.26}$$

We can now evaluate the denominator term that appears in (5.20), since this involves only n_k and not the average length. We can write this as

$$\sum_{k<L} n_k = \alpha A C [1 - 4^{p-1}] \sum_{k<L} 4^{k(p-1)}$$

$$= \alpha A C [1 - 4^{L(p-1)}]$$

$$= \alpha A C [1 - C^{p-1}] \tag{5.27}$$

In the last expression, we have used (5.26) to relate C to L. It remains now to achieve an expression for the average length of a connection at each level.

We shall treat only the two-dimensional array case here. In this approach, it may be assumed that the devices at the kth level are laid out in a $2^k \times 2^k$ array. To simplify the equations somewhat, we shall let $w = 2^k$, so that the array is now $w \times w$. Thus, the devices are situated at a set of locations which are indexed by the quantities i, j. The quantity we are interested in is the distance between a device at i, j in array A and a device at i', j' in array B. We can write this distance as

$$d = w + i - i' + |j - j'| \tag{5.28}$$

With this, we can now write the interconnection length as

$$r = \frac{\sum_i \sum_{i'} \sum_j \sum_{j'} [w + i - i' + |j - j'|]}{\sum_i \sum_{i'} \sum_j \sum_{j'} 1} \tag{5.29}$$

and the sums run from 1 to w. The denominator just counts the total number of devices on the level. This now becomes

$$r_k = w + (2/w^2) \sum_{i=1}^{w} \sum_{j=1}^{w} (i - j) = (4w/3) - (1/3w) \tag{5.30}$$

This holds for the cells that are on the array and displaced in the x and y directions. For diagonal directions, (5.28) needs to be modified to reflect an additional factor of w for the second displacement and to neglect the absolute value brackets. This changes the numerator factor in (5.29) and

$$r_k = 2w \tag{5.31}$$

We can now find the average of these two factors as

$$r_k = \{2(2w) + 4[(4w/3) - (1/3w)]\}/6$$
$$= [14w - 2/w]/9 \tag{5.32}$$

The numerator is then given as

$$\sum_{k=0}^{L-1} n_k r_k = \sum_{k=0}^{L-1} \alpha A C(1 - 4^{p-1})4^{k(p-1)}[14(4^{k/2}) - 2(4^{-k/2})]/9$$

$$= (2/9)\alpha A C(1 - 4^{p-1}) \sum_{k=0}^{L-1} [7(4^{k(p-0.5)}) - 4^{k(p-3/2)}] \tag{5.33}$$

where we have reinserted the value of w. If p is different from 0.5, this simplifes to yield

$$\langle R \rangle = \frac{2(1 - 4^{p-1})}{9(1 - C^{p-1})} \left\{ 7\left(\frac{4^{L(p-0.5)} - 1}{4^{p-0.5} - 1} \right) - \left(\frac{4^{L(p-1.5)} - 1}{4^{p-1.5} - 1} \right) \right\} \tag{5.34}$$

Before proceeding, we want to replace the number of levels with the actual number of gates C. Doing this, (5.34) becomes

$$\langle R \rangle = \frac{2(1 - 4^{p-1})}{9(1 - C^{p-1})} \left\{ \left(\frac{7(C^{p-0.5} - 1)}{4^{p-0.5} - 1} \right) - \left(\frac{C^{p-1.5} - 1}{4^{p-1.5} - 1} \right) \right\} \tag{5.35}$$

The limit we are interested in is that for which C is very large ($> 10^6$). This gives us

$$\langle R \rangle = A(p)C^{p-0.5}, \ p > 0.5 \tag{5.36}$$

where

$$A(p) = (14/9)[(1 - 4^{p-1})/(4^{p-0.5} - 1)] \tag{5.37}$$

On the other hand, for small p, we find that $\langle R \rangle$ is independent of C and given by

$$\langle R \rangle = A(p)[B(p) - 1] \tag{5.38}$$

where

$$B(p) = (4^{p-0.5} - 1)/7(4^{p-1.5} - 1) \tag{5.39}$$

For comparison, let us assume that $C = 2 \times 10^6$ gates and that $p = 0.55$ is a good estimation of the value expected for interconnection-limited circuits such as gate arrays. Then, $A(p) = 10.06$ and $\langle R \rangle = 20.8$ circuit pitches. On the other hand, for $p = 0.21$, as found for highly integrated circuitry, we find that $\langle R \rangle = 2.95$ circuit pitches. At this level, there is almost an order of magnitude difference in the average interconnection length, and in the interconnection capacitance that must be driven by an individual gate.

Finally, when $p = 0.5$, we find that the sums must be reconsidered carefully because of the divergences which appear in the above equations. The result still depends upon the number of gates, and the leading terms are

$$\langle R \rangle = (7/9)\log(C)/\log(4) \tag{5.40}$$

5.2.3 Scaling Interconnections

In the previous chapters, we have introduced the concept of scaling laws for the down-sizing of integrated circuits. In the functionally partitioned circuits that will find wide usage in ULSI, we expect that the newer forms of "Rent's Rule" will prevail, and that the average interconnection length will not be a function of the number of gates on the chip. Thus, this interconnection length will remain the same as the cell size and will scale downward in true length with the rest of the circuit. In the concept of the parameters of Table 4.1, we expect the thickness of insulators to scale with the voltage, while lengths scale as other lengths in the circuit. Thus, we expect the interconnection capacitance to scale as K/λ^2, while the line resistance will scale as λ. We thus see that the RC time constant of the interconnection scales as K/λ. In constant-field scaling ($K = \lambda$), we see that the line delay, given as the RC time constant, does not scale but remains constant. This will serve to limit the efficiency of scaling in the future. On the other hand, for the more usually applied constant-voltage scaling ($K = $ constant, unchanged), we find that the RC time constant actually is reduced by the factor $1/\lambda$ by the scaling process. Thus, this latter case actually follows the normal linear scaling results that are desired, in that the interconnection delay is reduced by scaling so that faster circuits can be obtained, and equivalent-speed circuits can result even if the transconductance is reduced by scaling. This result can be improved if the aspect ratio of the metallization is increased (by a factor s, for example). Then the RC time constant is reduced by the factor $1/\lambda s$ in constant-voltage scaling, which will result in improved performance in the scaled circuits.

5.3 HIGH-SPEED SWITCHING

As we shall see, the significance of the length of the inter-device interconnection lies in the achievable speed of operation of the individual gates in the circuit. Since the early days of logic interconnections, the speed-power product (or delay time-power dissipation product) has served as a figure-of-merit for digital integrated circuits. Other concepts such as functional throughput, the product of the number of gates and the clock frequency, have also arisen. In any case, the pertinent parameters are typically calculated from static transfer characteristics and the capacitances of the logic gate. This argument arises from very simple considerations, as

$$P = 2N_g f_c(P_D \tau_D) \qquad (5.41)$$

where N_g is the number of gates, f_c is the applied clocking frequency at the gate level, and $2P_D\tau_D$ is the gate energy required to switch through a complete cycle. By using the complete cycle definition, we average over variations between rise and fall transients. If we also have

$$P = N_g V_{DD} I_{dm}/2 \qquad (5.42)$$

where I_{dm} ($= I_{Dss}$) is the peak drive current through the pull-down transistor (in Si MOS circuits), then

$$P_D\tau_D = V_{DD}I_{dm}/2f_c \qquad (5.43)$$

clearly, the minimum speed-power product will occur at the largest f_c, but this is limited by the cutoff frequency of the transistors, or

$$f_c = g_m/C_G \qquad (5.44)$$

Here, however, C_G should be replaced by the total nodal capacitance C_N (discussed below), and

$$P_D\tau_D = V_{DD}I_{dm}C_N/2g_m = V_{DD}^2 C_N^2/2g_m\tau_D \qquad (5.45)$$

where we have approximated the charging current during switching as $I_{dm} = C_N V_{DD}/\tau_D$. An alternative form is to write $I_{dm} = K(V_G - V_T)^2 = KV_{DD}^2$, and $g_m = 2KV_{DD}$, so that

$$P_D\tau_D = V_{DD}^2 C_N/4 \qquad (5.46)$$

Although both (5.45) and (5.46) are very crude approximations, they contain elements of validity and agree with each other if $f_c = 2/\tau_D$. We will examine these simple approximations further below, but show that this relationship on the clock frequency is much too high to be realistic.

The pertinent parameters are not independent of each other. For example, one could conclude from these equations that a reduction in the quantity τ_D would actually degrade the speed-power product of the gate. However, to accomplish this reduction in delay time, one requires that either the current I_{dm} is increased or the interconnection capacitance C_N is decreased. Clearly this illustrates the importance of the much shorter interconnection lengths in the highly integrated circuits. However, these changes counter the effect of reducing the delay time on the speed-power product so that this latter quantity is in fact reduced by this effect in keeping with our intuition. Thus, when looking at such simple forms for the speed-power product, all parameters must be considered together. A further note is that if $P_D\tau_D$ is dominated by the interconnection capacitance C_N, then the actual technology used in the circuitry is unlikely to have a large effect upon the resultant total speed and power requirements of the circuit.

In any case, we discover that if we are to increase the functional complexity of a system by increasing the number of gates, the speed-power product and the individual device sizes must be reduced. To meet these goals, node capacitance and operating voltages must be reduced. Moreover, to accomplish faster switching, the drive current capability I_{dm} must be increased. Thus, I_{dm}, τ_D, and $P_D\tau_D$ are all factors that are important to high-speed logic.

Before turning to the actual circuit implications for the speed-power product, we must first discuss another limiting factor, the delay incorporated into the propagation of the clock pulse across the circuit itself. Operation of the circuit at speeds suggested by the individual gates presupposes that all gates across the chip can be toggled in unison if required. In fact, this is not the case. Generally, the clock signal is input, or generated, at one side of the chip. Communication of this important timing signal to all parts of the chip involves the propagation of the signal completely across the chip. Propagation delay variations to different portions of the chip will result in phase delays in logic signals occurring at these different portions of the chip. Circuit design must be flexible enough to incorporate these delays without upsetting the functional behavior. Either the clock must be routed to assure equal delays, or the actual speed utilized must be slow enough to allow the clock skew to be accommodated in the circuit behavior. Propagation times in properly designed transmission (L-C) lines is about 0.1 nsec/cm for Si. Clearly, this time is comparable to delay times for modern high-speed circuitry, so that it can be a limiting factor in ULSI, if clock distribution is poorly designed (where differences of this level are introduced between different parts of the circuit).

Let us now turn to the considerations of high-speed switching and the transient signals in the logic gate. If one wants to compare different technological implementations for high-speed logic, it is necessary to find various figures-of-merit, such as the speed-power product. In essence, minimizing this latter quantity involves determining the mean value of the minimum energy per logic operation, as well as the intrinsic time required to perform the logic operation. In the last chapter, we will examine the fundamental limits that can be expected to exist on the minimum energy dissipation per logic operation, but here we want to examine how these arise in circuit switching. In Figure 5.4, we illustrate the various intrinsic times associated with the switching of a logic gate. These include the rise time τ_R, the fall time τ_F, the intrinsic switching time τ_I, and the delay time τ_D. In the following, the quantities for energy W_I, switching time τ_I, and power P_I are the mean values obtained for the transitions from 0 to 1 or from 1 to 0 and they are valid for a simple inverter gate with minimum levels of interconnections. In this case, we mean that these are quantities intrinsic to the gate, and are the appropriate values that would be obtained from a circuit such as a ring oscillator, with a fan-out of unity. In this sense, they represent the basic inherent performance that can

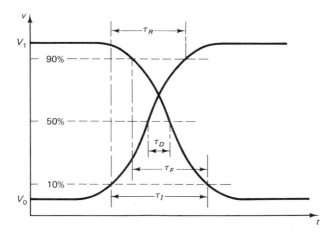

Figure 5.4   The various times involved in the switching of a logic gate.

be achieved from the gate itself. From the figure, we can see that the maximum frequency that can be achieved, in logic operations, is given by $f_{max} = 1/2\tau_I$.

We can estimate the power dissipated during the complete switching cycle (one 0 to 1 and one 1 to 0 transition) for a frequency f as [6]:

$$P(f) = \left[2W_I - P_{s1}(\tau_D + \tau_R) - P_{s0}(\tau_D + \tau_F)\right]f + P_S \qquad (5.47)$$

In most cases of high-speed logic, the pull-up and the pull-down transistors have been matched to achieve equal drive current for both parts of the cycle, although this is not the normal case for Si MOS circuitry. Rather, Si MOS is set to have the symmetry point at $V_D/2$, which is a different constraint. In the latter, setting a balanced switch point to $V_D/2$ often means that the pull-up transistor does not have sufficient drive capability to meet the above requirement. However, we are seeking average values for the quantities of interest, so that this will not greatly affect the results. In this average sense, we shall set $\tau_F = \tau_R$, and

$$\tau_I = \tau_D + (\tau_R + \tau_F)/2 \qquad (5.48)$$

Muller *et al.* [6] have carried out simulations for a number of logic families and they have found that in general $\tau_I = 2.5\tau_D$ is a very good approximation to use. Inserting this into (5.48) yields

$$\tau_D = 2\tau/3 \qquad (5.49)$$

We can then rewrite (5.47) as

$$P(f) = 2[W_I - P_S\tau_I]f + P_S = 2W_I f \qquad (5.50)$$

and

$$W_I = P_I\tau_I = 5P_I\tau_D/2 \qquad (5.51)$$

in agreement with earlier estimations. In fact, if the standby power P_S is small with respect to the switching power, then the speed-power product $P_D \tau_D$ is a good figure-of-merit to use in evaluating individual logic implementations.

The logic delay time can generally be split into three factors. The first part is caused by the finite electron transit time across the active region of the devices. If we are dealing with the saturated velocity of the carriers, then it requires about 2 psec to cross a 0.2 μm active region. The second component of the delay time is due to the parasitic reactances of the actual device and circuit and is usually of the same order of magnitude in size as the previous portion. Most of the delay, however, comes from the third part, which is the interconnection loading of the output node of the inverter circuit itself. We want now to discuss this portion.

Switching the inverter circuit from one level to another involves charging or discharging capacitances associated with the output node. In Figure 5.5, we show these capacitances for a simple enhancement-depletion inverter circuit. The gate capacitance C_G is split into the gate-source C_{GS} and the gate-drain C_{GD} portions separately. The channel capacitance C_C represents stored charge in the channel and includes particularly the above-mentioned transit-time delay factor. Including the transit time delay in this fashion is valid as long as $C_C \ll C_N$. In addition, C_L is the load capacitance, C_I is the interconnection capacitance, and C_{st} represents the stray capacitances. Then, the charge in the circuit is just [7]

$$Q_N = (C_{GS} + C_I + C_{st})V_o + C_{GD}(V_o - V_i) - C_L(V_{DD} - V_o) \quad (5.52)$$

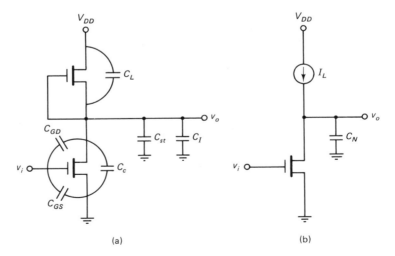

(a)   (b)

Figure 5.5   The equivalent circuit, with parasitic capacitances, that is normally encountered in integrated circuits.

The switching equation is just

$$dQ_N/dt = C_N(dV_o/dt) = I_L - I_D \tag{5.53}$$

where

$$C_N = C_{GS} + C_{GD}^* + C_I + C_{st} + C_L \tag{5.54}$$

is the total node capacitance, and

$$C_{GD}^* = C_{GD}(1 - \partial V_i/\partial V_o) \tag{5.55}$$

is the effective gate-drain capacitance. This differs little from the actual C_{GD}, since the Miller effect is not expected to be large in these circuits.

The output voltage transient $v_o(t)$, after a change in v_i, is found from the charge as

$$t = \int_{v_o(0)}^{v_o(t)} C_N(I_L - I_D)^{-1} dv_o \tag{5.56}$$

If both pull-up and pull-down transistors are saturated during most of the switching cycle, then the currents are relatively independent of the output voltage. In addition, if the transistors are nearly balanced, as discussed above, we may approximate $I_L - I_D = I_{dm}/2$ in magnitude for the rising and falling transients. Here, I_{dm} is the maximum value of the current in the pull-down transistor. We take V_m as the logic voltage swing in the circuit ($= V_{DD}$ in many circuits) so that we can now write (5.56) as

$$t = 2C_N V_m/I_{dm} \tag{5.57}$$

and the rise (or fall) time is

$$\tau_R = \tau_F = 1.6 C_N V_m/I_{dm} \tag{5.58}$$

Using (5.49), we find

$$\tau_D = C_N V_m/I_{dm} \tag{5.59}$$

as we have previously assumed. If we use $\tau_I = 2.5\tau_D$, $\tau_R = 0.4\tau_I$, and for the case $\tau_I = 1/2f_c$, we find $\tau_D = 1/5f_c$. The total energy required to switch is then

$$W_I = C_N V_m^2/2 = P_I \tau_I \tag{5.60}$$

or

$$P_D \tau_D = C_N V_m^2/5 \tag{5.61}$$

if the standby power dissipation is small, such as that expected for CMOS circuitry. Here, (5.61) should be compared (and preferred) to that obtained earlier in this section.

Above, we pointed out that the pertinent parameters are not independent of one another. The key equation for the speed-power product is (5.61), and although (5.45) appears more desirable, this latter equation can be deceiving. Indeed, as we pointed out earlier, (5.45) actually leads one to believe that reducing the delay time would hurt the speed-power product, but we see that this is not the case explicitly from (5.61). To actually decrease the delay time, one must either decrease C_N or increase I_{dm}, as can be seen from (5.59). If C_N is decreased, the speed-power product is improved. On the other hand, if I_{dm} is increased, g_m is also increased, and the speed-power product is changed very little, if at all. Thus all parameters must be considered together.

If the interconnection capacitance C_I dominates the node capacitance C_N, then $P_D \tau_D$ is often thought to be independent of the inverter technology, as we discussed above. However, τ_D need not be independent. If one can increase I_{dm} by appropriate transistor design or material choice, a smaller τ_D can be achieved without expense to the speed-power product. This will give rise to faster circuits and a higher maximum clock frequency. On the other hand, a technology giving a higher value of the transconductance g_m (arising from higher drive current at a given drive logic voltage) can achieve a given drive current level at a lower value of V_m, hence giving a smaller value of the delay time and a considerably smaller value of the speed-power product, even if the node capacitance remains the same. It is therefore apparent that the drive current level I_{dm} is a critical parameter in choice of technology, and it is this drive current consideration which most suggests that appropriate consideration of the full implications of any technology must be exploited.

5.4 OFF-CHIP DRIVE REQUIREMENTS

In the preceding section, we talked primarily of interconnections that resided on a single chip, rather than being from one chip to another. In many cases, it is the larger problem of long interconnections between chips which limits the overall system performance. Because of this, it is much more feasible to obtain top performance if all of the circuitry is on a single chip, but sometimes this is not practical. In early VHSIC circuits, for example, it was possible to achieve clock speeds of 100 MHz on-chip, but driving the external lines limited the effective speed to only 25 MHz. This illustrates a generic problem in system design, i.e., the desire to drive the off-chip circuit in a single clock cycle. This has usually been the case for micro-circuit design, but is not the norm in, say, supercomputer architecture. Indeed, the Cray 1 computers operated with an 80 MHz clock. Still, the length of the interconnects between the CPU and the memory were such that one normally would have had to slow the system down. However, the solution is to pipeline the memory transfer channels. This requires that a relatively large on-chip cache memory be available if the pipelining technique is to be usable.

In spite of the optimization suggestions above, it is still necessary to properly design the interconnection between chips. While impedance consider-

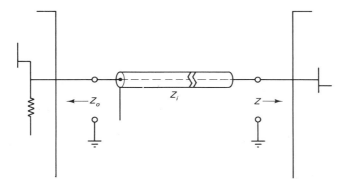

Figure 5.6 The presence of mismatch in impedances for off-chip lines used for interconnections.

ations are critical for on-chip interconnections, they are much more so for the off-chip lines. One is tempted to neglect the nature of the transmission line providing the interconnection in favor of power considerations on the chips to be driven at each end of the line. In fact, this cannot be done, and one must still take care that impedance matching is accomplished to minimize the drive power requirements of the lines [1]. It is difficult to construct interconnections, based upon transmission lines, that have characteristic impedances much different from that of normal coaxial cable, which is the free-space impedance modified by the presence of the dielectric material. Keyes [1] has presented a particularly cogent argument which shows that the line impedance should still be matched to that of the device (or more likely the converse). In Figure 5.6, we illustrate the presence of an interconnection line, with characteristic impedance Z_i, that is used to transfer the signal from one chip to another. For simplicity, we assume that the impedance levels of the two chips are equal with the value Z. At the source end of the line, the impedance seen by the source circuit is not Z, but is given from basic electromagnetic theory as

$$Z_a = Z_i[Z + Z_i\tan(\beta x)]/[Z_i + Z \tan(\beta x)] \qquad (5.62)$$

where x is the length of the interconnection, and β is the propagation constant of the line. For a lossless line (no power dissipated in the interconnection itself), $\beta = \omega/c_l$, where c_l is the velocity of light in the dielectric insulation of the transmission line. The efficiency with which the source circuit can deliver power to the line for eventual reception by the receiving circuit reaches a maximum when the impedances are matched, i.e., $Z = Z_a$. Note that this does not require that $Z = Z_i$, but rather that the input impedance matches the source impedance. If the line impedance differs from the source impedance, the difference can be corrected by properly *tuning* the line length x. In practice, however, proper matching cannot be achieved, although great care is usually taken to insure this matching in high-performance supercom-

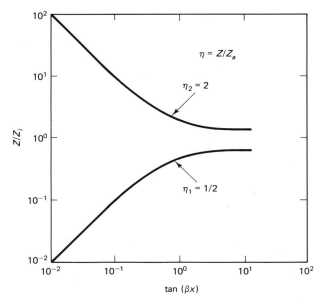

Figure 5.7 Range of mismatches and acceptable line lengths allowable for off-chip interconnections.

puters. For the purposes here, we may assume that a mismatch

$$\frac{1}{\eta} < |Z/Z_a| < \eta \tag{5.63}$$

If we combine (5.62) and (5.63), we find that Z is confined to a range of values that depends upon both η and βx. We illustrate this in Figure 5.7.

In general, one wants to minimize the power requirements by maximizing the impedance Z at a given voltage level ($P = V^2/Z$). Therefore, the area of most interest in Figure 5.7 is that for $Z/Z_i > 1$. It is apparent from this figure that rather large mismatches can be accommodated for short line lengths, i.e., when $\beta x < 1$. This condition can be rephrased as a line whose length is less than one wavelength. In normal coaxial cable, the wavelength at 100 MHz is about 2 meters, so that we are at this limit for all practical purposes, at least with systems generated from a small number of chips. In this case, we can use expansions for the tangent functions, and can write

$$\beta x = (Z_i/Z)[(Z/Z_a) - 1] < (Z_i/Z)(\eta - 1) \tag{5.64}$$

We note from this equation, that if we raise the frequency the wavelength is reduced, which requires that the impedance must also be reduced. Because of the relationship of the power required to the input impedance, we can now specify a limitation on the dissipation by

$$P > (V^2/Z) = (V^2/Z_i)\beta x/(\eta - 1) \tag{5.65}$$

Thus, we see that the power dissipation depends upon the propagation constant β, and hence on the frequency itself. Now, the maximum frequency is related to the delay time, or more importantly to the pulse rise time τ_R. We can set such a relationship as

$$\omega = g_o/\tau_D \tag{5.66}$$

At the limits discussed in the preceding section, g_o is about 5, but is more likely of the order of 10–20. Inserting these values into (5.65) gives us

$$P > \left(V^2/Z_i\right)g_o x/(\eta - 1)c\tau_D \tag{5.67}$$

Finally, we want to replace the intrinsic impedance of the transmission line by its capacitance and propagation velocity through the relationship $\beta/Z_i = \omega C'$, so that

$$P > \left(C'xV^2/\tau_D\right)g_o/(\eta - 1) \tag{5.68}$$

The first thing we now notice is that this result gives essentially a similar limitation on the power in the circuit as the device considerations earlier. The results differ only in the last terms (g_o and the subsequent factors). This is reassuring as the derivations have essentially grown from different sources. We can consequently gain a great deal of confidence in the general conclusions that derive from these discussions.

We note from this approach that the interconnections (even when they are composed of lossless transmission lines) cannot be disconnected from the power requirements on the drive circuits. This is to be expected since the drive circuits must ultimately provide the charge necessary to switch the voltage across the line capacitance. However, we note that this requirement is one of power level and not of speed. The limitations on speed and power are essentially uncoupled (although they interact of course). Even with the ideas of pipelining the interconnection lines, we cannot disassociate ourselves from the impedance considerations of the power necessary to drive the lines.

5.5 ALTERNATIVE INTERCONNECTION CONSIDERATIONS

5.5.1 Multi-Level Interconnects

Current VLSI approaches usually employ at least two levels of on-chip interconnection, which may be through the use of polysilicon for one level and metal for the second, or through the use of two levels of metal. However, future microelectronics has the problem that the polysilicon and many of the metals have too high a value of resistivity. As the line sizes are scaled down, the actual line resistance increases too rapidly and constitutes a significant limitation on down-scaling of devices and circuits. A future approach replaces the polysilicon level of interconnect with either a metal-silicide or a metal, giving effectively two levels of metal interconnects. This is not new, as it has been more or less the standard in GaAs circuitry for some time. The advantages are multifaceted, as this multi-level scheme offers a great deal of potential diversity for design. On the other hand, the crossing of different levels of interconnect offers a limitation as the device size is scaled downward. First, the crossing of different levels of metallization causes a localized capacitance which slows the propagation of signals through the circuit. Secondly, this local capacitance offers a direct *device-device interaction*, in that the signals from one device are parasitically coupled to a different metal layer and consequently to a different device set than originally planned in the layout. In both cases, this additional interaction creates a parasitic effect which affects circuit performance and limits the ultimate packing density that may be achieved with a given technology. It must be pointed out that these effects do not arise just from changing from polysilicon to metal, but from the downscaling of the individual circuit sizes.

5.5.2 Optical Interconnections

A relatively new concept that is receiving serious consideration for multi-chip architectures is the use of optical fibers for high-speed interconnections between chips and/or between boards. It is imperative in any new technology, such as this, to estimate the impact that this technology will have on future systems. However, the speed increase that can be expected in future high-density ULSI chips is so dramatic that one must also be aware of directions being pursued in this area. As we discussed above, the interconnections in large computer systems and between the individual chips or modules are both extensive and a limiting problem for further development of the technology. As these systems evolve, the interconnection problem can be expected to become ever more burdensome, since delays encountered by sending signals over these circuits eventually limit the processing speed of the network itself. Optical interconnection technology has the possibility of contributing significantly in this aspect of future computer networks.

Generally, board-to-board or chip-to-chip interconnections can warrant the high-speed advantage promised by optical interconnection technology. The integration of optical emitters/detectors with electronic switching elements on the same chip appears to be ready for research systems today. Two approaches must be considered, since the promise for optical interconnects usually focuses on the impact of multiplexed signals. In high-speed systems, multiplexing is not likely to be of much impact. For example, a 100 MHz system with 32 bit word lengths would provide a data rate of 3.2 GHz if bit-serially multiplexing is used. Although laser diode systems exist with data rates as high as 12 GHz, it is not clear that the support electronics to multiplex the signals onto the laser exist. For such systems, the more likely impact of optical interconnects lies in arrays of low threshold, quantum well lasers. These will provide a modest speed increase through the effective reduction of the dielectric constant in the propagation medium, providing that the modulation electronics do not slow the data transfer rate of the overall interconnection system.

A second application lies in the realm of relatively low data rate systems, where multiplexing allows the sending of many channels of data over a single high-speed laser channel. Here, GaAs lasers/modulators/multiplexers, integrated onto a single chip, offer a great deal of advantage over the normal interconnection channel. This gain does not come from improvement in the transmission medium, but in the reduction in the sheer number of interconnections that must be made.

REFERENCES

1. R. W. Keyes, *Proc. IEEE*, vol. 63, p. 740 (1975).
2. B. S. Landman and R. L. Russo, *IEEE Trans. Computers*, vol. C-20, p. 1469 (1971).
3. T. Chiba, *IEEE Trans. Computers*, vol. C-27, p. 319 (1978).
4. B. Gilbert, in *GaAs Technology*, ed D. K. Ferry (Sams Inc., Indianapolis, 1985).
5. W. E. Donath, *IEEE Trans. Circuits and Systems*, vol. CAS-26, p. 272 (1979).
6. R. Mueller, H.-J. Pfleiderer, and K.-U. Stein, *IEEE J. Solid State Circuits*, vol. SC-11, p. 1677 (1976).
7. K. Lehovec and R. Zuleeg, *IEEE Trans. Electron. Dev.*, vol. ED-27, p. 1074 (1980).

6

DEVICE-DEVICE INTERACTIONS

As we have seen in the previous chapters, the transition to ultra-large-scale integration confronts the industry with a major problem in handling the enormous complexity, as well as the reliability, of these systems. On the other hand, trends toward the integration of extensively concurrent architectures for computation opens the door to considerable opportunities. One aspect of the merging of these two ideas is that such a complex circuit may have system properties that are significantly different from those expected from just the array of individual devices. It is the purpose of this chapter to begin to discuss these largely cooperative effects. To see how this differs from conventional approaches, we have to recognize that an assumption of the validity of the partition principle is usually invoked. We will examine this below. First, however, it is important to note that new systems problems, which lead to a failure of the partition principle, can be regarded as drawbacks or as possible opportunities to generate new information processing structures.

In conventional descriptions of LSI/VLSI circuits, each device is assumed to behave in the same manner within the total system as it does when it is isolated. The full function of the system (or IC) is determined solely by the interconnection metallization specified to join the individual devices together. A different function can only be assigned to the system by redesigning the interconnection metallizations—a practical impossibility for most systems. The conventional clear separation of device design from system design thus depends ultimately on being able to isolate each individual device from the environment of the other devices except for planned effects occurring through the interconnection matrix. This simplification is likely to be seriously in error for the submicron-configured ULSI systems, where the isolation of one device from another (and by generalization, from the surrounding environment of metallizations) will be far more difficult to achieve.

The possible device-device coupling mechanisms are numerous and include such effects as capacitive coupling, of which line-to-line parasitic capacitance is one example, and wave-function penetration (tunneling and charge spillover) from one device to another. The former is significant, as many people restrict device-device interactions to only those regions where characteristic lengths are of the scale of the carrier wavelength. This would be a serious error. Indeed, for device sizes below, say, 0.4 μm, the line-to-line parasitic capacitance begins to dominate the direct line capacitance in determining the total capacitance of a logic gate. This parasitic capacitance leads to a direct device-device interaction outside the normal circuit or architectural design. The constraints imposed by device-device interactions will have to be included in future architectural design of compact VLSI systems, and this will most easily be accomplished if these constraints are reflected in the system theory description of the architecture itself.

In this chapter, we treat the current (albeit poorly understood) theory of the device-device interaction and its architectural limitations. We first show via a standard hierarchical approach of statistical mechanics that it is the pair-wise nearest neighbor interaction that dominates the device-device effects. (Those not wishing to deal with this complexity should skip this section.) Then, a simple system-theoretic approach illustrates the global restructuring that can occur. Following this, a number of real examples are considered in order to illustrate the effects. We then treat extensively one particular implementation, the lateral surface superlattice. This latter phenomenon is a cooperative (and positive) result of this device-device approach. Finally, we turn to a general automata view of the ULSI chip as a whole.

6.1 NEAREST NEIGHBOR DOMINANCE

At the total circuit (or system) level, control over the array of devices that compose the ULSI structure is exercised by means of control fields (or voltages) and input or feedback currents (or voltages). These make up a set of generalized forces $F_{i,\text{ext}}$, $i = 1, \ldots, N$, where N is the total number of devices which will exceed 10^7 in modern ULSI. These applied generalized forces are screened by a variety of interactions, but lead to a set of local applied forces F_i, which must be found by a total self-consistent method, just as is done in two-dimensional (and three-dimensional) device modeling. In the coupled N-device system, we can write the total Hamiltonian as

$$H = \sum_i H(x_i, F_i) + \sum_{i<j} H_E(x_i, x_j, F_{i,j}) \tag{6.1}$$

where

$$H_E = H_e + H_{ed} \qquad (6.2)$$

is the environment plus device-environment terms and thus represents the coupling between the devices i and j (which is assumed to be an instantaneous pair-wise interaction for simplicity). The variables x_i and x_j refer to complete sets of dynamical variables for the ith and jth devices, respectively. These variables relate to the voltages, currents, and charge characteristics of any one device. We use the generalized form here for simplicity. In the absence of inter-device coupling, the second term on the RHS of (6.1) is zero and we recover the Liouville equation result for which each individual device may be treated separately. Thus, the entire concept of the device-device interaction is contained in the second (interaction) term, and we need only examine how it enters the resulting equations of motion. The terms in (6.1) are assumed to be time-dependent only through the coupling to the generalized, time-dependent forces F_i. We note finally that the set of generalized variables x_i must also include any local, spatially delineated structure such as contacts and interconnects.

In the following, we adopt a matrix projection approach that yields a hierarchy of equations which illustrate the various correlations as they become important. We assume that we may formally separate the kinetic and potential energies as

$$H(x_i, F_i) = p_i^2/2m + \phi_F(x_i) \qquad (6.3)$$

where all external fields are reflected into the generalized local potential ϕ_F. Moreover, we assert that H_E is a pair-wise potential interaction. We have separated the generalized parameters into generalized coordinates x_i and conjugate momenta p_i. The total system density matrix satisfies

$$\frac{\partial \rho}{\partial t} = \hat{H}\rho \qquad (6.4)$$

where $\rho = \rho(x_i, \ldots, x_N; t)$ is an interacting N-device density matrix and $\hat{H}$ is the super-operator corresponding to the Hamiltonian of (6.1). By using the notation of (6.4), we do not have to specify whether we are dealing with quantum or classical systems, since these differ only in the formal form of $\hat{H}$. Let us now introduce the reduced density matrices $\rho_s(x_1, \ldots, x_s; t)$, which are symmetrical with regard to the set $x_1, \ldots, x_s$, time dependent, and normalized in such a way that the expression $\rho_s \, dx_1 \cdots dx_s/2V^s$ gives the probability that the dynamical states of the group of s devices are located, respectively, in the infinitesimal volume elements $dx_1, \ldots, dx_s$ around the points $x_1, \ldots x_s$ at the time t. Thus, we can write

$$\rho_s(x_1, \ldots, x_s; t) = V^s Tr_{s+1, \ldots, N}\{\rho(x_1, \ldots, x_N; t)\} \qquad (6.5)$$

where $1 \leq s \leq N$. Thus, we are producing the reduced density matrices by a trace (or an average) over the residual set $(s + 1, \ldots, N)$. The equation of usual interest is the equation for the distribution function of a single device, $\rho_1(x_1, t)$. It is also desirable here to know $\rho_2(x_1, x_2; t)$, the correlation function for the distribution of the dynamic states of pairs of devices.

We shall then proceed from (6.4), and using (6.1), represent the Liouville equation in the form

$$\frac{\partial \rho}{\partial t} = \sum_{i=1}^{N} \hat{H}(x_i)\rho + \sum_{i<j=1}^{N} \hat{H}_E(r_{ij})\rho \tag{6.6}$$

where $r_{ij} = |x_i - x_j|$ is the vector magnitude of the separation in phase space. In general, we will seek a development for ρ_s, the s-device density matrix. Multiplying both sides of (6.6) by V^s and taking the partial trace over the $s + 1, \ldots, N$ states, we obtain

$$\frac{\partial \rho_s}{\partial t} = \sum_{i=1}^{N} V^s Tr_{s+1,\ldots,N}\{\hat{H}(x_i)\rho\} + \sum_{i<j=1}^{N} V^s Tr_{s+1,\ldots,N}\{\hat{H}_E(r_{ij})\rho\} \tag{6.7}$$

Now, we can make use of the identities (shown here for the quantum case but easily proved as well for the classical case)

$$Tr\{[H(x_i), \rho]\} = Tr\{H(x_i)\rho\} - Tr\{\rho H(x_i)\} = 0 \tag{6.8}$$

$$Tr_{i,j}\{[H_E(r_{ij}), \rho]\} = Tr_{i,j}\{H_E(r_{ij})\rho\} - Tr_{i,j}\{\rho H_E(r_{ij})\} = 0$$

which follow from the cyclic properties of the trace operation in matrix algebra. We can further use the relations $(i, j \leq s)$

$$V^s Tr_{s+1,\ldots,N}\{\hat{H}(x_i)\rho\} = \hat{H}(x_i)V^s Tr_{s+1,\ldots,N}\{\rho\} \tag{6.9a}$$

$$V^s Tr_{s+1,\ldots,N}\{\hat{H}_E(r_{ij})\rho\} = \hat{H}_E(r_{ij})V^s Tr_{s+1,\ldots,N}\{\rho\} \tag{6.9b}$$

By considering the symmetry of the density matrix ρ with regard to the variables $x_1, \ldots, x_N$, we can also write

$$\sum_{i=1}^{s} \sum_{j=s+1}^{N} V^s Tr_{s+1,\ldots,N}\{\hat{H}_E(r_{ij})\rho\}$$

$$= (N - s) \sum_{i=1}^{s} V^s Tr_{s+1,\ldots,N}\{\hat{H}_E(|x_i - x_{s+1}|)\rho\}$$

$$= \frac{N - s}{V} \sum_{i=1}^{s} Tr_{s+1}\{\hat{H}_E(|x_i - x_j|)\rho_{s+1}\} \tag{6.10}$$

We can now use (6.8)–(6.10) in (6.7), so that we obtain

$$\frac{\partial \rho_s}{\partial t} = \hat{H}_s \rho_s + \frac{N - s}{V} \sum_{i=1}^{s} Tr_{s+1}\{\hat{H}_E(|x_i - x_j|)\rho_{s+1}\} \tag{6.11}$$

where

$$H_s = \sum_{i=1}^{s} \left\{ p_i^2/2m + \phi_F(x_i) \right\} + \sum_{i<j=1}^{s} H_E(r_{ij}) \tag{6.12}$$

is the Hamiltonian of an s-device system with the same dynamics as (6.1). These equations, however, are still rather complex, since in order to calculate the single-device density matrix ρ_1, we must know ρ_2, the two-device density matrix, which is in turn coupled to all higher correlation functions through the hierarchy (6.11). However, in many physical situations it is possible to approximate the second or some higher correlation function, or to ignore them altogether as is usually done in the isolated device case. This truncates the hierarchy and allows a closed result to be obtained. For example, a common approximation used is the full partition principle in which each device is assumed to be uncorrelated to others and to set $\rho_2(x_1, x_2) = \rho_1(x_1)\rho_1(x_2)$. Clearly, then *most* device-device interactions disappear, but read on!

In particular, we wish now to look at the one-device density matrix. To ease this, we introduce the two-device correlation function $g_2(x_1, x_2)$ through

$$g_2(x_1, x_2) = \rho_1(x_1)\rho_1(x_2) - \rho_2(x_1, x_2) \tag{6.13}$$

Then

$$\frac{\partial \rho_1}{\partial t} = \left[\hat{H}_1 + \frac{N-1}{V} Tr_2\left\{ \hat{H}_E(|x_1 - x_2|) \right\} \right] \rho_1(x_1)$$

$$- \frac{N-1}{V} Tr_2\left\{ \hat{H}_E(|x_1 - x_2|) g_2(x_1, x_2) \right\} \tag{6.14}$$

The second term in the square brackets is analogous to a Hartree energy for electrons. The potential seen by each device is determined from the average distribution of all other devices $(Tr_2\{ \ldots \rho_1(x_2)\})$. Therefore, if we set $g_2 = 0$, the terms in square brackets lead to the Hamiltonian for an equivalent Hartree equation for the one-device performance, in which each individual device can be treated in isolation only *if an average mean-field background potential is evaluated*. Even with no correlation, an effect due to the multiplicity of devices is observed. Clearly, the deviation from this simpler case arises when correlation between devices begins to become important, a case that already arises when line-to-line capacitance begins to significantly affect circuit behavior. There are in fact two effects here. The first is a global modification that occurs when the Hartree potential differs from zero, for example when a substrate current begins to produce global shifts in substrate bias levels. The second effect is the correlated device behavior. We will discuss these further in Section 6.3. below.

6.2 A CIRCUIT-THEORETIC APPROACH

From the above discussion, we begin to perceive that the onset of device-device interactions can occur even though spatial scales are large compared to an electron wavelength. Indeed, global shifts of bias levels (induced by other device variations) and capacitance coupling are the forerunner effects that can be expected. We want to pursue this idea by using a simple circuit approach to illustrate how global cooperative effects can arise. The basic principles of a system restructuring that can occur are illustrated by a simple circuit-theoretic analogy utilizing component-connection type approaches. First, a special case of isolated devices is developed. Then a connection function (such as the network of desired metallizations for interconnecting logic gates) is introduced to describe the system in terms of the devices and to show how the properties of the connection can alter the system's dynamics. As the individual device dynamics and connections will be nonlinear, it may be expected that although the equations used here are linear, the general result will allow nonlinear synergetic (cooperative) responses for the system.

First, the state equations are examined for an isolated integrator with input-out conditioning. The applicability of this example is examined later. The state equations for each device are then

$$\dot{u}_1 = a_i u_i + b_i y_i, \qquad z_i = c_i u_i \qquad (6.15)$$

where u_i is the state variable and y_i and z_i are the input and output variables for the single device, respectively. For an ensemble of N devices, these become

$$\dot{\mathbf{U}} = \mathbf{AU} + \mathbf{BY}, \qquad \mathbf{Z} = \mathbf{CU} \qquad (6.16)$$

where $\mathbf{A}$, $\mathbf{B}$, and $\mathbf{C}$ are square diagonal matrices and $\mathbf{U}$, $\mathbf{Y}$, and $\mathbf{Z}$ are column matrices. Solving for the transfer function of the individual devices gives (in the Laplace transform domain with a relaxed initial state)

$$\mathbf{Z} = \mathbf{C}(s\mathbf{I} - \mathbf{A})^{-1}\mathbf{BY} \qquad (6.17)$$

So far, it has been considered that each device was isolated from the others. If we describe the connection matrix F through the ansatz

$$\mathbf{Y} = \mathbf{FZ} + \mathbf{LG}, \qquad \mathbf{H} = \mathbf{MZ} \qquad (6.18)$$

where $\mathbf{G}$ and $\mathbf{H}$ are the total system input and output matrices, and $\mathbf{L}$ and $\mathbf{M}$ are conditioning matrices. The connection matrix $\mathbf{F}$ generally describes how the input of a particular device is related to the outputs of other devices, and is thus the system representation of the metallization interconnect chosen for a particular VLSI chip. Equations (6.17) and (6.18) can then be combined to yield the system transfer function as

$$\mathbf{H} = \mathbf{MCB}(s\mathbf{I} - \mathbf{A} - \mathbf{FCB})^{-1}\mathbf{LG} \qquad (6.19)$$

where we have used the fact that $\mathbf{A}$, and hence $(s\mathbf{I} - \mathbf{A})^{-1}$ is diagonal.

Equation (6.19), for the system transfer function, is a special application of the connection function theory of systems, applicable to the integrator. Although we have used this special case, the approach is far more general and is applicable to arbitrary circuits. Further, even though we have assumed an analog signal approach by employing the Laplace transformation for the time variation, the technique is currently extendable to a class of digital circuits, linear sequential circuits, through the description of the systems dynamics in the abstract mathematical concept of an extension field. However, this simple case is adequate to illustrate the major points discussed above, in that a simple extension to digital circuits can be made in the z-transform approach.

The quantity $(s\mathbf{I} - \mathbf{A} - \mathbf{FCB})^{-1}$ plays the conceptual role of a resolvant for the system and the zeroes of $\det(\mathbf{S}) = \det\{(s\mathbf{I} - \mathbf{A} - \mathbf{FCB})\}$ define the various modes of the operation expected. Since $\mathbf{B}$ and $\mathbf{C}$ are diagonal, any deviations of the system response from that defined by $\mathbf{A}$ must arise through the structure of $\mathbf{F}$. For example, if we consider that the system is logically connected, i.e., y_i is connected only to z_j if $j < i$, then $\mathbf{F}$ has elements only in the lower triangle below the main diagonal. Since $\mathbf{A}$ is diagonal, $\mathbf{F}$ does not modify the modes determined by $\mathbf{A}$, i.e., $\det(\mathbf{S}) = \det(s\mathbf{I} - \mathbf{A})$. Only when $\mathbf{F}$ has entries across the main diagonal does this result change. For example, if $y_i = z_{i-1}$, then $\mathbf{F}$ has entries along the diagonal just below the main diagonal. If now the last stage is fed back to the first stage, an entry appears in the upper right corner of $\mathbf{F}$ and one new mode is generated, the collective ring-oscillator mode. This last follows as the last entry altered the topology of the directed graph of $\mathbf{S}$, allowing a new, strongly connected graph to arise.

Let us examine this "ring-oscillator" mode more carefully. If each $y_i = z_{i-1}$ by a matrix element f_{21} in the $\mathbf{FCB}$, matrix, we have

$$\mathbf{S} = (s\mathbf{I} - \mathbf{A} - \mathbf{FCB})$$

$$= \begin{bmatrix} (s - a_{11}) & 0 & 0 & \cdots & +1 \\ f_{21} & (s - a_{22}) & 0 & \cdots & 0 \\ 0 & f_{21} & (s - a_{33}) & \cdots & 0 \\ \vdots & \vdots & \vdots & & \\ 0 & 0 & 0 & \cdots & (s - a_{nn}) \end{bmatrix} \quad (6.20)$$

where the 1 in the upper right corner causes the feedback (negative) from the last stage to the first. Then

$$\det(\mathbf{S}) = (-1)^{n-1} f_{21}^{n-1} + (s - a_{11}) \prod_{i=1}^{n} (s - a_{ii}) \quad (6.21)$$

We note here that all modes are changed. However, the $Tr(\mathbf{S})$ is unchanged, so that the sum of all eigenvalues is unchanged. Normally, each eigenvalue is $\lambda_i = a_{ii}$ (< 0 for stability). The new modes are found from ($a_{ii} = a$)

$$s = a - f_{21}^{1-1/n} e^{2ik\pi/n}, \quad k = 1, 2, \ldots n. \quad (6.22)$$

Now, because the $Tr(\mathbf{S})$ is unchanged, we must have

$$f_{21}^{1-1/n} \sum_{k=1}^{h} e^{2\pi i k/n} = 0 \tag{6.23}$$

which is automatically satisfied. In order to have the oscillator mode, we require n to be odd, so that (6.22) is modified to

$$s = a + f_{21}^{1-1/n} e^{i\pi(2k-1)/n}, \quad k = 1, 2, \ldots n \tag{6.24}$$

Usually, each device is the same as all others, so that $a_{11} = a_{22} = \cdots = a_{nn} = -a$, and the roots of the left-hand plane, unless f_{21} is sufficiently large that the rightmost complex pair just lie in the imaginary axis. Then for

$$f_{21}^{1-1/n} > \frac{a}{Re\left(e^{\pm 2i\pi/n}\right)} \tag{6.25}$$

Clearly, we now require that n, the number of stages, be an odd integer or that the net feedback is negative rather than positive. The gain f_{21} must be just enough to overcome the loss due to the delay time ($a = 1/\tau_d$). Both of these factors are contrary to the usual theory of analog oscillators. But, the ring oscillator is not a usual analog oscillator. Its operation depends upon the delay at each gate, and requires the negative feedback to maintain the alternate switching between on and off states at each gate. Thus, the period of oscillation (twice around in a simple approach) is just

$$T = 2n\tau_d \tag{6.26}$$

where τ_d is the gate delay of a single stage.

In general, the connection function $\mathbf{F}$ can be divided into two parts, $\mathbf{F}_1$ and $\mathbf{F}_2$, where $\mathbf{F}_1$ is the portion of $\mathbf{F}$ that represents the desired metallizations, i.e., the designed architectural circuit yielding

$$\mathbf{S}_1 = s\mathbf{I} - \mathbf{A} - \mathbf{F}_1\mathbf{CB} \tag{6.27}$$

Then $\mathbf{F}_2$ represents the parasitic interactions, such as the parasitic device-device couplings (e.g., the line-to-line coupling capacitance). Thus, a new resolvent S_2,

$$S_2 = S_1 - F_2 CB \tag{6.28}$$

arises with a new set of eigenmodes given by $\det(S_2)$, and the structure of the system is altered in the presence of $\mathbf{F}_2$. As $\mathbf{F}_2$ depends upon the states of $\mathbf{U}$ (voltages, for example), as well as the inputs $\mathbf{G}$, it is entirely conceivable that the system is now strongly nonlinear. In large-scale systems, where sizes are more than a micron in scale, $\mathbf{F}_2$ may reasonably be assumed to be negligible. In future VLSI and ULSI systems of submicron dimensions, this is no longer the case, and the presence of $\mathbf{F}_2$ will have to be accounted for in the design.

The terms in $\mathbf{F}_2$ play the role of the extra terms of (6.14). Contributions to $\mathbf{F}_2$ that do not depend on particular devices enter the effective Hartree potential, while device-dependent terms enter the correlation g_2. Let us illustrate the slaving principles by some further examples. We first consider the case where each y_i is coupled to its linear neighbors $z_{i\pm1}$. Then **FCB** is tri-diagonal, as

$$
\mathbf{S} = \begin{bmatrix}
(s+a) & -b & 0 & \cdots & 0 \\
-b & (s+a) & -b & \cdots & 0 \\
0 & -b & (s+a) & \cdots & 0 \\
\vdots & & & & \\
0 & 0 & 0 & \cdots & (s+a)
\end{bmatrix}
\tag{6.29}
$$

where we have assumed all $a_{ii} = -a$, $\mathbf{B}_{ii} = \mathbf{C}_{ii} = 1$, $\mathbf{F}_{i,i\pm1} = b$. If $b = 0$, $Tr(\mathbf{S}) = -na$ as previously. However, for $b \neq 0$, the eigenvalues span a smooth range from $-a - b$ to $-a + b$. The structure is equivalent to a "tight-binding" system and the range of eigenvalues form a "band" just as in solids. This leads us to an important conclusion: *the existence of device-device coupling that changes the performance of a circuit is not dependent upon the devices being placed in a regular array.*

Generally, we may be interested in time-dependent entries in the matrix $\mathbf{F_2CB}$. These entries may vary due to external time-dependent properties, such as soft errors, or global control functions intended to restructure the system performance. We can illustrate this latter by following an approach due to Haken [1]. We assume that b_1 and b_2 are two entries in the upper triangular region of S. The term b_1 represents the desired coupling, perhaps to achieve a ring-oscillator, but b_2 is a parasitic coupling in the system. Let us assume that

$$
\frac{\partial b_1}{\partial t} = -\gamma_1 b_1 - \alpha b_1 b_2
\tag{6.30}
$$

$$
\frac{\partial b_2}{\partial t} = -\gamma_2 b_2 - \beta b_1^2
\tag{6.31}
$$

Here, we have assumed that b_1 is controlled directly by state variable u_i through $\gamma_i = \gamma_i(u_i)$ and that b_2 depends strongly upon b_1. Hence, b_1 drives the interaction. Moreover, b_1 depends somewhat more weakly on b_2. Let us further assume that changes in b_2 occur rapidly with respect to changes in $b_1 (\gamma_2 \gg \gamma_1)$, so that b_2 follows b_1 without delay. Hence we can approximate (6.31) by

$$
b_2 = -(\beta/\gamma_2)b_1^2
\tag{6.32}
$$

$$
\frac{\partial b_1}{\partial t} = -\gamma_1 b_1 + (\alpha\beta/\gamma_2)b_1^3
\tag{6.33}
$$

If $\gamma_1 > (\alpha\beta/\gamma_2)$, then b_1 is a stable function, and the system performs as desired. However, we recall that γ_1 depends upon u_1 and γ_2 depends upon u_2, so that there is a nonlinear feedback in the system. Under certain conditions, we may be able to drive the system to a condition with

$$\alpha\beta/\gamma_2 > \gamma_1 \tag{6.34}$$

in which case the system goes unstable. In particular if γ_1 becomes such that (6.34) is satisfied, the system *bifurcates*, and the modes of operation are completely changed. We note also that we can modulate the terms α and β *from outside the system*, so that it is possible to use external control over the interconnects to induce bifurcations in the system performance.

6.3 CURRENT EXAMPLES

The effects of device-device interactions on device and circuit behavior currently can be found in ULSI structures. The most commonly observed effects are latchup and hot carriers with their subsequent substrate current and minority carrier current. While these effects can currently be controlled by either fabrication or circuit techniques, in ULSI circuits major device and circuit behavior modifications will occur.

A semiconductor-controlled rectifier (SCR) is composed of four alternating doped regions (see Figure 6.1). The structure can also be thought of as consisting of a PNP and an NPN bipolar transistor configured in a circuit such that positive feedback can saturate both transistors. This saturated condition is called latchup and is characterized by the sudden drop in output voltage as shown in Figure 6.2. The output voltage abruptly switches from V_{BE} to V_n, the holding voltage. A minimum of the holding current, I_n, must flow to keep the circuit latched-up. The important point is that once the circuit is in latch-up, it cannot be switched off without removal of the power supply.

In a CMOS n-well structure (see Figure 6.3) the SCR structure consists of the PMOS P^+ source, the N well, the P substrate, and the NMOS source. This SCR structure can be turned on by terminal overvoltage, radiation induced currents, internal switching transients or optically generated photocurrents. Once latch-up has commenced, functional upset and even chip destruction can occur—a truly destructive device-device interaction.

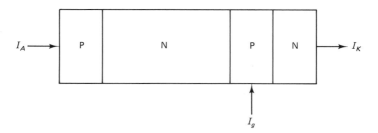

Figure 6.1   Semiconductor-controlled rectifier (SCR) structure.

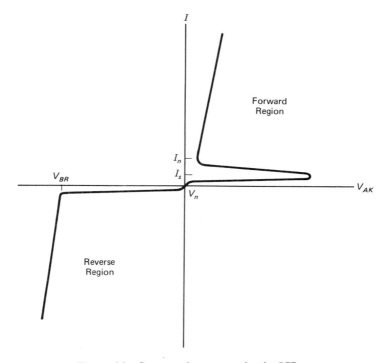

Figure 6.2   Current-voltage curves for the SCR.

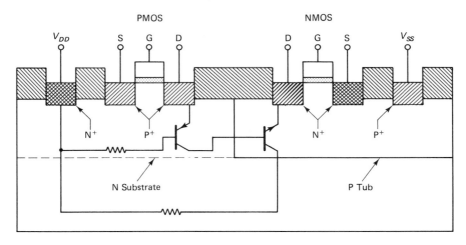

Figure 6.3   CMOS *n*-well structure that illustrates the lateral SCR that is thought to be responsible for latch-up.

The current latch-up prevention techniques being currently used are beta reduction, bias control, and layout. The beta of each transistor can be reduced by reducing the lifetime in the base region, degrading the collector efficiency, increasing lateral base width and the use of Schottky junctions. Bias control can be used externally to prevent the forward bias of the emitters. Also, the use of epitaxial layers to reduce resistance, and hence the forward-diode voltage drop, reduces the probability of forward biasing the emitter-base junctions.

Layout restrictions are one of the most common forms of latch-up reduction. Careful location of sources, guard rings, and deep isolation oxide trenchs are used to isolate devices from their neighbors. The sacrifice is reduced circuit density and complexity of layout.

Another example of device-device interaction is that which arises from substrate majority and minority carrier currents. The generation of these currents by impact ionization has previously been discussed in Chapter 2. Simply, the substrate current in NMOS results from the holes generated by electron-hole pair generation through impact ionization. These holes are swept out of the drain depletion region and become substrate current. This substrate current can interact with neighboring devices and cause debiasing of the source-substrate junction, which causes the $I_D - V_D$ output current to be modified, and can even cause device breakdown. Also, threshold voltage variations in neighboring devices have been observed from changes in the substrate potential. This also occurs in MESFET devices, under the guise of "back-gating" or "side-gating."

Another, and possibly more important, mechanism causing device-device interaction is minority carrier injection into neighboring devices. As holes are generated by primary impact ionization in the drain depletion region, they are accelerated out of this region. The probability exists that a second collision causing ionization can occur. This secondary impact ionization will cause another electron-hole pair to be created. The momentum of the collision can cause both of the created carriers to be injected into the bulk. This causes an increase in substrate current (holes) as well as injection of minority carriers (electrons) into the substrate. These minority carriers can drift for hundreds of microns, affecting memory nodes and causing logic state changes.

Recently, it has been suggested that secondary impact ionization is insignificant in the generation of minority carriers when compared with photons generated during primary impact ionization. These photons can travel hundreds of microns and then generate electron-hole pairs. The reason that the difference in generation mechanism is important is that, if secondary impact ionization is dominant, in CMOS devices a reverse biased tub will keep the minority carriers from drifting and interfering with nearby circuits. If photon generation is dominant, reverse biasing the tub will not have an effect on minority carriers. Therefore, device-device isolation could be very difficult at small geometries.

6.4 LATERAL SURFACE SUPERLATTICES

As semiconductor technology continues to pursue the scaling down of IC device dimensions into the submicron and ultra-submicron regimes, many novel and interesting questions will emerge concerning the physics of charged particles in semiconductors. One of the more important topics to be considered is that of carrier confinement in structures that reduce the dimensionality of the system. Notable among these structures are MOS quantized inversion layers discussed earlier, and the heterojunction superlattice. In particular, the fabrication of the quantum-well superlattice has been possible due to the advent of molecular-beam epitaxy (MBE) and metal-organic CVD (MO-CVD) technology.

The concept of a superlattice, as it is currently interpreted, was first put forward by Esaki and Tsu [2] in terms of a layered semiconductor structure, such as obtainable by MBE and MO-CVD. Indeed, the general potential and superlattice energy structure have been verified by careful optical experiments.

Lateral superlattices, in which the superstructure lies in a surface or hetero-structure layer [3, 4], offer considerable advantages for obtaining superlattice effects in planar technology. We shall illustrate here how such lateral superlattices can be prepared by standard MOS processing. The surface MOS structure is formally similar to an array of CCD devices, and these superlattices can be fabricated through the use of electron-beam or ion-beam lithography. Other approaches, using selective area epitaxial growth are discussed below. If superlattice gate arrays can be fabricated with a spacing less than the appropriate correlation length, then superlattice effects should manifest themselves in the planar surface. While being a distinct limitation to down-scaling of semiconductor device arrays, the collective effects which arise due to these lateral superlattices are interesting in their own right and offer new device capabilities.

The lateral superlattice offers conceptual as well as technological advantages over the layered superlattice in terms of achieving the desired quantum-well transport effects. In essence, the reason for this is that the mini-bands in the one-dimensional layered superlattice are not separated by real mini-gaps, but are "connected" by the two-dimensional transverse continuum of states. In order to create true mini-gaps, a multi-dimensional superlattice is required. This can be achieved by a lateral superlattice imposed in a quantized inversion layer. We discuss the quantum mechanics of these structures in this section. Those not versed in this language may choose to skip on to Section 6.5.

6.4.1 Surface Structure

The concept of a lateral superlattice along a surface has considerable advantages, among which is the ability to control the magnitude of surface

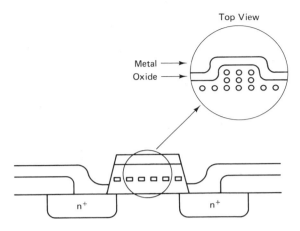

Figure 6.4 The MOS surface superlattice in which an array of metal gates induces a super potential.

potential seen by an inversion layer. The basic structure is shown in Figure 6.4. The periodic gate array buried in the dielectric differs from a normal CCD array in that a blanket top gate structure has been added to provide gap potential control without requiring critical alignment of successive levels. If the periodic gates are biased positively, the surface potential for electrons decreases under the gate electrodes, and to a lesser extent in the gaps. Minority carrier generation, injection from an FET source, or optical pumping, creates the carriers necessary to form the inversion layer under the gates. Thus, in addition to the normal average surface potential, a periodic super-lattice potential is seen by the inversion layer electrons. The presence of the top electrode allows for critical control of the relative strengths of both the average potential and the superlattice potential.

The effective superlattice potential $U(x, y)$ can be expected to vary along the structure in a form given by

$$U(x, y) = 4U_o\cos(2\pi x/d)\cos(2\pi y/d) \tag{6.35}$$

By introducing a change of variables $u = x + y, v = x - y$, with

$$\frac{\partial}{\partial x} = 2^{-1/2}\left(\frac{\partial}{\partial v} + \frac{\partial}{\partial u}\right), \qquad \frac{\partial}{\partial y} = 2^{-1/2}\left(\frac{\partial}{\partial u} - \frac{\partial}{\partial v}\right) \tag{6.36}$$

the effective two-dimensional Schrödinger equation for the interface electrons in the inversion layer is given by

$$\left\{\frac{d^2}{dv^2} + \frac{d^2}{du^2} + \frac{2m^*}{\hbar^2}\left(E - 2U_o\cos\left(\frac{2\pi u}{d}\right) - 2U_o\cos\left(\frac{2\pi v}{d}\right)\right)\right\}\psi_1(u, v) = 0 \tag{6.37}$$

This equation is now separable using a product form $\psi_1(u)\psi_2(v)$, which yields two effective one-dimensional Schrödinger equations of the form

$$\left\{\frac{d^2}{du^2} + \frac{2m^*}{\hbar^2}\left(E_1 - 2U_o\cos\left(\frac{2\pi u}{d}\right)\right)\right\}\psi_1(u) = 0 \qquad (6.38)$$

Introducing the reduced variables (with $g = 2\pi/d$)

$$\xi = \frac{gu}{2}, \qquad a = \frac{8m^*E}{\hbar^2 g^2} = \frac{m^*d^2 U}{\hbar^2\pi^2}, \qquad q = \frac{8m^*U}{\hbar^2 g^2}\frac{m^*d^2 U}{\hbar^2\pi^2} \qquad (6.39)$$

(6.38) can be rewritten as

$$\frac{d^2\psi(\zeta)}{d\zeta^2} + [a - 2q\cos(2\zeta)]\psi(\zeta) = 0 \qquad (6.40)$$

which may be immediately recognized as the Mathieu equation. For $q = 0$, all values of a (and hence of the energy E) are allowed. However, when $q \neq 0$, gaps open in the spectrum of a. For small q, the lowest gap is centered approximately at the point $a = 1$, and higher gaps occur approximately at $a = 4, 9, \ldots, n^2$. The general energy structure is shown in Figure 6.5. It is very important to note that the general solution to the Mathieu equation is of Bloch form

$$\psi(\zeta) = e^{ik\zeta}p(\zeta) \qquad (6.41)$$

where $P(\zeta)$ is a periodic function of period π. This is of course expected for the periodic potential. For the first mini-gap to be centered at a particular energy W, we require $a = 1$, and from (6.39)

$$\hbar^2\pi^2/2m^*d^2 = W \qquad (6.42)$$

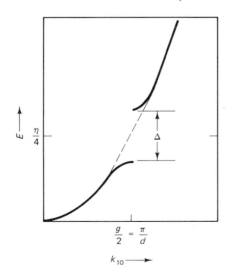

Figure 6.5 The general energy structure of the minigaps in the energy spectrum opened by the periodic potential.

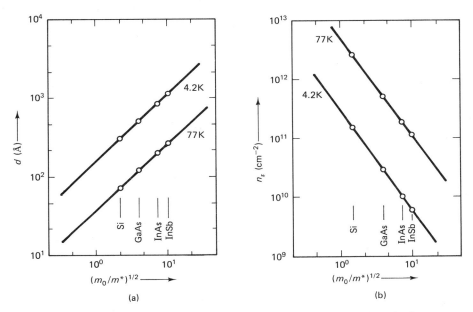

Figure 6.6 The first miniband for a bandwidth of $6k_BT$. (a) Spacing. (b) State density.

or the required spacing is

$$d = \left(\hbar^2\pi^2/2m^*W \right)^{1/2} \tag{6.43}$$

In Figure 6.6, we show a plot of the d values required to achieve an energy width of $W = 6k_BT$ in the lowest band ($\eta/4 = W$). We also show the number of states in the lowest miniband, which is closely related to the surface carrier density required in the inversion layer to fill the first miniband. It will be noted that these densities correspond to a relatively strong inversion layer existing at the surface. For these densities, the Fermi level at low temperature will be well into the conduction band.

The first mini-gap will have a value for $q < 1$, given approximately by $\Delta_a = a(\Delta) = 1.9q$. For $U = 0.01$ V, we find that $\Delta_a = 2.9k_BT$ at 77K and $52.4k_BT$ at 4.2K, corresponding to rather large gaps when compared to the mini-band energy width. It is clear that relatively small induced superlattice potentials are required to produce the mini-band/mini-gap structure. Indeed, surface band-bending corresponding to roughly one trapped electron under each gate could produce sufficient potential to be noticeable at 4.2K. Evidently, from Figure 6.6, lower effective mass material is favored. Whereas Si requires d ~ 100 Å in order to produce such superlattices, the effects should be observable in InAs and InSb for d ~ 500 Å. The size of the potential is also crucial. For example, if we want the gap to be equal to the band-width, we

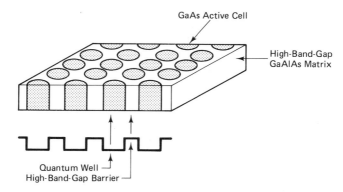

Figure 6.7   The heterostructure surface superlattice in GaAlAs.

require $U = (\eta/4)^{2/3}$. We note that, while the sizes of the gaps and bands are determined by the electron wavelength, we really require the inelastic mean free path to be large compared to d.

A second possible structure is shown in Figure 6.7. Here it must be assumed that a thin GaAlAs epitaxial layer is patterned by high-resolution lithography [5]. Thus, holes can be physically etched in the epitaxial layer and GaAs regrown in these holes be selective-area epitaxy. (This is just one of a large number of possible schemes for fabricating such a structure.) In such a structure, the electrons are tightly bound in the GaAs regions. For an energy barrier of 0.5 V, and a GaAs well diameter of 75 Å, only two energy levels are found in the wells. We can solve the cylindrical boundary value problem, in which the energy levels of the isolated well are given by the solutions of the transcendental equation

$$T_n(\gamma a) K_n'(\mu a) - (\gamma/\mu) T_n'(\gamma a) K_n(\mu a) = 0$$

where

$$\gamma = \left(2m^*E/\hbar^2\right)^{1/2}, \qquad \mu = \left(-\gamma^2 + 2m^*U/\hbar^2\right)^{1/2}$$

and a is the well radius. The index n refers to the $\exp(in\phi)$ rotational component of the wave function, and the prime denotes differentiation with respect to the argument. For $2a = 75$ Å, the lowest eigenvalue has $n = 0$, while the second eigenvalue has $n = 1$.

The above eigenvalues can be used in a tight-binding calculation of the structural array, which gives results equivalent to Figure 6.5. For a well spacing of 150 Å, the energy levels remain tightly bound, with values of 0.164 eV and 0.318 eV. For comparison, the Mathieu equation approach also shows non-dispersive energy levels on this size scale, but gives the eigenvalues as 0.2 eV and 0.41 eV. However, if the peak-to-peak amplitude of the cosine potential is reduced by 10% (to 0.45 eV rather than 0.5 eV), the eigenvalues are reduced to 0.16 eV and 0.32 eV. Thus, weakening the potential slightly counteracts the tendency of the cosine function to raise the energy levels in the well. Now, this structure is probably of only theoretical interest. The important point, however, is that the two extremes of approach yield the same results. This is encouraging as the relationship of Mathieu functions to Bloch functions is important for transport calculations.

If suitable materials are selected, it appears that lateral superlattices can be fabricated by next generation technology, or indeed can be expected to arise in ULSI arrays. In fact, the *I-V* relationships discussed below have been seen in a preliminary HEMT structure in which the lateral superlattice is patterned in the gate metal by *e*-beam lithography [6]. The fact that these structures can show synergetic behavior under conditions of population inversion (discussed below) suggests that new functional performance characteristics may be important for their operation as devices. Here, "new" is used in the sense that normal device operation is hindered due to strong device-device interactions so that other modes of operation will arise. In such MOS structures as discussed here, filling of a mini-band readily presents the conditions for what is called a Kohn anomaly, or dielectric instability. Therefore, if a population inversion is induced by some technique, there exists the possibility of zeroes appearing in the dielectric function. In this case, a non-zero value of superlattice potential could arise without an applied potential, leading to a charge instability. Although such synergetic behavior may be expected here, it can also arise in the device arrays due to the device-device interaction, and could conceptually be programmed by system structure, as we discussed in Section 6.2. We return to this further below.

6.4.2 Transport

As we have seen above, various superlattice structures give rise to energy mini-bands that vary sinusoidally across the mini-zone, in at least one dimension, and which have relatively narrow widths. The shape of such bands results in interesting electrical transport properties. The one-dimensional superlattice is one such structure, and the surface superlattice is another. In this section, the average velocity and the energy are found by taking the first and second moments of the Boltzmann transport equation with an assumed form for the distribution function. A constant electric field is assumed to be applied in the plane of the sinusoidal bands, while the energy shape in the other two dimensions is arbitrary. Here, we shall take a Wigner representation as the initial equilibrium distribution. This treatment is valid for a single energy band at low to moderate fields with the sinusoidal band less than half-filled with carriers. For a band over half-filled, the Pauli exclusion principle must be taken into account. Also, a constant relaxation time is assumed, which is not strictly valid since the density of states for cosinusoidal bands in two dimensions show Van Hove singularities which lead to peaks in the scattering rates. Nevertheless, we shall see below that the constant relaxation time approximation is not too bad an approximation due to the high scattering rates. Finally, the distribution function is assumed to be homogeneous in space.

The form of the time-independent, homogeneous Wigner transport equation in the relaxation time approximation is

$$\frac{eF}{\hbar}\frac{\partial f(\vec{k})}{\partial k_z} = -\frac{f(\vec{k}) - f_o(\vec{k})}{\tau} \tag{6.44}$$

where the field and the direction of the superlattice are taken to be the z-direction. $f_o(\vec{k})$ is found from the equilibrium quantum density distribution by using the Hamiltonian equivalence principle, followed by a Wigner transformation, which leads to the form $E = \varepsilon - \varepsilon \cos(dk_z)$ to give

$$f_o(k) = e^{\beta\{\varepsilon - \varepsilon\cos(dk_z)\}} f_o(k_x, k_y) \tag{6.45}$$

in which ε is the half-width of the energy band of the sinusoidal band and d is related to the periodic spacing of the superlattice.

Taking the first moments of the velocity in the z-direction and the second moment (the total energy) results in the following two equations

$$\frac{eF}{\hbar}\int_{-L}^{L}\!\!\!\int v_z \frac{\partial f(\vec{k})}{\partial k_z} d^3k = -\frac{n\langle v_z\rangle}{\tau} \tag{6.46}$$

$$\frac{eF}{\hbar}\int_{-L}^{L}\!\!\!\int E \frac{\partial f(\vec{k})}{\partial k_z} d^3k = -\frac{n\langle E\rangle}{\tau} + \frac{n\langle E_o\rangle}{\tau} \tag{6.47}$$

where $L = \pi/d$ and $\langle S\rangle$ is defined as the average of the quantity S. Here, E_o is the equilibrium energy without an applied field.

To proceed further, the analytical expressions for v_z and E must be assigned. We use here the assumed energy band shape, and

$$v_z = (\varepsilon d/\hbar)\sin(dk_z) \tag{6.48}$$

$$E = \{\varepsilon - \varepsilon\cos(dk_z)\} + E(k_x, k_y) \tag{6.49}$$

The LHS of both moment equations may be integrated by parts in the z-direction to yield

$$\frac{eF}{\hbar}\iint d^2k \left\{ Ef(\vec{k})\Big|_{-L}^{L} - \int_{-L}^{L}\frac{\partial E}{\partial k_z}f(\vec{k})\,dk_z \right\} = -\frac{n\langle E\rangle}{\tau} + \frac{n\langle E_o\rangle}{\tau} \tag{6.50}$$

$$\frac{eF}{\hbar}\iint d^2k \left\{ v_z f(\vec{k})\Big|_{-L}^{L} - \int_{-L}^{L}\frac{\partial v_z}{\partial k_z}f(\vec{k})\,dk_z \right\} = -\frac{n\langle v_z\rangle}{\tau} \tag{6.51}$$

Since v_z vanishes at L and $-L$, the first term on the left-hand side of (6.51) is zero. Further, the distribution function is periodic with regard to the reduced Brillouin zone and thus the first term on the left of (6.50) also vanishes. After some further simplifications, these reduce to a form that can be written as

$$(efd^2/\hbar^2)n\{\langle E\rangle - (\varepsilon + \langle E_t\rangle)\} = -n\langle v_z\rangle/\tau \tag{6.52}$$

$$-eFn\langle v_z\rangle = -(n/\tau)\{\langle E\rangle + \langle E_o\rangle\} \tag{6.53}$$

where $\langle E_t\rangle$ is the average energy perpendicular to the field. Solving the above equations simultaneously gives the expressions for the velocity and energy as

$$\langle v_z\rangle = \{(\varepsilon + \langle E_t\rangle) - \langle E_o\rangle\}\left(\frac{eF\alpha^2}{1 + (eF\alpha)^2}\right) \tag{6.54}$$

$$\langle E\rangle = \frac{\langle E_o\rangle - (\varepsilon + \langle E_t\rangle)}{1 + (eF\alpha)^2} + (\varepsilon + \langle E_t\rangle) \tag{6.55}$$

where $\alpha = 2\pi/\hbar L$.

The velocity as a function of field has the same basic analytical form as that obtained earlier by Lebwohl and Tsu [7] except for the energy factor in front of the expression for the field. The difference is caused by the different equilibrium distribution chosen. In this latter work, the authors assumed the initial distribution to be a zero temperature Fermi-Dirac. Here, the distribution is a real temperature one that includes the details of the band shape. Note that the velocity as a function of the electric field shows negative differential conductivity (NDC) and also exhibits the general shape expected.

The energy at zero field is just the equilibrium energy for zero drift as expected. As the field is increased toward infinity, the energy approaches the half-band energy, which is the contribution for the sinusoidal band itself, plus the energy in the transverse directions. The energy in the z-direction approaches this limit asymptotically due to the tendency of the electrons to undergo Bloch oscillations in the reduced Brillouin zone. Although we have assumed only a particular band shape and obtained the NDC, the cause must be carriers cycling through the bands by these Bloch oscillations. As mentioned above, preliminary studies have shown the presence of the NDC in a structure fabricated in a HEMT [6].

To compare with the simple approach above, we have also carried out a Monte Carlo calculation of the transport in an LSSL, using standard techniques. The model chosen was that of Figure 6.7, although the effects differ little from those of the MOS array. The square lattice array of GaAs cylinders in the background of GaAlAs creates a square array of potential wells, as discussed above. The scattering processes for the surface superlattice are calculated for acoustic and polar optical phonons using the two-dimensional density-of-states appropriate to the cosinusoidal energy bands. A Van Hove singularity occurs in the density-of-states at the half-band energy and produces a singularity in the scattering rate. This singularity was removed by including the self-energy corrections due to the phonons, which become important in the vicinity of the singularity. The widely spaced discrete energy levels in the third dimension allows scattering and transport in that dimension to be neglected.

In this surface superlattice, as in others, the conduction band splits into subbands. The lowest energy mini-band was nearly flat, so that transport dominantly occurs in the second mini-band. This energy dispersion of this mini-band is given by

$$E = E_o - (E_o/2)\{\cos(dk_x) + \cos(dk_y)\}$$

where $E_o = 0.05$ eV is the half-width of the energy band and $d \sim 100$ Å is the periodic distance. The satellite valleys and next subband are at energies of 0.3 eV and 0.2 eV, respectively, above the subband under consideration, so that their contribution to the transport of electrons is insignificant, since there are no intermediate states through which the electrons can scatter to these upper levels.

The overall transport properties of this system were calculated by an ensemble Monte Carlo technique, and the results are shown in Figure 6.8, where the velocity-field curves are displayed. The dashed curves are for transport in the (10) direction while the solid curves are for transport along the (11) direction. At low fields, both curves show a linear region as expected for most structures. At approximately 8–10 kV/cm, the curves begin to bend over to the peak near 13 kV/cm. As the field is further increased, the velocity begins to decrease for this model, and continues to decrease to zero as the field tends to infinity.

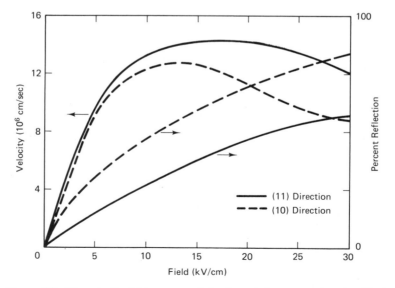

Figure 6.8 The velocity field curves and fraction of electrons undergoing Bloch oscillations.

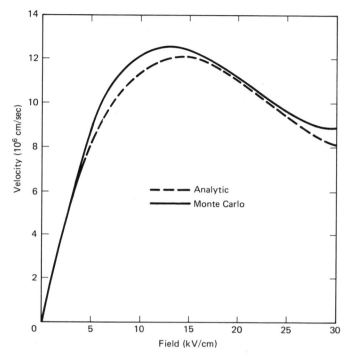

Figure 6.9 Comparison of the Monte Carlo results with the simple, analytic theory.

The negative differential conductivity is the result of electrons being able to cycle through the reduced Brillouin zone many times before they are scattered. The process of the electrons cycling through the zone is called a Bloch oscillation, and can only occur when the band is narrow enough to allow a moderate field to move the electrons beyond the half-band energy. The percentage of electrons undergoing Bloch oscillations is also shown in Figure 6.8.

One can compare the two methods of calculating the transport to determine the validity of the general results of (6.54) and (6.55). This is done in Figure 6.9, where the low field mobility has been taken as the one fitting parameter. The agreement is quite good, better in fact than one would normally expect. It is felt that this is because of the relatively high scattering rates in the structure.

6.4.3 Dielectric Response

In situations where the lowest mini-band is full (or the Fermi energy lies in the mini-gap), it can be expected that excitations of carriers across the mini-gap will produce potential contributions that lead to renormalization of the mini-gap. These effects are well known in bulk semiconductors, leading for example to correlation and exchange energy contributions to band-gap narrowing. Whereas a Coulomb contribution to the potential of a few millivolts is small when compared to a band gap of 1–2 V, it can be a dramatic effect on a mini-gap whose total value is only 10 mV or so. This effect was carefully examined by Kroemer [8] for the case of a one-dimensional superlattice, such as can occur in an organic chain polymer. In the following, the general approach of Kroemer is followed for the LSSL. The basic idea is of course that charge fluctuations across the mini-gap lead to a Coulomb potential that screens the applied potential. However, when a fluctuation arises with $q = 2k_F$, instabilities can arise.

Indeed, even the instability follows from a general treatment of electron-electron interactions and their role in screening of an external potential. In the normal case, the instability at $q = 2k_F$ arises as a logarithmic singularity (in three dimensions) that leads to a very high value of the dielectric constant ε. The electron-electron contributions to the static dielectric constant will be negative if there exists a region where $\partial f_o / \partial E > 0$. If the electronic contribution is large enough, this negative sign will allow the total dielectric constant to be driven to zero. This corresponds physically to a population inversion such as occurs in a laser. In the following we take the value of the principal mini-gap to be $2U$ (rather than $1.9U$ as found above) for simplicity.

The superlattice potential $U(x, y)$ can be considered to be composed of two portions as

$$U(x, y) = U_a(x, y) + U_e(x, y) \tag{6.56}$$

where U_a is the intrinsic (or applied) potential if the electrons were uniformly distributed and U_e is the electronic contribution to the total potential. The intrinsic potential will have the same form as (6.35). For simplicity, we concentrate primarily now on excitations along either the x-axis or y-axis, so that $q = 2^{-1/2}(g, g)$ (in the u, v coordinates). It may be assumed that the electronic contribution will have the same periodicity as the gates themselves and as the intrinsic potential.

The total resulting potential is just the screened potential U. By introducing a spatial Fourier transform representation, this can be written in terms of the effective dielectric function as

$$U = U_a \varepsilon^{-1}(q, \omega \to 0) \tag{6.57}$$

where

$$\varepsilon(q) = 1 - \frac{e \Delta\rho(q)}{U \varepsilon_s q^2} \tag{6.58}$$

Here

$$\Delta\rho = -\frac{eU}{w}\sum_{\vec{k},\alpha}\frac{f_\alpha(\vec{k}) - f_\alpha(\vec{k} - \vec{q})}{E(\vec{k}) - E(\vec{k} - \vec{q})}$$

is the non-uniform space charge, where $\vec{q}$ is the wave vector associated with the potential field, $\vec{k}$ is a two-dimensional wave vector of the electrons and w is the thickness of the inversion layer. The electron population is characterized by $f_\alpha(\vec{k})$, where α is a spin or band index. In the Mathieu equation approach, we take

$$q = g(1 + \gamma)(a_u + a_v)/2^{1/2} \tag{6.59}$$

where $\gamma = 2|\vec{k}|/g - 1$ is the normalized value of k measured from the zone edge. This is appropriate to the case where E_F lies in the mini-gap. Then for $\vec{k} = (q/2)\vec{a}_x$,

$$E(\vec{k}) - E(\vec{k} - \vec{q}) \sim 2\{U^2 + \eta^2\gamma^2\cos^2\theta\}^{1/2} \tag{6.60}$$

where $\eta = \hbar^2 g^2/2m^*$ and θ is the planar angle away from the x-axis.

We break the k-summation into parts with the general form

$$\sum \rightarrow \frac{1}{4\pi^2}\int_0^{2\pi}d\theta\int_0^\infty k\,dk = \frac{g}{16\pi^2}\int_0^{2\pi}d\theta\int_1^\infty(\gamma + 1)\,d\gamma \tag{6.61}$$

The angular integration is relatively straightforward and

$$I_o = \int_0^{2\pi}(U^2 + \gamma^2\eta^2\cos^2\theta)^{-1/2}\,d\theta = \frac{4}{U}K(i\eta\gamma/U)$$

$$= (U^2 + \gamma^2\eta^2)^{-1/2}K\{\eta\gamma/(U^2 + \eta^2\gamma^2)^{1/2}\} \tag{6.62}$$

where $K(\cdot)$ is a complete elliptic integral of the first kind.

In order to carry out the γ-integration, it is necessary to have a form for $f(k)$. The simplest choice, representing a population transfer from the lowest mini-band to the second mini-band (along the x-axis) is given by Figure 6.10. This form essentially is a zero-temperature Fermi-Dirac in equilibrium, but which has been supplemented by the charge transfer. Analytically, this can be written

$$f(\gamma) = \begin{cases} 1, & -1 < \gamma < -F_T \\ 1 - \delta, & -F_T < \gamma < 0 \\ \delta, & 0 < \gamma < F_T \\ 0, & \gamma > F_T \end{cases} \tag{6.63}$$

Inserting (6.61)–(6.63) into (6.58), we arrive at

$$\varepsilon = 1 + \lambda S(U)/\lambda_0 \tag{6.64}$$

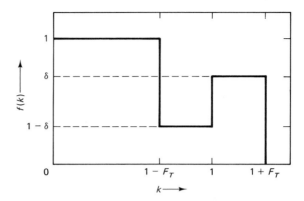

Figure 6.10 Form of the distribution function assumed, with a fractional population inversion.

where

$$\lambda = \frac{2m^*d^2\varepsilon_o}{wm_o\varepsilon_s}, \qquad \lambda_o = \frac{\pi^2\eta^2\varepsilon_o}{e^2m_o} = 16.4 \text{ Å}$$

and

$$S(U) = \eta \int_0^{F_T} K(\eta\gamma/L)\left(\frac{\gamma - 1}{L}\right) d\gamma - 2\eta\delta \int_0^{F_T} K(\eta\gamma/L)\frac{\gamma}{L} d\gamma$$

$$= \frac{\eta}{U}\int_0^{F_T} K(i\eta\gamma/U)(\gamma - 1) d\gamma - \frac{2\eta\delta}{U}\int_0^{F_T} K(i\eta\gamma/U)\gamma d\gamma$$

where $L = (U^2 + \eta^2\gamma^2)^{1/2}$ and the first form of (6.62) has been reintroduced. These integrals may be readily evaluated to give

$$S(U) = \frac{U}{\eta}\left\{\left(1 + \eta^2/U^2\right)^{1/2} + 2U/\eta\right\}\left\{K(\alpha) - E(\alpha)\right\}$$

$$- \frac{2\delta U}{\eta}\left(1 + \eta^2F_T^2/U^2\right)^{1/2}\left\{K(\alpha') - E(\alpha')\right\} \qquad (6.65)$$

where $\alpha = \eta/(\eta^2 + U^2)^{1/2}$, $\alpha' = \eta F_T/(\eta^2F_T + U^2)^{1/2}$, and we have used several properties of the elliptic integrals to reach the final form.

The form in (6.65) is not very transparent, but it can be simplified by noting that $U < F_T$ (or ηF_T) will generally be applicable. With this in mind, noting that $\alpha, \alpha' \le 1$, and using asymptotic limits of K and E, (6.65) may be rewritten as

$$S(U) \sim \frac{1}{3}\ln\left\{\frac{4(U/\eta)^{2\delta F_T - 1}\left(1 + U^2/\eta^2\right)}{\left[4\left(F_T2 + U^2\eta^2\right)^{1/2}\right]^{2\delta F_T}}\right\}^{1/2} \qquad (6.66)$$

It should be noted that the nature of $S(U)$ changes dramatically for $2\delta F_T > 1$. In this case $S(U)$ is negative and can lead to conditions where $\varepsilon = 0$. This point will be returned to in the next paragraph. The condition $2\delta F_T > 1$ corresponds to one-half of the free carriers being transferred into the upper mini-band, a condition of true population inversion.

If a population inversion is induced by some technique, the negative value of $S(U)$ leads to the possibility of zeroes appearing in the dielectric response. In this case, a non-zero value of U can exist without the application of the external field U_a. This means that the superlattice potential can be set up by a charge instability under the gates themselves. The charge instability spontaneously leads to a charge-density wave which creates the superlattice potential. The condition for $\varepsilon = 0$ can readily be found by combining (6.64) and (6.66) as

$$U \sim (\eta/4) F_T^{(\nu+1)/\nu} \exp(-3\lambda_o/\nu\lambda) \tag{6.67}$$

where $\nu = 2\delta F_T - 1$. For $\nu = 0$, the superlattice is zero, but for $\nu > 0$, $U > 0$. These conditions of population inversion, such as can occur under intense optical pumping, can lead to a spontaneous charge-density effect.

Such spontaneous self-organization of the space-charge potential is a relatively good example of synergetic switching phenomena, which we discussed in general for the device-device interaction. This can be illustrated further by plotting U/η as a function of U_a/η, i.e., plotting (6.57) using (6.64) and (6.65). We do this for two conditions: $\nu = -0.2$ and $\nu = 0.5$, corresponding to conditions just below or well above the inversion threshold. The results are shown in Figure 6.11. Here, it is also assumed that $\lambda \sim 90$ Å, corresponding to a structure on InSb. The system shows clear bifurcation, in that the $U(U_a)$ characteristic changes its nature from a single-valued function to a multi-valued function at the onset of inversion. For $U/\eta \ll 1$, it appears that $U(U_a)$ shows a simple cusp catastrophe, governed by the single parameter ν.

If a suitable material is selected, it appears that an LSSL can be fabricated by today's technology. The fact that these structures show synergetic behavior under conditions of population inversion suggests that new operational characteristics may be achieved. It should be remarked that if the array is operated as a CCD, then the carriers are transferred from one well to another in a non-equilibrium condition, so that a degree of population inversion can be expected in the normal course of operation. Thus, optical pumping, although the most obvious source of creating the population inversion, is not the only method for doing so. Rather, inter-device charge transfer by barrier lowering (CCD mode) or by direct tunneling can also lead to inversions. It is also worth noting that the transition from the second mini-band to the first mini-band is a direct transition and carriers relaxing across the mini-gap should release radiative energy, such as has been seen from transitions between Landau levels or between subbands in MOS inversion layers. In the present case, the superlattice structure could be used for conversion of

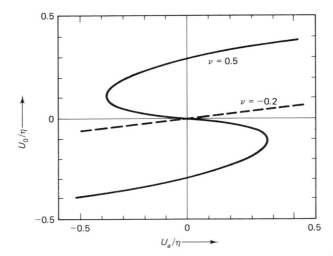

Figure 6.11 Relationship between the applied potential U_a and the total self-consistent potential U ($U_a = V_a$, $U = V_o$) for just below inversion, $\nu = -0.2$ and well above inversion, $\nu = 0.5$. The multi-valued structure leads to switching behavior in the arrays.

optical, or near-infrared radiation (valence to second mini-band excitation) to far-infrared radiation.

6.5 CELLULAR AUTOMATA

In the previous sections, we discussed a number of cases where the individual devices interacted with one another, either intentionally or parasitically. The result, in particular, of the parasitic interaction was a large array of devices which were totally interconnected. The interconnection could result in a major change in the *functional behavior* of the chip itself. In this section, we want to explore in a more general manner the operation of general arrays of devices which are interconnected in a (more or less) controlled manner. The general approach has been given the name cellular automata by Von Neumann [9], and he had shown that such structures could fully implement a Turing machine. This is not surprising as current microprocessors fit the description of a cellular automaton.

Most of the above discussion can be cast into the form of the interconnection matrix **F**, introduced in (6.18). Two particular examples have been considered. First, we discussed the linear case where device j was fed from device $j - 1$, and in turn fed device $j + 1$. While this was a unidirectional connection, the general case of bidirectional connects device j to devices $j \pm 1$. This is shown in Figure 6.12a, and is termed a 2-connected system.

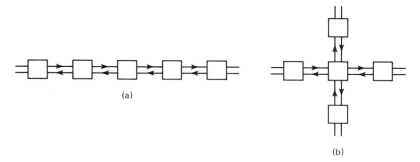

Figure 6.12 Examples of cellular automatons. (a) 2-connected. (b) 4-connected.

Here, the interconnections are specified by elements of **F** given by

$$T_{ij} = b\delta_{j, i \pm 1} \tag{6.68}$$

where δ_{kl} is the Kronecker delta function, and a is the general coupling strength. **F** is a tri-diagonal matrix with 0s on the main diagonal, as discussed following (6.29). The structure leads to eigenvalues of **S** that form a band of values from $-a - b$ to $-a + b$. If b is varied, these eigenvalues all vary as well, so that control of the system may be exercised through control of the interconnections, a result well in keeping with current VLSI design.

The second example considered was the two-dimensional lateral surface superlattice, in which direct coupling from a device to its four neighbors was assumed. This is shown in Figure 6.12b, and is a 4-connected system. Here, the device denoted by the pair of indices (i, j) is connected to the device at $(i, j \pm 1)$, $(i \pm 1, j)$. Can we describe an interconnection matrix **F** for this system?

Indeed we can. We can write the resultant interconnections via

$$\hat{F}\mathbf{U} \tag{6.69}$$

where **U** is a two-dimensional array of devices, and $\hat{\mathbf{F}}$ is a 4-tensor, whose elements are F_{klij}, representing a super-operator. Quite simply, a super-operator merely is a function of operators, which here is the anticommutation described by the matrix operations

$$\hat{F}\mathbf{U} = \mathbf{F}\mathbf{U} + \mathbf{U}\mathbf{F} \tag{6.70}$$

where **F** is given once again by (6.68). Thus the element (i, j) of 6.70 is

$$(\hat{F}\mathbf{U})_{ij} = b\left[U_{i, j+1} + U_{i, j-1} + U_{i+1, j} + U_{i-1, j}\right]$$

The fact that **F** reappears here unchanged is a result of the simple reorganization that is possible on the network. Any two-dimensional array, representing a principle axis system, can be renumbered as a single-dimensional column matrix, e.g., if $\mathbf{U}$ is $N \times N$, the new $1 \times N^2$ has elements

$$(U')_e = U_{i + N(j-1)}$$

Obviously, the new $\mathbf{F'}$ has strong similarities to the old $\mathbf{F}$, but larger. Indeed, this new $\mathbf{F'}$ is a sparse matrix dominated by its tri-diagonal entries.

Perhaps even more interesting is the fact that we may use these interconnections to describe the motion of charge, or information, through the system. If we write the state at $t + \Delta$ in terms of the state at t, we can say

$$U(t + \Delta) = U(t) + \hat{F}\mathbf{U}(t) \tag{6.71}$$

or

$$U_{ij}(t + \Delta) = U_{ij}(t) + b\left[U_{i, j+1}(t) + U_{i, j-1}(t) + U_{i+1, j}(t) + U_{i-1, j}(t)\right]$$

If we let $b = D\Delta/4h$, where h is the spatial scale corresponding to the spacing of devices, then we find

$$\frac{\partial U}{\partial t} \doteq D\nabla^2 U \tag{6.72}$$

This is a significant result since it implies that charge, or information, tends to diffuse through the system. In reality, devices are strongly nonlinear in their usage in VLSI, so that the basic behavior of (6.72) is modified somewhat. However, this strongly interconnected system is one of the bases, upon which the neural analogy with integrated circuits is predicated. Moreover, (6.72) corresponds to one of the more popular smoothing functions utilized in image processing, itself a cellular automata function. We want to pursue these analogies a little further below.

6.5.1 Threshold Switching

Since the two-dimensional arrays can readily be rewritten as one-dimensional arrays, we will concentrate on these latter systems for the time being. Quite often, a binary system can be utilized, so that the ith element has the setting $V_i = 0$ or 1, corresponding to the on or off state of a simple logic device (clearly, the 1 represents the normalized value of the maximum logic level voltage). Threshold logic is defined by applying the test:

$$\sum_j T_{ij}V_j - U_i \begin{cases} > 0 \rightarrow V_i = 1 \\ < 0 \rightarrow V_i = 0 \end{cases} \tag{6.73}$$

This can be more formally described as

$$V_i = Tr\left\{ \sum_{j \subset R} T_{ij}V_j - U_i \right\} \tag{6.74}$$

where U_i is the threshold of the ith element, T_{ij} is an element of the interconnection matrix **F**, Tr represents the logical "truth" function ($Tr \rightarrow 1$ if the argument is positive, so that this function really is the Heavyside step function), and R is a region or neighborhood of i. Here R might correspond to the 2-neighbors, 4-neighbors, or 8-neighbors, or might be the complete array of N elements.

Neural networks are commonly modeled by the representation of the individual neurons, or groups of neurons, by threshold elements. In ULSI circuits, however, pure threshold logic is seldom used. Rather, the setting of a state relies upon a logic *function* which computes a result. An example is the "exclusive or" circuit for two inputs. Here, the output is true for either of the inputs alone, but not for both. A simple way of looking at this is that the

$$EOR(A, B) = (A + B)_{\mathrm{mod}\,2}$$

is a function in which the computation is carried out in modulo 2 arithmetic. For systems like these, (6.74) must be replaced by

$$V_i = Tr\left\{ f\left[\sum_{j \subset R} T_{ij} V_j U_i \right] \right\} \tag{6.75}$$

where $f(\cdot)$ is the desired logical function. We can continue to use the ideas of the state of the system being represented as the set $\{V_i\}$ of values at any one instance. Then, (6.71) can be rewritten as

$$\mathbf{U}(t + \Delta) = [\mathbf{I} + \hat{F}]\mathbf{U}(t)$$

which is a special form of (6.75). Here **U** is the matrix of values V_i. This form and (6.75) are particularly useful, as they allow us to talk about *mappings* of the system. A map is the transition from one state vector, here $\mathbf{U}(t)$, to the next, here $\mathbf{U}(t + \Delta)$, produced by the function (6.75). The connection to the idea of maps in automata theory is obvious. The entire system dynamics is now described by the characteristics of the mapping function. Indeed, the form of (6.75) is that of a Liouville equation in mechanics, so that $\hat{F}$ describes the evolution of **U** in the system phase space.

There are important differences in the system that develop between synchronous and asynchronous mappings. In synchronous mappings, the system is clocked and all elements are tested at the same instant of time. A test such as (6.75) will map one initial state onto only one output state, although the mapping is not necessarily 1 : 1. Such synchronous systems are typical of normal ULSI circuits. On the other hand, for asynchronous switching, only a single element is tested at a particular time, so that many different mappings are possible results of a given initial system state. An important feature of the threshold test is its unidirectionality. If this test is applied to some element, the resulting setting will not be changed by a future test unless the settings of some other elements are changed first. This unidirectionality of the threshold test means that all asynchronous and most synchronous maps do not have an inverse. This noninvertibility can have profound implications, the most important of which is that the corresponding logical operations may themselves be logically irreversible and therefore thermodynamically irreversible as well.

The directed nature of the threshold test leads to bifurcations when the thresholds are varied. The general behavior will be illustrated here for a simple three-element asynchronous system in which all elements have the same threshold U. The interconnection matrix is taken to be

$$I = \begin{bmatrix} 0.0 & -0.5 & 0.2 \\ 0.4 & 0.0 & -0.3 \\ -0.7 & 0.4 & 0.0 \end{bmatrix} \qquad (6.76)$$

and the simple threshold dynamics of (6.74) will be used. The diagonal elements are zero as they do not appear in the threshold test. The behavior of this system will be explored for a range of threshold values.

For $U < -0.7$ the various states and mapping are shown in Figure 6.13a. Here the state (000) is a garden-of-Eden state (must be created at $t = 0$ by an external agent) and the state (111) is a stable state. Note that the threshold is lower than any linear sum of elements from the same row of the interconnection matrix. For any size system, either synchronous or asynchronous, when the threshold satisfies the above linear combination condition, the state of all 0s is a garden-of-Eden state and the state of all 1s is a stable state. For the system shown, the transition (100) → (101) changes its direction

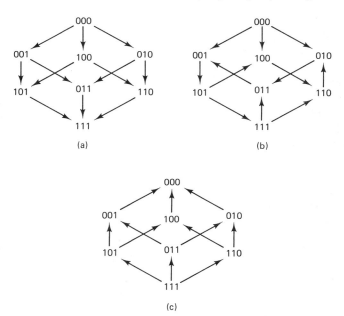

Figure 6.13 Activity topology for the **I** matrix of (6.76) for various threshold values. (a) **U** < 0.7. (b) −0.3 < **U** < 0.0. (c) **U** > 0.4.

to (101) → (100) if the threshold is raised to a value above -0.7. Further increasing the threshold changes the direction of other transitions as well. In Figure 6.13b, the transitions are shown for thresholds in the range $-0.3 < U < 0.0$. Note that now there are no stable states and some looping structures also exist. These looping structures represent oscillating cycles. For $U > 0$, the state (000) ceases to be a garden-of-Eden state and becomes a stable state. For $U > 0.4$, the system becomes essentially reversed from the original system shown in Figure 6.13a. This reversed system is shown in Figure 6.13c. Again, for any size system, either asynchronous or synchronous, when the threshold is larger than any linear sum of elements lying in the same row of the interconnection matrix, the state of all 1s is a garden-of-Eden state while the state of all 0s is a stable state which serves as an attractor in the system state space.

The results discussed above explain one difficulty found when networks of this sort are utilized as content addressable memories [10]. An algorithm proposed for storing a set of states with state vectors V^s, $s = 1, 2, \ldots, n$, consists of the interconnection matrix

$$T_{ij} = \sum (2V_i^s - 1)(2V_j^s - 1) \tag{6.77}$$

The contribution to T_{ij} made by a given vector s is the complement of the "exclusive or" function, i.e., $-T_{ij} = -2(V_i^s + V_j^s) + 1$. This algorithm works well for randomly generated vectors V^s. However, we find that the algorithm works poorly for systems where the stored states are largely 0s with only a few scattered 1s (or the converse). These latter states are those found in character recognition, where a character consists of a pattern of 1s written into a background of 0s. (A physical two-dimensional array has been used and transformed into the formalism discussed here by assigning a numerical identifier to each element, i.e., counting the elements.) For such patterns, one finds mostly positive contributions are made to the interconnection matrix from each individual pattern, with the result being a total interconnection matrix whose elements are almost all positive. Therefore, the system has only one stable state for a threshold which is non-positive. This is the state $\{V_i = 1,$ for all $i\}$. Since the memory algorithm works by associating some stable attracting state with each memory state, it certainly fails for pattern recognition unless threshold weighting is employed.

The above problem is clearly understood from the above analogy with a random spin glass. Equation (6.77) is just one model of the Hamiltonian of such a spin glass. Randomly filling the matrix T corresponds to a Monte Carlo simulation of this system. In systems, such as those of the preceding paragraph, T_{ij} has mostly $+1$ elements, so that the threshold lies below the sum of any row or column, and the system approaches the global stable state. In physical terms, the net magnetization is far above the phase transition. Thus, random V^s with nearly equal numbers of 0s and 1s must be used. One should remark, however, that care must be exercised in pursuing this analogy as spin glasses are usually simulated by nearest-neighbor coupling only.

6.5.2 General Remarks

In the above discussion, the general features of cellular automata have been briefly discussed, especially in regard to threshold logic. The key feature here is that cellular automata may be viewed as representations of dynamical systems. Consequently, they have found applications as filter systems (e.g., image processing and matrix multiplications) as well as fundamental paradigms of parallel computation (e.g., the Illiac IV machine). In general, any computer architecture that aims to maximize the density of active devices, while minimizing the delay inherent in interconnections, leads to a layout endemic to cellular automata. What we seek in future ULSI is not games played with cellular automata (a characteristic of much of the pathological science present in current treatises on the topic) but the nature with which cooperative phenomena are exhibited in these systems, and the extent to which these cooperative phenomena offer new techniques for information processing.

In some sense, the current applications to image processing and to matrix multiplication (applications popularized by systolic architectures and NASA's Tse computer) are more examples of treating cellular automata as mere computational tools. What we really need are, as mentioned above, cellular automata models treated as hierarchial dynamical systems, in which the overall topology of the system graph can be varied by the hierarchial control. Only in this way can we use the general information processing paradigm of dynamical systems as a role model for learning to control the cooperative dynamics of a cellular array. It is hoped that the discussion in this chapter will lead the reader to explore these connections, as the field is essentially unexplored.

REFERENCES

1. H. Haken, *Synergetics*, pp. 194–200 (Springer-Verlag, Berlin, 1978).
2. L. Esaki and R. Tsu, *IBM J. Res. Develop.*, vol. 14, p. 61 (1970).
3. R. T. Bate, *Bull. Am. Phys. Soc.*, vol. 22, p. 407 (1977).
4. D. K. Ferry, *Phys. Stat. Sol. (b)*, vol. 106, p. 63 (1981).
5. G. J. Iafrate, D. K. Ferry, and R. K. Reich, *Surf. Sci.*, vol. 113, p. 485 (1982).
6. G. Bernstein and D. K. Ferry, *Superlattices and Microstructures*, vol. 2, p. 373 (1986).
7. P. A. Lebwohl and R. Tsu, *J. Appl. Phys.*, vol. 41, p. 2664 (1970).
8. H. Kroemer, *Phys. Rev. B*, vol. 15, p. 880 (1977).
9. J. Von Neumann, in *Essays on Cellular Automata*, ed. J. W. Burks (Univ. Illinois Press, 1970).
10. J. Hopfield, *Proc. Nat. Acad. Sci. USA*, vol. 79, p. 2554 (1982).

7

FUNDAMENTAL LIMITS ON LOGIC

A general argument that has made the circuit of various computer science and electrical engineering departments, as well as numerous industrial facilities, is that almost any calculation is feasible if enough graduate students are pressed into service. This is of course a tongue-in-cheek description, but it serves to illustrate the principal question that must be asked about continued miniaturization in ULSI. That is, Are there any fundamental limits to the energy that must be dissipated within a single logic gate, so that there will be an absolute end to scaling theory? There are various factors that are certainly relevant to such discussions, such as the decay of information stored in a memory system or the problems of long calculations done with imprecise computers.

Much consideration has in fact been given to the transmission of data through various interconnection (telecommunication) circuitry in the field of information theory, and methods of error correction coding are commonly used to reduce these errors. We note here that in this regard, memory circuits have strong analogs to such communication channels and we find error correction used in storing information in large memory systems. Do these considerations, however, carry over to the general case of computational systems?

In this chapter, we want to spend some time investigating the limits on computation which are set by thermodynamics and quantum mechanics. We will see from this investigation that such limits by and large are expressable in terms of a minimum speed-power product, just as we have evaluated current technological implementations of logic.

7.1 REQUIREMENTS OF LOGIC

There have been many treatises in the past several years which have addressed the physical requirements of logic elements. For example, it is clear that the requirement of signal restoration at each logic node really means that the devices must be saturating devices, with the saturation levels at "on" and "off" well characterized in terms of the system logic levels. In addition, the need for large noise margins and sharp transitions between logic levels implies that the devices must be highly nonlinear. Certain very-high-gàin semiconductor devices of course satisfy both of these requirements, but this also means that signal levels (the difference between the two logic levels) must be large compared to the thermal voltage k_BT, since it is only with these voltage levels that the device is nonlinear. Moreover, the thermal noise in the system is also of this same order of magnitude (k_BT), so that the large signal level is necessary to discriminate against noise in the logical computation.

What other requirements for logic are there? Certainly, one view is that the logical operations that occur in a computer can be described as the nonlinear interactions between two data streams. This reinforces the above view of the necessity for strongly nonlinear devices, but is not complete as logic also involves the necessity for branching and decision points in the data interaction. Thus, there is a need for uniformity in logic levels throughout the array of devices as well as a need for ease of measurement of the current state of selected devices. The former is reflected as a limit in logic as non-uniformity in threshold voltage in MOS devices. In fact, a fairly stringent requirement is placed on the control of this quantity in ULSI chips, as we have seen in previous chapters. In some sense, this variation of parameters within the array of devices can be expressed as an additional noise source in the circuit.

As we have mentioned, the concepts of information theory have been applied to set limits on logical operations. In one sense, the concept of channel capacity can be utilized for this purpose. However, a few authors suggest that the channel capacity argument is for linear channels of information flow and should therefore be restricted to treating the information storage in memory circuits, but not applied to the logic circuits themselves. This is not really the case, though, as channel capacity refers to the limitations that arise when trying to measure the presence of a signal in a noisy environment. In the application at hand, the noisy environment is generated by the thermal background in which the logic elements are working, and the measurement is in fact the required determination of the state of the logic elements or of the memory cell. This measurement is a fundamental part of the computer process, and is basic to the operation of the theoretical Turing machine [1]. The results of the measurements are particularly important in making decisions on the branching operations. There are of course certain *procedures* in which a series of logic operations are carried out without the necessity for intermediate measurements, as only the results are necessary to the overall computation. But this does not eliminate the need for the measurements themselves.

The first to suggest the presence of such a noise/measurement induced limitation in line with the channel capacity arguments was Von Neumann [2], and this argument leads to the relation that the minimum energy required in the logic element is

$$E_{\min} > k_B T \ln(2) \qquad (7.1)$$

In Figure 7.1a, we show a simple double well potential energy diagram, in which the two wells are labeled as "0" and "1," in analogy with the bistable logic element. This analogy was first put forward by Landauer [3], but has been utilized extensively by others since then. In principle, a particle representing the logic state of the system can reside in either of the two potential minima, and the barrier between them protects the system from switching states. If the two potential minima are at the same energy, then there is no thermodynamic preference for either of the two states, and the barrier separating them is a kinetic barrier which must be surpassed for switching. Given a long enough time span, the particle will fluctuate over this kinetic barrier (or tunnel through it), so that the system will equilibrate to a state characterized by the random sampling of both minima by the particle during this long time span. For this reason, information is usually considered to be stored in this system by raising one of the minima to a high energy relative to the other. This then introduces a thermodynamic barrier as well. In principle, this latter system is out of equilibrium with its environment (but not necessarily so). We think of flip-flops as this type of circuit, where the non-equilibrium steady-state is maintained by the dissipation of energy. Landauer was apparently the first

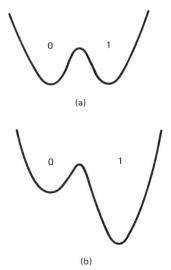

(a)

(b)

Figure 7.1 A double-well potential used to illustrate storage in a computer. (a) The equilibrium case. (b) The case in which one state is far from equilibrium.

to refer to this state as the *dissipative steady-state*. Nearly all latching type devices are of this nature, so that we can easily discuss the generalities by using such a simple two-well potential.

Landauer [3] also introduced the idea of logical irreversibility, in which the output of a logic element does not uniquely define the logical inputs. This is true of almost all logic operations in current use. One of his main points was that logical irreversibility *required* physical irreversibility, although the converse to this has never been proven, i.e., it is clear that logical reversibility has little to do with physical reversibility. This was crucial to a major statement put forth by this latter author. In Figure 7.1b, we show the system in the dissipative steady-state with the logical "1" state preferred. Rather than waiting for the system to equilibrate through removing the separation between the two states, we can perform a restore-to-one operation by simply removing the kinetic barrier between the two states. Landauer asserted that this removed one-half of the available states and thus contributed an energy loss given by (7.1) above. However, he quite correctly pointed out that if the actual state of the particle were known, it could be switched (slowly) in such a manner that no dissipation would be incurred. If it were already in the "1" state, nothing would be done, but if it were in the "0" state the potentials could be manipulated in such a manner that the particle could be moved to the "1" state sufficiently slowly that no dissipation would be involved. This suggests that the dissipation is really contained in a *reading* operation to ascertain the actual state of the machine.

On further consideration, we may say that the bit really can exist in only a single state, either "0" or "1." Bit operations are always physical $1:1$ mappings and may be accomplished without dissipation, as pointed out above for sufficiently slow switching. Landauer's phase space argument above would only apply if a bit sampled the two possible states in a random fashion, or the states were randomly occupied in the presence of thermal noise [4]. Then, however, these bits could not be used for computation as they are changed stochastically rather than according to a defined program. Rather, the bit must be maintained in either the "0" or the "1" state, and this requires a non-equilibrium system. The key factor for the Turing machine, and hence for any computational machine, is the reading operation needed for decision making during the process. The measurement itself must be described by an application of information theory (or statistical mechanics), which indicates a dissipation of the level given in (7.1). As mentioned above, there are certain procedures which do not involve reading operations within them, so that the average energy loss *per bit operation* may be less than that of (7.1), and this will depend upon the actual architecture implemented.

The requirement of dissipation, that arises from the necessary reading operations, adds to that necessary to maintain the nonequilibrium steady-state of the total machine. In this sense, we may think of these two sources of dissipation as the switching power and the standby power, the latter of which can be made very small, such as in CMOS circuitry. Thus, in high-speed machines, it is the switching power that dominates; the reading energy dissipation and the rate at which these are made dominates the total energy dissipation of the computer. However, the dissipation and the non-equilibrium steady-state of the system all conspire to introduce a preferred direction for the computation and its representation by a physical system with a preferred direction of time. In this sense, discussions of logical reversibility are interesting, but are irrelevant to a discussion of dissipation in the computational process.

7.2 THERMODYNAMIC LIMITS ON SWITCHING

In the previous section, we briefly introduced the idea that the dissipation at a given logic gate can be reduced by operating the gate sufficiently slowly. We would like to investigate this further by addressing the question of the inherent limitations on energy dissipation. For this, we shall actually utilize a quantum system in order to more accurately set these limits, and follow an approach put forward by Bate [5]. In this case, we are actually seeking to establish some fundamental limits set by real physical laws, fully recognizing that the actual minimum speed-power product may in fact be limited by the acceptable error rate in the data rather than by these fundamental limits. In fact, such limits as these provide very valuable guidance in evaluating real limits on system performance, even in the absence of precise information on the system itself. Moreover, such limits may provide insight into new failure modes not previously expected for the system and may also provide guidance on the difficulty of achieving desired system performance goals. The models to be treated are in fact rather simplified, but they do give us certain insights.

As we discussed in Chapter 5, two of the most significant parameters to be used in evaluating system performance are the power dissipation P and the speed, characterized by the delay time τ_D. From these, we can construct the speed-power product which gives the average energy E dissipated in the logic operation. Now, if a computation requires N_c operations, the total energy required is simply

$$E_T = N_c E = N_c P \tau_D \tag{7.2}$$

This energy could ultimately become the final obstacle in future ULSI, and is already recognized as a limiting factor. Generally, one major problem is the calculation of the parameter N_c, and most computer scientists must rely upon minimization procedures based upon mathematical complexity theory. This is beyond the scope of the current discussion, but an important point is that N_c must ultimately be less than the number of available states of the total computational system (for stored program machines), which of course impacts circuit size.

The real system is somewhat more complicated than this simple-minded approach, since E is a decreasing function of the probability p_e of an error occurring in the logical operation. Thus, as E is reduced, we are faced with the result that the confidence in the results is also reduced (in a simple sense, there is much more noise in the system as system voltages are reduced). In general, error-correction schemes can be employed, but only at the expense of increasing N_c. The trade-off between switching energy and acceptable error rate depends upon the actual time over which the computation is performed, providing that this time is relatively short. Because of this, we expect that quantum mechanical limits will surpass the thermodynamic limits at very fast clock rates, say, > 10 GHz. These limits are such that they increase linearly with speed beyond this level.

7.2.1 The Abstract Gate Model

The simple two-well potential utilized above is rather difficult to extend to the quantum mechanical case. For this reason, Bate [5] has suggested a different approach, in which two energy levels are assumed. Available switches, or gates, in the system must be in one or the other of these two levels, and the two levels are assumed to be in thermal equilibrium with each other and with the environs. In particular, there is some relaxation time τ which characterizes the approach to equilibrium of the system. Throughout, we assume that Fermi-Dirac statistics will be employed to describe the occupancy of the two levels. The general scheme is shown in Figure 7.2, and the two levels are assigned energy values E_1 and E_0 for obvious reasons. In equilibrium, the "0" state is assumed to be the lower energy state, and if $E_1 - E_0 > k_B T$, nearly all of the particles will be in this lower energy state. Switching is then assumed to occur by the application of an external potential which reverses the position of the two levels. If this occurs on a time scale fast compared to τ, the switching time is given approximately by τ, i.e., by the relaxation of the system. On the other hand, if the switching of the levels is done slowly compared to τ, then the overall switching is on this slower time scale. No state gain is included so that the absolute limits will be obtained.

One crucial question that must be asked is the number of particles that must be switched in the system for it to represent a realistic logic gate.

Figure 7.2   The two energy levels used to simulate the states 0 and 1.

Landauer above assumed only a single particle, and this carries through in general for a classical system. In quantum systems, however, switching single particles really involves too much energy, and systems with many particles may be switched more economically. Still, the optimum number of particles to be switched must be odd so that more than one-half of the particles must be in the wrong state for an error to be recorded. If the individual bit error rate is p_e, then the system logic gate error rate is $p_e^{(n+1)/2}$. Since any combination of individual particles, subject to the sum $(n + 1)/2$ can occur, the net error rate is

$$P_e = {}_n C_{(n+1)/2} \, p_e^{(n+1)/2} \tag{7.3}$$

with $p_e \ll 1$, and the binomial coefficient is

$$_n C_k = n!/k!(n - k)! \tag{7.4}$$

Because the individual error rates are assumed to be small, we can ignore the possibility that more than $(n + 1)/2$ are in the wrong state as being small in comparison with (7.3). In general, p_e is a function of the energy expended in the switching of the single state. If $E_T = nE$, then we may also write (7.3) as

$$P_e = {}_n C_{(n+1)/2} \left[p_e(E_T/n) \right]^{(n+1)/2} \tag{7.5}$$

Clearly now, (7.5) is an expression that can be optimized to yield the lowest P_e (as a function of n) whenever the dependence of p_e on E is known.

7.2.2 Thermodynamic Limits

Let us now turn to the limits imposed in the strictly thermodynamic case. We assume that there are $N_0 = Nf_0$ particles in the "0" state and $N_1 = Nf_1$ particles in the "1" state, where N is the total number of particles and f_i is the Fermi-Dirac distribution (Fig. 7.3)

$$f_i = \left\{ 1 + \exp\left[(E_i - E_F)/k_B T \right] \right\}^{-1}, \; i = 0, 1, \ldots \tag{7.6}$$

where E_F is the Fermi energy level (the equilibrium chemical potential of this system). We must always have $N_0 + N_1 = N$, so that $f_0 + f_1 = 1$, or

$$E_F = (E_0 + E_1)/2 \tag{7.7}$$

Thus, this critical energy level is midway between the two logic levels themselves. For simplicity, we shall take $E_F = 0$, so that $E_1 = E/2$ and $E_0 = -E/2$, where $E = E_1 - E_0$ is the separation in the two levels. These distributions are the equilibrium values

$$f_0 = \left[1 + \exp(-E/2) \right]^{-1} \tag{7.8a}$$

$$f_1 = \left[1 + \exp(E/2) \right]^{-1} \tag{7.8b}$$

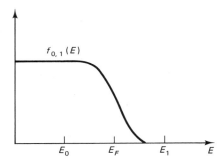

Figure 7.3 The switching levels of the two voltages.

and are the appropriate values at $t = 0$. In general, with $E \gg k_B T$, $f_0 = 1$ and $f_1 \ll 1$.

Let us now consider the fast switching case, in which the two levels are reversed in a time small compared to τ. For this non-equilibrium case, the distributions satisfy a relaxation equation

$$df_i/dt = -[f_i(t) - f_{ei}]/\tau \qquad (7.9)$$

and

$$f_i(t) = f_{ei} + [f_i(0^+) - f_{ei}]e^{-t/\tau} \qquad (7.10)$$

After switching, we have that

$$f_{e1} = f_0, \; f_{e0} = f_1$$

$$f_1(0^+) = f_1, \; f_0(0^+) = f_0$$

Inserting these values, as shown in Figure 7.3, we find that

$$f_0(t) = [1 + \exp(E/2k_B T)]^{-1} + \tanh(E/4k_B T)e^{-t/\tau} \qquad (7.11)$$

Equation (7.11) gives us the probability that the particle stays in the zero state, which is now the upper energy level. If t_s is the allotted switching time, the error probability is just $p_e = f_0(t_s)$, and if $t_s \gg \tau$,

$$p_e = [1 + \exp(E/2k_B T)]^{-1} \qquad (7.12)$$

which should be small as expected. The energy dissipation is just E per particle, as each particle dissipates this much energy in the downward transition.

In the case of quasi-static switching, the relaxation time is rapid when compared to the slow variation of the energy levels. Here, the position of the two levels is very slowly reversed (this is accomplished by reducing the "1" state slowly to zero and slowly raising the "0" state so that absorption is not a significant problem), and we can write

$$f_{e0} = [1 + \exp(\varepsilon/2k_BT)]^{-1} \tag{7.13a}$$

$$f_{e1} = [1 + \exp(-\varepsilon/2k_BT)]^{-1} \tag{7.13b}$$

where $\varepsilon = \varepsilon(t)$ is the slowly varying switching function. Then, we find that $f_i(t)$ is still given by (7.10), and

$$f_0(t) = [1 + \exp(\varepsilon/2k_BT)]^{-1}$$
$$+ \{[1 + \exp(-E/2k_BT)] - [1 + \exp(\varepsilon/2k_BT)]^{-1}\}e^{-t/\tau} \tag{7.14}$$

For $E \gg 2k_BT$, this reduces to

$$f_0(t) = [1 + \exp(\varepsilon/2k_BT)]^{-1}\{1 + \exp(\varepsilon/2k_BT)\exp(-t/\tau)\} \tag{7.15}$$

For long, slow switching such that $t_s \gg \tau$, we find that

$$p_e = f_0(t_s) = [1 + \exp(E/2k_BT)]^{-1} \tag{7.16}$$

which is the same result obtained for fast switching. Thus, the error probability depends primarily upon the thermodynamic separation of the two energy levels and not upon the details of the switching process, as long as $t_s \gg \tau$. The energy dissipation, on the other hand, varies significantly with the switching process. The rate of energy dissipation is just $-N\varepsilon \, df_0/dt$, so that

$$E_T = \int_0^{t_s} (-N\varepsilon \, df_0/dt) \, dt = -N \int_{f_0(0)}^{f_0(t_s)} \varepsilon \, df_0$$

Now, we must approach this problem carefully, as dissipation does not begin until the crossover point of the two slowly varying levels. Thus, we may choose a new time axis such that $f_0(t_0) = 0.5$, $\varepsilon(t_0) = 0$, and $\varepsilon(t_s) = E/2$. Then

$$E = \int_0^{E/2} [1 + \exp(\varepsilon/k_BT)]^{-1} d\varepsilon$$
$$= k_BT\{\ln(2) - \ln[1 + \exp(-E/2k_BT)]\} \tag{7.17}$$

For large energy separations, this just gives the result given in (7.1). The important point is that this energy dissipation is a function of the temperature alone. Since thermodynamics really places no limit on the value of τ, we are free to reduce it as much as we want. We can then in principle achieve the lower limit (7.1) as long as the switching time $t_s \gg \tau$. At the same time, we can increase E in order to lower the error probability.

Finally, one should consider just what the optimum form should be for the switching function $\varepsilon(t)$. Bate [5] points out that this is a variational problem which is quite complex. We merely reproduce his result, which is

$$E_{\text{opt.}} = k_BT \ln(2) + E\left[1 + (\pi t_s/2\tau)^{1/2}\right]\exp(-t_s/\tau) \tag{7.18}$$

This result differs little from that of (7.17), especially in the limiting case for which $t_s \gg \tau$.

7.2.3 Quantum Limits

We want now to extend the above discussion to the case in which quantum effects are explicitly included, not in actual quantization as that is already implied in the limitation of two levels, but in level lifetime effects. The mere presence of transitions between the two levels in our system implies the presence of an interaction between them. This interaction gives rise to a "renormalization" of the levels which appears (in any measurement) as a *broadening* of the levels. It is this primary effect which we want to now consider, as it directly affects the error probabilities with which we were concerned above.

From the above discussion, we concluded that in order to switch with any degree of reliability we needed to have $t_s > \tau$. However, the finite lifetime τ of the levels gives rise to the broadening, as it represents the gradual loss of coherence in the state represented by the level. This loss can be through interaction of the levels, as mentioned in the previous paragraph, or through interaction with the ambient background. In the above discussion, we took the actual width (in energy) of the levels to be the classical value of essentially zero; that is, we assumed that the level could be represented by a probability density function

$$P_i(E) = \delta(E - E_i) \tag{7.19}$$

where $E_i = E_0$ or $E_i = E_1$. Quantum mechanically, the broadening of the level by the lifetime τ causes the δ-function to evolve into a finite-width function whose area still retains the overall strength of the δ-function. The simplest approximation to this is the Lorentzian function

$$P_i(E) = \left(h/2\pi^2\tau \right) \left[\left(E - E_i \right)^2 + \left(h/2\pi\tau \right)^2 \right]^{-1} \tag{7.20}$$

The introduction of this probability density function now allows us to talk about the noise margins and error probabilities of the levels themselves. In Figure 7.4, we indicate the two broadened levels and the Fermi-Dirac function (occupation probability), where the limit $T \to 0$ is taken in the latter function. The error probability is now related to the portion of the line width that overlaps into the region dominated by the opposite level. For example, the error probability is related to the cross-hatched region for the supposed "0" state. It is clear how the noise margin is now defined in relation to the level widths, as the error probability can be made small for narrow lines or large level separation, but becomes rather larger if $E_1 - E_0$ is of the same order as the level width. The noise margin itself is not a quantum mechanical quantity, but arises in logic circuits from the same physical sources—the broadening of

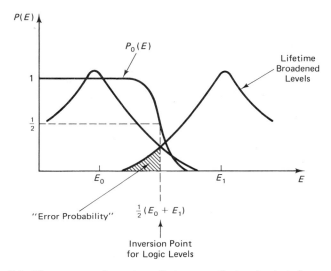

Figure 7.4 The presence of quantum effects causes the two levels to have a finite width, which introduces noise margins.

the actual levels due to interactions. For the following, we shall continue to invoke the low temperature limit to ease the integrals.

As in the previous section, we can determine the position of the Fermi level by requiring equal weights for the two levels, i.e.,

$$\int_{-\infty}^{\infty} f(E)[P_1(E) + P_0(E)] \, dE = 1 \qquad (7.21)$$

Each of the probability density functions is normalized so that

$$\int_{-\infty}^{\infty} P_i(E) \, dE = 1 \qquad (7.22)$$

as well. Now, the Fermi-Dirac distribution has the properties in the low temperature limit that $f = 1$ for $E < E_F$ and $f = 0$ for $E > E_F$, so that we may manipulate (7.20) to give

$$\int_{-\infty}^{E_F} [P_1(E) + P_0(E)] \, dE = \int_{E_F}^{\infty} [P_1(E) + P_0(E)] \, dE = 1 \quad (7.22)$$

which tells us that the Fermi level must be placed such that the two lines are symmetrically located about it. Thus, we obtain

$$E_F = (E_1 + E_0)/2 \qquad (7.23)$$

just as was previously derived. This now allows us to evaluate the error probability (for either level) as

$$p_e = \left(h/2\pi^2\tau\right) \int_{-\infty}^{(E_0 + E_1)/2} \left[(E - E_1)^2 + (h/2\pi\tau)^2\right]^{-1} dE$$

$$= (1/2) - (1/\pi)\tan^{-1}\left[\pi\tau(E_1 - E_0)/h\right] \tag{7.24}$$

Since we can drive the second term arbitrarily close to 0.5 by increasing the level separation or the lifetime, we can make this error probability arbitrarily small. The result (7.24) is the steady-state result, and is modified by the transient solutions for the distribution functions and occupation probabilities. However, for times $t \gg \tau$, the steady-state result reappears. For shorter times, the error probability can be as much as 0.5 at the switching time, but drops off quickly.

The energy lost during switching is found in the same manner as for the previous section. For fast switching, the energy lost per particle is $E_a = (E_1 - E_0)$, just as in the classical case. In the quasi-static switching case (or nearly so), the variational approach gives the result that

$$E' = E_a\left\{0.5 - (1/\pi)\tan^{-1}(x) + (1/2\pi x)\ln(1 + x^2)\right.$$

$$\left. + \left[1 + (\pi t_s/2\tau)^{1/2}\right]\exp(-t_s/\tau)\right\} \tag{7.25}$$

where $x = \pi E_a\tau/h$. As the lifetime τ decreases, the exponential term goes toward zero, but the coefficient increases and x decreases. We can in fact use τ as a variational parameter to further minimize the error probability and the switching energy. For large x, we can expand the above to give the limiting relations

$$p_e = (1/\pi x) + 0.5e^{-t/\tau} \tag{7.26}$$

and

$$E' = (E_a/\pi x)\ln(x) + (E_a/\pi x) + E_a\left[1 + (\pi t_s/2\tau)^{1/2}\right]e^{-t/\tau} \tag{7.27}$$

Minimizing the error probability leads us to the appropriate delay time

$$\tau_o = t_s/\ln(\pi^2 E_a t_s/h) = t_s/\ln(u_o) \tag{7.28}$$

where we have introduced the dimensionless parameter u_o. This gives the minimum error probability

$$p_e = (1/2u_o)\left[1 + \ln(u_o)/\pi\right] \tag{7.29}$$

and the corresponding switching energy

$$E' = (E_a/u_o)\left\{1 + \left[\pi\ln(u_o)/2\right]^{1/2}\right.$$

$$\left. + \ln(u_o)/\pi\left[1 + \ln(u_o)\ln(u_o)/\pi p\right\} \tag{7.30}$$

It is clear that there are two cases here depending upon the speed. Moreover, it appears that the limit appears in the form of an action, i.e., as an energy-time

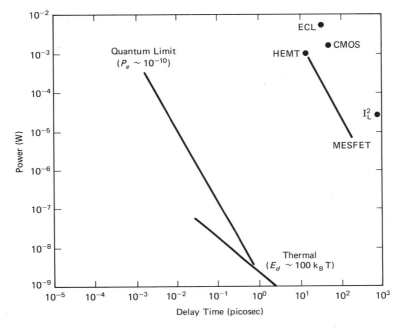

Figure 7.5 The expected quantum limits on speed and power. $P\tau^2$ values for various technologies are also plotted for comparison.

product, as suggested in Chapter 5. For slow switching, we have $Q = E't_s$ as the relevant action, while for fast switching, we have $Q' = E_a t_s$ as the relevant action. These are shown in Figure 7.5 along with the Pt_s^2 curve obtained in Chapter 5 from Keyes' considerations. The quantum mechanical considerations yield ultimate limits which are clearly well beyond the current state-of-the-art, but still within what could be considered in the next few decades. It is reassuring that the basic limitation on the action first obtained classically by Keyes actually is also obtained from the quantum approach.

7.3 SUMMARY

The considerations that have been taken here are well beyond those that would normally appear in considerations of VLSI or ULSI. However, when dealing with the limitations of scaling down integrated systems, it is always useful to be aware of whether one is approaching fundamental, rather than technological, limits. Here, we have tried briefly to evaluate where the fundamental limits might appear. In short, the mere requirement of measurement during the computational process invokes a dissipation of energy. This dissipation can be evaluated in an approximate form by simple quantum mechanical, or classical thermodynamic, models. These models indicate that, although we are a long way from the fundamental limits today, the distance to them is not that great, perhaps only a few orders of magnitude in speed-power product.

REFERENCES

1. A. Turing, *Proc. London Math. Soc.*, vol. p. 42, 230 (1936); vol. 43, p. 544 (1937).
2. J. Von Neumann, cited in *The Computer and the Brain* (Yale Univ. Press, 1958).
3. R. Landauer, *IBM J. Res. Develop.*, vol. 3, p. 183 (1961).
4. W. Porod, R. O. Grondin, D. K. Ferry, and G. Porod, *Phys. Rev. Letters*, vol. 52, p. 232 (1984).
5. R. T. Bate, in *VLSI Electronics: Microstructure Science*, ed. N. Einspruch, vol. 5, p. 359 (Academic Press, New York, 1982).

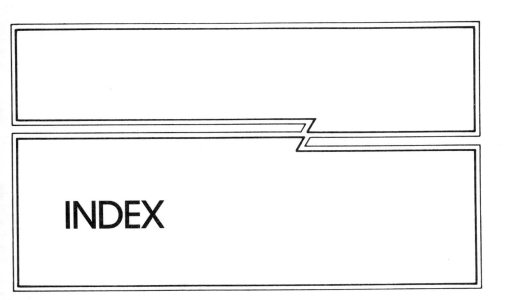

INDEX